WORLD® AIR POWER

J O U R N A L

Aerospace Publishing Ltd

AIRtime Publishing Inc.

Published quarterly by
Aerospace Publishing Ltd
179 Dalling Road
London W6 0ES
UK

ISSN 0959-7050
Aerospace ISBN 1-86184-027-6
                (softback)
             1-86184-028-4
                (hardback)
Airtime ISBN 1-880588-07-2
                (hardback)

Published under licence in USA and
Canada by AIRtime Publishing Inc.,
USA

Editorial Offices:
WORLD AIR POWER JOURNAL
Aerospace Publishing Ltd
3A Brackenbury Road
London   W6 0BE   UK
     E-mail: info@aerospacepbl.co.uk

Publisher: Stan Morse
Managing Editor: David Donald
     E-mail: dave@aerospacepbl.co.uk

Editor: Robert Hewson
     E-mail: rob@aerospacepbl.co.uk

Deputy Editor: Dave Willis
     E-mail: willis@aerospacepbl.co.uk

Sub Editor: Karen Leverington

Editorial Assistant: Tim Senior
     E-mail: tim@aerospacepbl.co.uk

Origination by Universal Graphics
Printed in Italy by Officine Grafiche
       de Agostini

Correspondents:
General military: Jon Lake
USA Washington: Robert F. Dorr
USA Southwest: Randy Jolly
Europe: John Fricker
Russia/CIS: Yefim Gordon
Asia: Pushpindar Singh
Canada: Jeff Rankin-Lowe
Argentina: Jorge Núñez Padin
Chile: Patrick Laureau

The *World Air Power Journal* web site can be
found at:

http://www.airpower.co.uk

The Editor extends thanks and appreciation to
the following individuals who made an
important contribution to this issue of
World Air Power Journal:

For their help with the 366th Wing feature thanks are due to
Brigadier Gen. Randall M. Schmidt, Commander 366th
Wing, Mr Bob Jensen, Air Force News Service, Lt Shane
Balken, 366th Wing Public Affairs, Capt. Chris Azzano,
391st FS (F-15E chase pilot), 1Lt Shawn Cotton, 390th FS
(F-15D chase pilot), 391st Fighter Squadron, 'Bold Tigers',
Life support section, A1C Bennie Davis, 366th
Communications Squadron.

For their help in the preparation of the US Navy Air Power
Analysis, the author would like to express his thanks to:
Michael Weeks, Rick Morgan, Brad Elward, Davide Reade
(Raytheon), Cdr David Foy USNR (OPNAV), Rob Koon
(NAVAIR PAO), Stephen W. Walsh (TECHMATICS) and
Jan Jacobs. Thanks are also due to Roy Grossnick, Mark
Evans and Todd Baker, at the Naval Aviation History Office.

For their assistance with the Mi-24 feature thanks are due to
David F. Brown, Alexander Mladenov, Jaroslev Spacek and
Gábor Szekeres.

World Air Power Journal is a
registered trademark in the
United States of America of
AIRtime Publishing Inc.

World Air Power Journal is
published quarterly and is
available by subscription and
from many fine book and hobby
stores.

**SUBSCRIPTION AND BACK
NUMBERS:**

**UK and World (except USA and
Canada) write to:**
Aerospace Publishing Ltd
FREEPOST
PO Box 2822
London
W6 0BR
UK

**(No stamp required if posted in
the UK)**

USA and Canada, write to:
AIRtime Publishing Inc.
Subscription Dept
10 Bay Street
Westport
CT 06880, USA
(203) 838-7979
Toll-free order number in USA:
1 800 359-3003

**Prevailing subscription rates are
as follows:**
Softbound edition for 1 year:
       $59.95
Softbound edition for 2 years:
       $112.00
**Softbound back numbers
(subject to availability) are
$16.00 each, plus shipping and
handling. All rates are for
delivery within mainland USA,
Alaska and Hawaii. Canadian
and overseas prices available
upon request. American Express,
Discover Card, MasterCard and
Visa accepted. When ordering
please include card number,
expiration date and signature.**

U.S. Publisher:
     Mel Williams
Subscriptions Director:
     Linda DeAngelis
**Charter Member Services
Manager:**
     Janie Munroe
Retail Sales Director: Jill Brooks
Shipping Manager: E. Rex Anku

WORLD AIR POWER ®

J O U R N A L

CONTENTS

Volume 37   Summer 1999

Military Aviation Review

International

Eurofighter production launched

Resolution in September 1998 of UK MoD concerns regarding logistic support cleared the way for an initial DM14 billion (£5 billion) four-country order for the first 148 Eurofighters, plus 363 Eurojet EJ 200 turbofans. Also included in the fixed-price Supplement 2 contract were spare powerplants and role equipment, plus long lead-time items for the planned second batch of 232 aircraft, each costing £34 million.

Orders for additional spares, ground equipment and training aids were finalised within the following few months, to support initial deliveries from 2001. As the biggest initial Eurofighter recipient, the UK will receive 55 aircraft, followed by 44 for Germany, 29 for Italy and 20 for Spain. Five instrumented production aircraft will supplement the seven development prototypes, plus a production test aircraft, and 37 with initial operating capability.

Although lacking such planned features as an infra-red search and track system (IRST) and GEC-Marconi Crusader helmet-mounted sight, the 37 IOC Eurofighters will equip operational conversion units in all four countries. They will be upgraded later to the full combat capability standards of Eurofighters Nos 44-148, for delivery by 2005, when the next 232 aircraft and 519 engines, also with spare powerplants, will follow on until 2010.

Production economies will reduce second-batch aircraft costs, including first export Typhoons. These would add to the similarly-sized third production batch, for 2010-2014 deliveries, to complete initial four-country commitments of 620 Eurofighters and 1,382 EJ200 turbofans. Eurofighter is hoping to secure up to 50 per cent of a projected fighter export market of 800-1,000 aircraft between 2005 and 2025.

ETOM 52 'Tontouta' operates a mixed fleet from Noumea in New Caledonia. The unit has recently gained Airtech CN.235s in place of Transalls. The badge (right) has a silhouette of New Caledonia and a Polynesian totem.

Europe

BULGARIA:

MiG-21bis upgrade

The BVVS announced in late 1998 that it intends to begin the upgrade of a limited number of MiG-21bis – a total of 70 of which are in service or storage – in 1999 and 2000, for which IAI and VPK-MAPO are competing. It is understood that IAI had gained a certain advantage due to its active marketing efforts in 1998. Only some of the 36 MiG-21bis of the 3rd IAB at Graph Ignatievo, delivered in 1983, will be the subject of the upgrade. The type's service life is expected to be extended to 40 years/4,000 hours during the upgrade, which will be combined with a major overhaul.

Aircraft life extension programmes

The BVVS has initiated a series of life extension initiatives of some of the main fleet types, aimed at improving the airworthiness of its fleet. The service life of the last 26 of the BVVS's 102 Aero L-29 Delfin jet trainers (delivered in 1970 and originally slated for retirement in 2000-01) will be extended to 37 years, thus making possible their use until 2007. Other types subject to extension programme are the MiG-23BNs and MFs delivered between 1978 and 1980 and originally slotted for retirement in 1996 and 1998 at the end of their 18-year life. Five BNs and three MFs underwent a general overhaul combined with the replacement of some airframe parts in the TEREM VRZ 'G. Benkovsky' facility in 1996-1998, and now are expected to be useful until 2004-2006. Life extension of more BNs and MFs was hampered by the lack of funds in the 1999 defence budget.

The time between overhauls (TBO) of the 21 MiG-29s delivered from 1989 was also extended from eight years – as originally required according to the design bureau's specification – to 10 years, based on the maintenance experience of the Slovak, German and Belarussian air forces. The expired hours of the MiG-29's accessory gearbox, and lack of funds for its general overhaul, caused serious serviceability problems that grounded most of the fleet. At one time in mid-1998 there was only one flying aircraft. In late 1998 the situation was considerably improved by the introduction of a set of new gearbox maintenance procedures to extend its TBO. Further improvement of the MiG-29's serviceability is expected in mid-1999 with the delivery of a spare parts package, as a part of the deal for the write-off of the $48-million trade debt owed to Bulgaria by Russia. The deal also included the restoration of the airworthiness of up to 10 Su-22M-4/UM-3s. The remaining 11 Su-22s were offered for sale to Third World countries in early 1999.

CROATIA:

Lancer upgrade planned for MiG-21s

Following an Israeli government veto on Aerostar/Elbit's proposed upgrade of 11 Ethiopian air force MiG-21s, the Croatian air force (HRZ) could be the first customer for the Romanian Lancer III upgrade of the MiG-21bis. Croatia has a requirement to modernise 28 MiG-21s equipping its two combat squadrons, although only some $50 million is initially being authorised for the upgrade of a dozen 'Fishbed-Js', plus two MiG-21UM two-seat combat trainers.

CZECH REPUBLIC:

Russian transport purchase

Recent Czech Defence Ministry acquisitions from Russia have included a Tupolev Tu-154 'Careless' tri-turbofan transport, which carries an 18144-kg (40,000-lb) payload, or up to 180 passengers. Its $22 million cost is being offset from Russia's $3.4 billion debts to the Czech Republic.

FRANCE:

Rafale programme progress

Final negotiations for French government multi-year orders for 28 more Dassault Rafale multi-role fighters

If funds permit, the MiG-21bis fighters of the Dobrich-based 3/26 IAE will be included in Bulgaria's upgrade programme.

costing FFr10.3 billion ($1.82 billion), plus options for another 20 (21 two-seat Rafale Bs, 12 single-seat Cs, and 15 naval single-seat Rafale Ms in all) for FFr5.5 billion, were in progress late in 1998, against a background of further company restructuring and privatisation to facilitate European aerospace merger moves. In December, the Dassault Aviation board finally approved the transfer of the state's 46 per cent shareholding in the fighter company to Aérospatiale, leaving the Dassault family with its original 49 per cent. Aérospatiale privatisation also began from its mid-1998 merger with MATRA's defence interests, giving the Lagardere group a 30-33 per cent stake in the former state company.

As one of the 13 Rafales on order at that time, the first production B1 two-seater of three then funded for the French air force (AA), the remaining 10 being for the navy, made its initial flight at Bordeaux-Merignac on 24 November. Accepted by the AA on 2 December, it joined the four prototypes in the development programme at Istres, where Rafale B2 and the first production naval M1 will follow in 1999, with initial F1 software limited to only air-to-air roles with MATRA/BAeD Magic and MICA AAMs.

The Aéronavale is expecting its first of 60 F1 standard Rafale Ms for operational service with Flottille 14F in October 1999, and anticipates having seven by 2001, of the 12 required for work-up trials on the carrier *Charles de Gaulle*.

GREECE:

Trainer acquisitions

Replacement of the 20 or so remaining HAF Cessna T-37B/Cs at Kalamata is planned from a $200 million Greek order with Raytheon for 45 Beech

Above: This VIP transport-configured Mi-8S of the 36 SPLT displays a new colour scheme. The unit flies from Warsaw-Okecie, and also operates the Tu-134, Tu-154 Yak-40 and Bell 412HP.

Right: 18. eskadra (C) of the Brygada Lotnictwa MW (Polish naval aviation) displayed this PZL W-3RM Anakonda in Amsterdam harbour, including a demonstration of the flotation equipment.

Mk II T-6A Texan turboprop trainers, selected in preference to the EMB-314 Super Tucano and the Pilatus PC-9G. The urgency of this programme is indicated by its initial delivery target of July 1999, with completion by 2002.

The Greek New Trainer Aircraft programme is also considering replacement of 30 or so HAF Rockwell T-2E advanced jet-trainers by up to 50 ex-German air force Alpha Jets, plus spare Larzac 04-C20 turbofans, airframe spares and ground training equipment. Most of the Luftwaffe Alpha Jets were operated in single-seat close air support roles, and, with upgraded avionics, could be adaptable for lead-in fighter training. They are being evaluated against offers of new Aero L-159T, AMX-T and BAe Hawk 100 lead-in fighter trainers.

Erieye selected for HAF AEW programme

A joint Brazilian/Swedish bid for the twin-turbofan EMBRAER ERJ-145, fitted with Ericsson's FSR890 Erieye planar phased-array dorsal antenna, as developed for the FAB's SIVAM Amazon air defence programme, was selected in late December 1998 for the Greek air force (HAF) airborne early-warning requirement. Negotiations were then being finalised with Ericsson, in conjunction with Thomson-CSF in France and EMBRAER in Brazil, for four NATO-compatible aircraft, with options for two more, for a mid-1999 contract worth more than $500 million.

For this second Erieye export order, Thomson-CSF will be responsible for some mission system avionics, including the DR3000 electronic support measures (ESM) system, IFF transponders, and radio and communications equipment. Initial deliveries to Greece are expected from late 2001.

MALTA:

Second Islander delivered

A refurbished Britten-Norman BN-2B-26 Islander utility light transport was delivered to the Armed Forces of Malta in September 1998. With two new 260-bhp (194-kW) Textron Lycoming O-540-E4C5 engines and new interior trim, the 1987 Islander joined an earlier similar aircraft in patrolling Malta's 25-nm (46-km) fishing zone, as well as monitoring pollution, illegal immigration and smuggling, plus airborne policing roles.

POLAND:

Preparing for NATO

NATO requirements for Polish entry call for three squadrons of Su-22s and MiG-29s. Half of the MiG-29 squadron is to be NATO-compatible by mid-1999, and an Su-22 squadron is to reach operational status by the end of 1999. The full squadron of MiG-29s is to be operational by the end of 2000 and the second squadron of Su-22s by the end of 2001.

The lack of an upgrade programme has forced the grounding of more than 100 aircraft over the next two years, leaving in the front line only some 150 MiG-23s and MiG-21bis, as well as a few Su-22s. The air force states that it is losing its operational capabilities and needs new equipment. Less expensive equipment such as indigenous Irydas or upgrades and modern avionics systems could be the cheapest and fastest solution, but this has not been pursued.

According to current plans, wider upgrades are to be made only to NATO-dedicated aircraft, i.e., the MiG-29s and Su-22s. It is expected that apart from new communications systems and IFFs, they will receive TACAN and GPS.

Iryda gets green light

The Ministry of National Defence and WSK PZL-Mielec have signed a contract under which three unfinished PZL I-22s will be put into flying condition, including all structural modification and installation of French avionics. The aircraft will be used for certification and evaluation, which is to last 18 months. The Ministry is to give the troubled company some PLN7-8 million ($2 million) to cover expenses for the modification and tests; it is thought that the whole project will be much more expensive and costs may reach PLN16-18 million.

The agreement ends almost 14 months of conflict over the Iryda and brings hope that new aircraft might finally enter service early in the next century. In total, 17 aircraft have been manufactured at a programme cost of around $300 million. Six of those

In December 1998 CASA flew the first production C.295 tactical transport, although a prototype (illustrated) has been flying since November 1997. The type is on the shortlist for the RAAF's Caribou replacement competition.

aircraft are new-build, and the remaining 11 have temporarily been withdrawn from service for modifications.

Polish multi-role fighter

Competitors to supply multi-role fighters to the Polish air force have been reduced to BAe/Saab/DASA and Boeing, the French having bowed out and New Zealand having bought the stored Pakistani F-16s offered by Lockheed Martin.

Boeing is offering its F/A-18 Hornet in A/B+ versions, and quantities of seven, 18, 24 and 36 are available. The company has proposed that Poland lease 18 F/A-18s and be responsible for infrastructure changes necessary to keep the aircraft operational. Maintenance would be carried out locally by Polish-US joint ventures. The addition of the L-159 to the package was rejected strongly by the Poles. First Hornet deliveries could start at the end of 1999, with the final aircraft arriving in 2001. The whole leasing would be completed by 2004, for Polish costs estimated at $250 million. To match the European offer, English language lessons for both flying and ground crews were also included, of six months duration and carried out at US bases.

The team of BAe, DASA and Saab has not proposed a lease option even though such types as Viggens, Tornadoes and Jaguars would be available. Instead, a joint effort upgrade of Polish MiG-29s would be undertaken and might cover radio equipment, IFFs, 1553 databus and online maintenance strategies. Polish financial straits rule out the introduction of full 'glass' cockpit and armament conversion, but such modifications are possible. The British suggest that four groups of Polish pilots per annum attend 10-week language courses specially focused on aviation language, and that all participants would have the opportunity to visit BAe Hawk-equipped No. 100 Squadron, where they would take part in planning air operations, flying in the back seat and finally joining debriefing. Polish instructors would be given the opportunity to train in Canada at NATO's flying school, which would hasten the conversion.

The Swedish air force is offering space on its own aircraft. Initially, Viggens would be made available but from mid-2000 Gripens would be added. In return, JAS 39s would be allowed to operate from Polish airfields. It is expected that such a solution would help the Polish air force to quickly build up the flying time of its pilots, which currently is around 50 hours per annum, to 150. It is anticipated that up to 1,000 hours could be flown with the Swedes.

BAe is reviewing an opportunity to obtain 20 Hawks from their current customers and lease them to the Polish air force to support operational and weapon training, for one-third the costs of flying front-line fighters.

PORTUGAL:

More F-16s ordered

Twenty-five surplus USAF F-16A/Bs, plus 20 upgrade kits, will be supplied in 1999 to Portugal from a $268 million letter of offer and acceptance (LOA) signed with the US on 30 November. Under the new Peace Atlantis II programme, 16 of the 21 F-16As and all four F-16Bs will undergo a three-phase upgrade, to supplement the FAP's 1994 Fighting Falcon procurement. This comprised 17 new-build F-16As and three F-16B two-seat combat trainers, which have already undergone NATO mid-life updates (MLU) to Block 15OCU standards.

Above: This Russian AF Let 410T was seen at the LET factory at Trencin, awaiting overhaul and return.

Below: '01' is the first production MiG-29SMT for the Russian air force, rolled out at Zhukhovskii on 29 December 1998.

After two prototype installations by Lockheed Martin in late 1999, OGMA will incorporate Falcon UP structural modifications, NATO-standard avionics and cockpit MLUs, plus modernisation requirements for their F100-PW-220E turbofans, in 18 surplus USAF F-16A/Bs in Portugal, from kits supplied by the US manufacturers. The remaining five F-16As will be cannibalised for spares, including their engines.

ROMANIA:

Lancer III first flight

Aerostar/Elbit's prototype upgraded MiG-21bis Lancer III with new digital avionics, shown statically at Farnborough in September 1998 with five weapons pylons, began its flight-test programme at Bacau on 6 October. For its 25-minute 'in-house receiving flight' in the hands of Israeli test-pilot Yehuda Shafir, a two-seat Romanian air force Lancer I/B acted as chase aircraft. A second sortie of only 12 minutes on 9 October by the same pilot was described as the first official test-flight of 40 planned for the Lancer III, which is being widely promoted among the many remaining MiG-21bis operators.

The first Romanian air force squadron from Grupul 95 Aviatie Vanatoare (95th Fighter Group), which became fully-equipped on 8 May 1997 with MiG-21MF Lancers upgraded jointly with Elbit Systems Ltd with similar digital avionics, is now operational. All 110 RoAF Lancers on order, comprising 75 I/A ground-attack versions, 10 two-seat MiG-21UM Lancer II/B combat trainers with similar mission-system avionics, and 25 II/C air-superiority variants with an additional Elta EL-2032M fire-control radar, will be delivered by the end of 1999.

TURKEY:

F-5 upgrade contract

A $70 million three-year contract awarded in September 1998 by the Ankara government to an Israel Aircraft Industries-led team will involve major upgrades of 48 Turkish air force (THK) Northrop F-5A/Bs for use as lead-in fighter trainers. In conjunction with Elbit Systems and Singapore Technologies Aerospace, IAI will produce a prototype installation and production kits for the THK F-5 upgrade, for completion entirely within Turkey. Structural upgrades and replacements will also be done where necessary by Turkish Aerospace Industries (TAI).

Installation of F-16-type digitised avionics, including cockpit layout and displays, HUD, HOTAS, nav/attack and weapons systems enhancement, will be based on previous IAI F-5 upgrades in Chile and Singapore, although without radar replacement which is possible only in the F-5E/F. IAI upgrade kits, plus integration and flight-testing, will be installed under Israeli supervision at THK's Eskisehir air base by 2001. IAI is already upgrading 54 THK F-4Es at Eskisehir from an earlier $640 million contract.

Attack helicopter procurement problems

Ambitious Turkish army plans for buying 145 attack helicopters costing $3.5 billion from local co-production between 2002-2010 were delayed late in 1999 by a change in government, and political disputes with potential supplier countries concerning Turkey's hostile handling of Kurdish claims for independence. These disputes effectively vetoed earlier national clearances for submissions to Turkey from Eurocopter for the Tiger, and from Agusta, teamed with IAI, for the A 129 International.

Prospects of US State Department clearance being maintained for the Bell Helicopter Textron AH-1W and upgraded AH-1Z, or Boeing/MDH AH-64D Longbow Apache, also began to seem increasingly unlikely. A clear run could therefore possibly result for the remaining submission, made jointly by Russia's Kamov and Israel Aircraft Industries for a developed Ka-50/52, with mainly Israeli avionics and missions systems equipment. The two-seat Ka-50-2 Alligator prototype, fitted with some Israeli equipment, was airlifted to Turkey in an Ilyushin Il-76 in October 1998 for trials and evaluation.

Transport helicopter plans

Fifty UH-60 Black Hawk transport helicopters ordered in October 1998 through a $500 million contract, to follow 45 delivered earlier, will also be Sikorsky-built, rather than under licence as originally planned, for delivery within about a year. In a long-standing parallel programme, the Turkish government has also allocated up to $300 million for eight heavy-lift helicopters, for which Sikorsky CH-53E Super Stallions were originally selected. Late in 1999, however, the Ankara government decided to reopen this requirement to competitive bids, which had earlier also included the Boeing CH-47D and Mil Mi-26.

Licence-production by Turkish Aerospace Industries, through a joint consortium with Eurocopter known as EuroTAI, started late in 1998 of 28 of the 30 AS 532 Cougar Mk I transport helicopters ordered from a $430 million 1997 contract. Following receipt in early 1999 of the first two Eurocopter-built Cougars, which will feature Mk II cockpit systems, deliveries of Turkish-assembled examples will follow from October 1999. Twenty were ordered for THK SAR roles, while the Turkish army will operate the remaining 10 in transport and utility roles.

CN.235M production

Following earlier Turkish military procurement of 52 CN.235Ms, of which 50 were licence-built by Tusas Aerospace Industries at its Akinci facility for THK operation, further national orders were confirmed late in 1999 for nine CASA/IPTN CN.235M twin-turboprop transports, costing some $108 million. Six will be modified for maritime patrol roles for the Turkish navy, and three for the Coast Guard Command. Export orders were also being negotiated by TAI with Croatia and Israel, plus a confirmed lease by Turkey of two CN.235Ms to the Royal Jordanian air force.

UNITED KINGDOM:

EH101 Merlin roll-out

Roll-out at GKN Westland's Yeovil facility on 25 November of ZJ117, the first of 22 Anglo-Italian EH101 Merlin HC.Mk 3 transport helicopters ordered for the RAF in March 1995 through a £750 million contract, inaugurated a 44 per cent increase over the next few years in its medium vertical-lift tactical capability. After factory and service trials leading to Controller Air clearance at the MoD's Defence Evaluation and Research Agency (DERA) at Boscombe Down, the Merlin Mk 3s will begin equipping the RAF's No. 28 Squadron at Benson, in Oxfordshire, on 1 April 2000.

The maximum range of 1000 km (621 miles) on internal fuel can be extended by air-to-air refuelling, giving it a 12-hour flight endurance. The Merlin HC.Mk 3 is also designed for shipboard operation, and has a night-vision goggle-compatible cockpit. All HC.Mk 3s have provision for a chin-mounted GEC-Marconi FLIR turret and air refuelling nose probe, for rapid installation when required, from RAF procurement of about half-a-dozen of each system.

An integrated defensive aids suite, including Hughes Danbury laser detection system, GEC-Marconi Sky Guardian 2000 radar-warning receiver, and Tracor ALE-47 countermeasures dispensers, is being installed by GKN Westland from a recent £28 million MoD contract.

RN Merlin HM.Mk 1 IFTU commissioned

Initial service delivery schedules established under the MoD's 1991 fixed-price programme contract for 44 GKN Westland-built EH101 Merlin HM.Mk 1 ASW helicopters were met on 1 December 1998 with the formal commissioning of the Royal Navy's No. 700M Squadron at RNAS Culdrose.

Merlin HM.Mk 1 autonomous mission equipment is claimed to incorporate the most advanced engineering and electronics of any current ASW helicopter, based on twin computers, integrated with dual digital databus and Ultra Electronics Data Link 11 systems. Also included are GEC-Marconi Avionics (GMAv) Blue Kestrel 7000 pulse-compression radar with 360° coverage and multiple target track-while-scan; Thomson-Marconi AQS-950/952 FLASH low-frequency active dipping sonar suite with a GMAv AQS-903 acoustic processor and Ultra sonobuoys; and Racal Orange Reaper passive electronic warfare (EW) and support measures (ESM) equipment.

No. 700M Squadron, commanded by Lieutenant Commander Phil Shaw, is scheduled to operate as an intensive flight trials unit (IFTU) until mid-2001

The EH101 Merlin achieved two important milestones on its way to full UK service. On 1 December 1998 No. 700M Squadron formally stood up at Culdrose to begin the operational evaluation task of the Navy's Merlin HM.Mk 1 (right), while on 24 December the RAF's Merlin HC.Mk 3 made its first flight from Westland's Yeovil plant (above).

to establish service training and operating procedures, while assessing future development potential. It will have four early production Merlin HM.Mk 1s, starting with ZH825 (build number RN05, the first for the RN being ZH821/RN01). An early task will be to check the viability of the Merlin's planned automated single-pilot operation, with an observer and a weapons systems operator to complete the three-man crew.

From GKN Westland production of currently one aircraft per month, delivery of the 12th Merlin to the Royal Navy by 31 March 1999 will mark the official in-service date. It will allow formation of the first operational training unit, No. 814 Squadron, to start Westland Sea King AS.Mk 6 replacement from 2000, with deliveries continuing between mid-2001 and 2004. No. 824 Squadron is expected to form as the first front-line Merlin unit in 2001, for embarkation on the carrier HMS *Ark Royal* after completion of its major refit later in that year.

Service clearance is then expected for ASW roles, carrying up to four GEC-Marconi Stingray or similar homing torpedoes or four Mk 11 depth charges over a 200-nm (370-km) range, to be followed by similar qualification for ASuW operations.

WAH-64 progress

Several major milestones in Britain's £2 billion Army Air Corps programme for the acquisition of 67 WAH-64D Apache attack helicopters were reached in the past year. They included the first flight of the prototype with Rolls-Royce/Turboméca

RTM322 turboshaft engines on 29 May and delivery of the first production example from Boeing to GKN Westland Helicopters, following its initial flight on 25 September.

Flight development of the RTM322-powered Apache started after less than two months of ground-running, following installation at Boeing's Mesa facility, in Arizona, in a prototype AH-64D on loan from the US Army. As prime contractor, GKN Westland accepted delivery of the first production WAH-64, with its US civil registration N9219G, on 28 September at Mesa. Although this was only three days after it first became airborne, the WAH-64 immediately continued flight development of its RTM322 turboshafts, Longbow millimetric-wave fire-control radar, and unique avionics system specified by the UK MoD.

BAe receives RAF Hawk upgrade contract

Long-term RAF proposals for a major upgrade of its 140 or so BAe Hawk T.Mk 1/1A advanced jet trainers, to rectify fuselage fatigue problems and extend their planned out-of-service date to 2010, finally resulted in an initial £100 million MoD contract in December 1998 with British Aerospace Military Aircraft and Aerostructures Division (MA&AD). BAe will now undertake design, development, and manufacture of 80 centre- and rear-fuselage sections for fatigue-limited RAF Hawks, based on its current Hawk Mk 60 export design, to maintain at least 120 in service to the extended retirement date.

Known as the Kasatka (killer whale), Kamov's Ka-60 utility helicopter made its first flight from the bureau's Lyubertsy facility on 24 December 1998. Although developed to a Russian army requirement, no funding has yet been allocated for procurement of this Mi-8 replacement.

Middle East

EGYPT:

SH-2G delivery completed

The last two of 10 Kaman SH-2G(E) Super Seasprite ASW helicopters ordered in 1995 for the Egyptian air force base were delivered on schedule in November 1998, to Burg el-Arab, near Alexandria. Their delivery also marked completion of the EAF Super Seasprite training programme for Egyptian air and ground crews at the US Naval Air Station at Pensacola, Florida.

ISRAEL:

New fighter decision imminent

Evaluations were continuing late in 1998 of the relative merits of more Boeing/MDC F-15Is or later model Lockheed Martin F-16s for the IDF/AF's $2.5 billion requirement for up to 110 new advanced combat aircraft to replace 90 MDC A-4H/N and TA-4Hs, some F-4s and early F-16A/Bs. Boeing's F/A-18C/D and the Lockheed Martin F-22 have not been entirely excluded from Israeli consideration, but IDF/AF opinion in early 1999 appeared to be inclining towards a compromise split purchase decision for the F-15 and F-16.

Since January 1998, Israel has been receiving two examples per month of the 25 two-seat F-15Is ordered earlier from McDonnell Douglas by the IDF/AF from a $2.5 billion contract. They are strike-optimised with Hughes APG-70 synthetic-aperture radar, Kaiser holographic HUD, and some Israeli mission and weapons systems, including Elbit flat-panel colour cockpit displays and helmet-mounted sight/display, Elisra SPS-2100 integrated EW suite, plus Rafael Python 4 advanced AAMs, and a new contract could at least double this total.

US Defense Department letters of offer and acceptance were recently extended to Israel for 30 F-15Is with a

lower $52 million programme unit cost, or 60 Block 50/52 F-16C/Ds costing about $2 billion, with various radar and equipment options. These are not expected to include Northrop Grumman's new agile-beam radar, however, nor Israeli proposals for installation of an indigenous Elta EL/M-2032 radar, among much other locally-produced equipment, in its new FMS-funded F-16s. A split procurement decision expected early in 1999 would, of course, mean reduced numbers of both US fighter types in the new programme.

Israeli/US upgrade agreement

A memorandum of understanding agreed between Lockheed Martin and an Israeli consortium led by Israel Aircraft Industries (IAI), signed in October 1998, is expected to lead to joint upgrades of some of the 250 or more early production F-16A/B air superiority fighters operated by countries other than the US. Excluded are those F-16s already undergoing mid-life upgrades, notably the 325 from Belgium, Denmark, the Netherlands and Norway, plus others elsewhere. It does include the remaining Fighting Falcons from 67 Block 10 F-16As and eight two-seat F-16Bs delivered to Israel in 1980, plus 37 similar ex-USAF F-16As and 13 Bs from 1994, although the IDF/AF has no immediate plans for their further upgrade.

They have already been extensively modified and updated since delivery by Israeli companies, including the current consortium members of Elbit Systems, Elta Electronics, El-Op Industries and Rafael Armament Development Authority, as well as IAI. Operational capability improvements for IDF/AF's F-16A/Bs have included integration by Elbit of its DASH display and sighting helmet, in conjunction with advanced Israeli air-to-air and air-to-surface missiles, and digital communications systems.

7

Military Aviation Review

Only the small Israel Air Force 50th anniversary badge next to the forward door reveals the ownership of this IDF/AF EC-707 seen on a visit to the UK. The boards around the aircraft warn of an explosive cargo.

Wearing muted US national insignia and USAF serial, this is one of a batch of F-15Ss which passed through RAF Lakenheath on its delivery to Saudi Arabia. All 72 are due to be delivered before the end of 1999.

Elbit F-16 products have also included advanced stores management systems (SMS), on a sub-contract basis to General Dynamics; multi-function cockpit displays (MFDs), as co-producer from a Honeywell licence; and two generations of Elbit-developed fire-control computers (FCCs). Over 700 F-16s have been equipped with Elbit-produced SMS sets, and nearly 2,000 of its MFDs have been supplied.

Other IDF/AF F-16 upgrades, including such indigenous weapons systems as fourth-generation DASH-controlled Rafael Python 4 AAMs and precision-guided munitions, plus the addition of Elta EL/M-2032 fire-control radar and El Op 967 head-up displays, are planned by the Israeli consortium through its Netz (Hawk) programme in a demonstrator aircraft, due to fly by late 1999. Following the recent MoU, Lockheed Martin's technical support is now expected for any structural work involved in F-16 upgrade programmes. Israeli proposals to install advanced Elta radar in new production IDF/AF F-16s have been rejected by the US, however, which is not prepared to release the software source codes required for weapons systems integration.

SAUDI ARABIA:

Tornado deliveries completed

On 24 September 1998 British Aerospace delivered at Warton the 48th and last Tornado IDS aircraft to complete the Royal Saudi air force's 1993 Al Yamamah II contract, marking the end of production of the three-nation Panavia project. As the sole export customer for the Tornado, Saudi Arabia took delivery of 24 air defence versions and 96 interdictor-strike examples in two batches from 1986, the latter including 12 similar to the RAF's GR.Mk 1As, for electro-optic reconnaissance. Some 992 Tornados were built in all by the Panavia consortium, including prototype and development aircraft.

UNITED ARAB EMIRATES:

F-16 procurement deferred

US restrictions on radar, ECM and weapon software source codes delayed signature of the UAE's $6.7 billion commercial contract for 80 new Lockheed Martin Block 60 F-16C/D

variants, originally planned for late 1998. Similarly affected was the $2 billion associated US weapons package, from FMS funding, for Raytheon AIM-9M Sidewinders, AIM-120 AMRAAMs, AGM-65D/G Mavericks, and AGM-88 HARMs, plus Boeing AGM-84 Harpoon 1Gs, and laser-guided bombs.

While further negotiations continued, the UAE reportedly resumed discussions with Dassault in November on its previously short-listed Rafale submission for the new fighter contract, for which deliveries are required from 2002. At the same time, the UAE finalised its $3.4 billion contract for 30 new Mirage 2000-9 multi-role fighters, plus upgrades to similar standards of its 33 earlier Mirage 2000-8s. Up to $2 billion has also been allocated to Thomson-CSF for RDY multi-role AI radars with enhanced air-to-surface software for new precision-guided munitions, new ECM suites, and additional related equipment.

A further $2.1 billion is being spent, mainly with MATRA/BAeD, on associated weapons, including the first export order for the Black Shaheen version of the Storm Shadow/SCALP EG cruise missile, as well as IR- and radar-guided MICA AAMs. Selected in preference to GEC-Marconi Electronic System's PGM 4 Centaur version of its Al Hakim, developed specifically for the UAE, Black Shaheen is being released for export to approved customers by the British and French governments. Both claim that it does not infringe International Missile Technology Control Regime (MTCR) Category 2 limitations, despite its range of more than 300 km (186 miles), since its warhead weighs less than 500 kg (1,102 lb).

Africa

ERITREA:

MiG-29s acquired

Moldova was thought to be the source of up to 10 MiG-29s acquired by Eritrea towards the end of 1998, to provide a viable combat element for its embryo air force. Hitherto this has been restricted to six Aermacchi MB.339FD lead-in fighter trainers, which have light ground-attack capa-

bilities. Eritrea's MiG-29s are believed to be the airworthy remainder of 34 taken over by Moldova from the USSR after its 1991 collapse, following pre-emptive US Defense Department acquisition of six 'Fulcrum-As', one two-seat MiG-29UB, and all 14 'Fulcrum-Cs' from this total in October 1997. Unconfirmed reports suggest that one had been shot down in February 1999.

ETHIOPIA:

Su-27s supplied

Ten surplus VVS Sukhoi Su-27 'Flanker' advanced combat aircraft, with associated weapons and support equipment, as well as Mil Mi-24 and Mi-8 attack and transport helicopters, were reportedly included in a Russian arms package deal agreed with the Ethiopian government in late 1998. The Su-27s were immediately airlifted from Krasnodar to Ethiopia in VVS Antonov An-22s, and represent a major advance in Ethiopia's combat capabilities over its current 20 or so MiG-21bis fighters. An upgrade contract for 11 of these, agreed in July 1998 with Elbit Defence Systems, was reportedly suspended by the Israeli government following representations from Eritrea, which is involved in border disputes and an arms race with Ethiopia. Its MiG-21s were to have received similar digital avionics and Elta EL/M-2032 multi-mode radar to those being installed by Elbit and Aerostar for Romania's Lancer upgrade programme.

SOUTH AFRICA:

European arms selected

Contracts worth up to R30 billion ($5.2 billion) were being negotiated in late 1998 with major European arms contractors, following South Africa's November announcement of preferred suppliers of the main items for its National Defence Force (SANDF) modernisation programme. Apart from $1.9 billion of naval procurement from Germany of four corvettes and three submarines, most SANDF appropriations were allocated for the aerospace package.

This included the first export order for the Saab/BAe JAS 39 Gripen, although the SAAF's revised total of 28, costing around $1.76 billion with spares and support equipment, falls

short of South Africa's original new combat aircraft requirement of 38, to replace Cheetahs and Atlas-built Aermacchi MB.326 Impalas. Six two-seat JAS 39B combat trainers were also originally expected, but SAAF procurement is now thought likely to include no more than two or three. Submitted jointly with BAe, from its 35 per cent shareholding in the Swedish aerospace group, the Gripen won preference over the Dassault 2000-5 and DaimlerChrysler Aerospace's projected AT2000 Mako supersonic advanced trainer/light combat aircraft.

The SAAF is expected to receive its first examples, incorporating Denel-built components, from about 2003. Authorisation to re-export the substantial US content of the Gripen, including its GE F404-derived Volvo RM12 turbofan, to South Africa – previously the subject of an arms embargo – was received by Sweden only last August.

BAe is also benefiting from its first order for the lead-in fighter trainer (LIFT) version of its Hawk Srs 100, costing some $830 million, for the 24 aircraft specified by the SAAF. Equipped with similar digital avionics, including three multi-function cockpit displays, to those in the Gripen and Eurofighter, SAAF Hawks will assume from 2005 some operational conversion roles originally planned for a larger number of two-seat JAS 39Bs. They will also have seven weapons pylons for up to 6,800 lb (3085 kg) of ordnance for light attack roles.

South Africa's selection of four Super Lynx 300 ASW/ASV helicopters in preference to Eurocopter's AS 532SC Cougar for its new corvettes could be worth some £80 million to GKN Westland. This would also represent the first Super Lynx 300 export order, with new FADEC-controlled Rolls-Royce/AlliedSignal CTS800 turboshaft engines offering 30 per cent more power than the previous RR Gems, and a full 'glass' (EFIS) cockpit with digital avionics. Up to eight Super Lynxes may eventually be required to replace the South African navy's six Westland Wasps for the new corvettes.

Agusta, GKN's Italian partner in the EH101 and other helicopter projects, was also selected to meet SANDF requirements for up to 60 light utility and combat support helicopters to replace venerable Sud Alouette IIIs. Contracts for some $380 million were planned for an initial batch of 40

Aero India '98

Held at Bangalore between 8 and 12 December, the show provided a rare occasion to review India's ongoing efforts to become more self-sufficient in defence procurement. Despite some interesting new developments, the long-awaited LCA fighter failed to appear yet again.

Right: The Lancer is a new light attack variant of the HAL Cheetah (licence-built SA 315 Lama), with two weapon pods, each containing a 12.7-mm machine-gun and three 70-mm rockets.

Below: This An-32 is fitted with prominent chaff/flare dispensers.

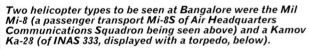

Above: HAL is still producing Jaguars under licence for the IAF. The final single-seater is due for delivery in 1999, but work is beginning on a new batch of two-seaters, potentially for use in a deep strike role. This is a maritime radar-equipped Jaguar M from No. 6 Squadron.

Two helicopter types to be seen at Bangalore were the Mil Mi-8 (a passenger transport Mi-8S of Air Headquarters Communications Squadron being seen above) and a Kamov Ka-28 (of INAS 333, displayed with a torpedo, below).

Above: The green/white/saffron markings were originally applied to some of the Su-30s of No. 24 Squadron for their public debut, but the colours have been retained, although now looking decidedly worn. The first full-specification Su-30MKI has been completed at the Irkutsk works, and deliveries of the canard-equipped, thrust-vectoring 'Flanker' are due to begin in 2000.

Left: The HAL ALH (Advanced Light Helicopter) has entered the pre-production phase, with three pattern aircraft being built (one each for the army, air force and navy). Two powerplants are available, the Turboméca TM 333 and LHTEC CTS800, with each service free to choose. Three hundred are expected to be ordered, comprising 120 each for the navy and army, and 60 for the air force. Seen here in company with a Chetak is the army/air force prototype, one of four so far produced.

9

Seen at the Moma Stanojlovic repair centre at Belgrade-Batajnica in 1998 were four Iraqi air force aircraft which have been held for some time since undergoing overhaul, with no immediate intention of redelivery. These include a MiG-21bis (above) and MiG-23MF (below).

Agusta A 109s, with provision for light armament, plus participation by Denel Aviation in production and sales of the new A 119 Koala utility helicopter.

Additional SANDF requirements then remained for light and medium transport, tanker and maritime patrol aircraft, plus attack helicopters. Offset contracts for at least R50 billion ($8.7 billion) are being specified for all new procurement by South Africa's Armscor defence procurement agency for national industries over the next 15-20 years, and could generate up to twice that amount.

ZIMBABWE:

Russian arms package

A new lease of life for the badly run-down Zimbabwe armed forces, for which some $60 million was sought by Defence Minister Moven Mahachi in mid-1998, was promised by news of an arms deal with Russia for £32 million in November 1998. Virtually grounded through funding problems, from a national defence budget of little more

than $250 million per year, the Air Force of Zimbabwe (AFZ) was reportedly one of the main beneficiaries of this deal, from deliveries of unspecified new combat aircraft, Mil Mi-24 'Hind' attack helicopters, and reconnaissance types, plus associated weapons, before the end of 1998.

Limited AFZ operations with its dozen or so Chinese-built Chengdu F-7II/N (MiG-21) fighter-bombers at Thornhill air base, and similar number of venerable Hunter FGA.Mk 9s, are now expected to be supplemented, after operational training with the new equipment, in Zimbabwe's support of President Kabila's opposition to Tutsi-led rebels in the neighbouring Congo Republic (formerly Zaïre). An AFZ MiG-21 and one of the newly-delivered Mil Mi-24 attack helicopters were claimed by Tutsi-led Congolese rebels to have been shot down in December 1998 in operations around the southeastern town of Kabalo.

Other AFZ aircraft deliveries in 1998 reportedly included an additional six SIAI-Marchetti SF.260F piston-engined basic trainers.

Southern Asia

INDIA:

IAF MiG-21 upgrade programme stretched

Budget constraints and Russian economic problems are delaying for up to three years the IAF's Rs15 billion ($388 million) three-year modernisation programme for 125 MiG-21bis 'Fishbed-Ns', for which MiG-MAPO, ANPK Sokol, Sextant Avionique and Elta Electronics are joint contractors with HAL. Following formal roll-out on 20 August 1998 of the prototype IAF MiG-21bis, upgraded by the Sokol plant of Russia's VPK MAPO group at Nizhni Novgorod, flight trials started there on 6 October, although

they were originally scheduled for April. A two-seat prototype was also expected to follow from the Sokol factory, before the remaining IAF MiG-21s are upgraded by 2004 from 123 component kits by Hindustan Aeronautics Ltd at Bangalore, as original constructors of the IAF 'Fishbeds', including 220 IAF MiG-21bis. Apart from the Phazotron Kopyo lightweight multi-mode fire-control radar, Sextant is supplying most of the new digital nav/attack avionics for the IAF programme, including a Totem ring laser-gyro INS with embedded GPS, and a liquid-crystal display and control unit.

India's upgrade contract also includes advanced Russian air-to-air and precision-guided air-to-surface

missiles, for continued IAF MiG-21 service until at least 2015.

Jaguar production extended

Indian government funding was authorised late in 1998 for 18 more two-seat BAe Jaguar B combat trainers for the Indian Air Force, according to reports from the Aero India 98 trade show at Bangalore in December. Following initial deliveries of 40 Jaguar Internationals from British Aerospace from 1981, assembly and licence-production by Hindustan Aeronautics Ltd continued until 1997 with completion of its 91st aircraft. These included 15 Jaguar Bs, which will now be supplemented over the next three years by the 18 new combat trainers. Unlike the IAF's earlier two-seat Jaguars, the new aircraft will have upgraded digital avionics from Elbit and Sextant Avionique for ground-attack and close-support roles with precision-guided munitions. Similar retrofit upgrade programmes

are also planned for another 45 or more of the IAF's existing Jaguars.

PAKISTAN:

FC-1 interest hardens

Having finally abandoned any hopes of fulfilling its original requirement for a total of 72 more F-16s, because of US arms embargoes resulting from Pakistan's nuclear weapons programme, the PAF was reportedly planning procurement of up to 100 Klimov RD-33-engined Chengdu FC-1 or Super 7 developments of the MiG-21, with Western avionics. Although the Chinese air force is apparently not interested in the acquisition of the FC-1, four Klimov RD-33N (RD-93) turbofans with lower-mounted accessory gearbox for installation in MiG-21, Mirage III and Mirage F1 variants, had been delivered to Chengdu by mid-1998 for this programme. A prototype FC-1 is expected to fly in China later in 1999 or in early 2000.

Far East

CHINA:

Su-27 co-production begins

Assembly began in mid-1998 by the Shenyang Aircraft Corporation (SAC) of the first two of 200 Sukhoi Su-27SK (J-11) advanced air superiority fighters scheduled for co-production from initial kits of parts from the KnAAPO Aviation Production Association at Komsomolsk-on-Amur. Some 15 Su-27SKs are scheduled for completion in China by 2000, of the 200 currently ordered for the co-production programme, supplementing 26 delivered from Russia in 1992, and 24 more in 1996.

JAPAN:

F-2 delivery plans

Withdrawals have started from the Japanese Air Self-Defence Force (JASDF) of the Mitsubishi F-1 close air-support fighter, in anticipation of their replacement by the first of 130 planned Mitsubishi/Lockheed Martin F-16-derived F-2s, including 47 two-seat F-2B versions. From original

deliveries of 77 F-1s by 1986, 59 remained in operation early in 1999 in three squadrons of the 3rd Air Wing at Misawa air base and at Tsuiki. This total will decrease to 24 by 2002, following scheduled delivery in March 2000 of the first F-2s to Misawa. In addition to four flight prototypes, 39 F-2s are planned for delivery by 2002, of which 28 have been ordered to date, with funding continuing for about nine aircraft per year until around 2011. F-2s will also begin replacing some of the JASDF's current 107 F-4EJ Kai Phantoms in the early 2000s, although 103 will still remain in service in FY 2002, alongside 197 F-15J/DJs.

FY99 aircraft requests

Despite major reductions in purchasing power caused by recent Far Eastern

In January 1999 the JGSDF received its first Raytheon King Air 350 (local designation LR-2) to begin replacement of the MU-2 (LR-1) in the liaison/reconnaissance role. The first user will be Dai 1 Herikoputa-dan at Kisarazu AB.

After 55 years of service to the RAAF, the Dakota was withdrawn from service in December 1998. Four aircraft were left in ARDU service, with plenty of useful hours left. No replacement has been found and the 'Daks' may yet fly on.

currency devaluations, FY99 defence budget requests of Yen4,960 billion ($35 billion) remained virtually unchanged from previous years. As in FY98, the Japanese Defence Agency requested 48 new aircraft costing over $2 billion for the three Self-Defence Forces, comprising (in millions of dollars, with previous year procurement in parentheses where applicable, and current cost requests):

Air SDF: Mitsubishi (MHI) F-2A/B combat aircraft, eight (nine), $868.4 million; Kawasaki (KHI) T-4 advanced trainer, 12 (nine), $235.9 million; Fuji T-7 primary trainer, two, $4.8 million; Raytheon Hawker/BAe U-125A SAR aircraft, two (three), $75.9 million; KHI/Boeing CH-47J airlift helicopter, two, $76.3 million; Sikorsky/MHI UH-60J SAR helicopter, two (two), $59.17 million. Total, 28 (25) aircraft costing Yen174 billion in all.

Maritime SDF: ShinMaywa US-1A SAR amphibian, one, $67.7 million; SH-60J ASW helicopter, 10 (seven), $383.4 million; Beech TC-90 instrument trainer, three, $18.5 million. Total, 14 (10) aircraft costing Yen62 billion.

Ground SDF: UH-60JA utility helicopter, three (five), $83.7 million; KHI OH-1 scout helicopter, four (two), $65.8 million; FHI/Bell UH-1J utility helicopter, five (four), $55.1 million; KHI/Boeing CH-47J airlift helicopter, two (one), $87.4 million; Beech LR-2 liaison aircraft, two, $23.5 million. Total, 16 (13) aircraft costing Yen42 billion.

T-3 trainer approved

Turboprop conversion of some 50 piston-engined Fuji T-3 basic trainers (licence-built Beech T-34 Mentor developments), operated by the JASDF since 1978, was approved late in 1999 on economy grounds, in preference to competing submissions for their replacement by the EMBRAER Tucano, Pilatus PC-7 or Raytheon-Beech T-6A. T-3 re-engining to KM-2F or T-7 standards, with 450-shp (336-kW) Rolls-Royce/Allison 250-B17F engines costing up to $24 million, is expected to be similar to the modifications made to the Beech

Since February 1998 this MD369FF of the Ejército de Chile's Regimiento de Aviación N° 1 has had a rapid VIP transport role, for which it has been repainted in this smart scheme. There are no visible national insignia or serials.

T-34C Turbo Mentor. The work will be done locally by Fuji, as original prime contractor, for JASDF service from about 2000 onwards. Fuji's conversion will probably be based on its JMSDF T-5 turboprop trainer, which is a four-seat T-34 development with a 420-shp (313-kW) Allison 250-B17D turboprop. The last of 36 Japanese navy T-5s, each costing $4.3 million, was funded in FY98.

SOUTH KOREA:

Caravan II delivery begun

The first three of five Cessna F406 Caravan II twin P&WC PT6A-powered light transports ordered in 1997 from a $24 million Republic of Korea contract were delivered late in 1998 from Reims Aviation's Prunay facility in France. F 406 delivery is due for completion in June 1999, and the aircraft will fulfil RoK navy fleet support, utility and gunnery target-facility roles.

NORTH KOREA:

Mi-8 deliveries thwarted

Attempts by unspecified agencies to deliver five ex-Russian air force Mil Mi-8T armed transport helicopters to North Korea in October were reportedly frustrated by border guards southwest of Vladivostok. They apparently found no customs clearances or other required paperwork for the Mi-8s, which had set out to fly across the narrow border between Russia, Manchuria and North Korea.

PHILIPPINES:

F-5 strength increased

Delivery was reported late in 1998 to Manila of the five surplus Northrop F-5As promised earlier by the South Korean government, increasing reported PhilAF fighter strength to 11 F-5As and a single two-seat F-5B combat trainer. However, planned procurement of a dozen new air combat aircraft, as a priority programme within the Philippine government's 15-year Peso164.4 billion ($4 billion) armed forces modernisation programme, has been deferred because of the Far East economic slump.

TAIWAN:

Fighter deliveries continue

From initial deliveries in May 1997, the last of 48 Dassault Mirage 2000-5E multi-role fighters and 12 2000-5D two-seat combat trainers ordered for the Republic of China air force (RoCAF) from a $5.4 billion 1992 contract, arrived in Taiwan in November 1998. With them were their associated air superiority weapons, including MATRA/BAeD Magic 2 and 1,200 MICA short- and medium-range air-to-air missiles. The new Mirages have completely replaced the RoCAF's last Lockheed F-104Gs in two squadrons of the 2nd Tactical Fighter Wing at Hsinchu AB.

By mid-October 1998, two squadrons of the 4th TFW at Chiayi had also replaced their Northrop F-5E/Fs with 103 of 120 Lockheed Martin Block 20 F-16As and 30 two-seat F-16Bs similarly ordered in 1992, as part of $17 billion worth of Taiwan's current FMS contracts. A RoCAF F-16 training unit had also been formed at Luke AFB, Ariz., and the 4th TFW will complete its re-equipment by late 1999. It will then also receive the first of 28 sets of Lockheed Martin LANTIRN Pathfinder and Sharpshooter navigation and targeting pods from a recent $160 million FMS contract. They will be used with Taiwan's AGM-65 Maverick and AGM-84 Harpoon ASMs and AShMs, although, to meet Chinese objections to US offensive arms supplies, they will not have their customary laser target designators.

Chinook order reduced

US clearance was announced in October 1998 for Taiwan's Foreign Military Sales acquisition of nine Boeing CH-47SD Chinook MLHs costing $486 million, for delivery from 2000. Also included in the FMS package were three spare Lycoming T55-L-714A turboshafts, plus chaff/flare dispensers and radar warning receivers. Taiwan's original requirement was for 12 Chinooks, but the order was reduced as part of the defence economies imposed by the currency devaluation of some 25 per cent in the past year.

RoC army plans to acquire 100 or so utility helicopters costing some $1 billion, for which the Bell Helicopter Textron 412EP, Eurocopter AS 532U2 Cougar Mk II and Sikorsky SH-70 were competing, has been deferred for the same reasons.

Taiwanese procurement is going ahead, however, of 13 Bell OH-58D Kiowa Warrior armed scout helicopters, costing $172 million, as is a $160 million programme for 21 Bell AH-1W Super Cobras. Procurement sought in the $8.9 billion 1999 equipment budget includes Lockheed P-3C Orions, AIM-120 AMRAAMs, UAVs and other items.

THAILAND:

F-5 upgrades approved

Funding made available from Thailand's withdrawal, after major currency devaluations, from its $392 million contract for eight MDC F/A-18s, less its $74.5 million initial deposit, is now being applied to a low-cost upgrade of about half of the RTAF's 35 or so Northrop F-5E/Fs by Israel's Elbit Systems. As in Elbit's F-5S upgrade for Singapore, this will include new digital avionics and twin multi-function colour cockpit displays, plus a HUD. To minimise costs, however, the RTAF's F-5s will retain their original Emerson fire-control radar. As Elbit's partners in the F-5S project, neither Singapore Technologies Aerospace nor IAI is apparently participating in the RTAF F-5 programme, for which they also reportedly bid.

VIETNAM:

More Su-27s sought

Vietnamese air force requirements for up to 24 more Sukhoi Su-27 advanced air combat aircraft have been reported, to follow on from 12 initially delivered from 1994. Two attrition replacement Su-27UB combat trainers, destroyed on the December 1997 delivery flight in the Antonov An-124 crash at Irkutsk, are reportedly being replaced by twin-stick Su-30s.

Yak-52 delivery confirmed

With deliveries of 12 Yakovlev Yak-52 basic trainers in 1997, recently confirmed by Aerostar SA in Romania, the VAF may be the last major customer for this tandem-seat piston-engined aircraft. More than 1,800 have been produced by the sole-source Romanian company since 1978, mostly for the former Soviet Union. This received its last Yak-52 in 1991, although 12 were delivered to the Szolnok military school in Hungary in early 1994.

Australasia

AUSTRALIA:

Transport disposal sought

Offers were invited in November 1998 for two HS 748-229 twin-turboprop transports of 10 operated since 1966 by the RAAF for VIP and navigational training roles. Both aircraft were withdrawn from service in 1999 and, with six Rolls-Royce Dart turboprops and other spares, offered for public tender.

NEW ZEALAND:

F-16 lease-purchase deal

Long-standing US attempts to dispose of the 13 GD-built PW F100-220-powered Block 15OCU F-16As and 15 similar two-seat F-16Bs completed for Pakistan, but embargoed before delivery in 1992 because of Islamabad's nuclear policies, finally succeeded in late 1998. On 1 December, New Zealand's Defence Minister Max Bradford announced two consecutive five-year lease agreements at $NZ12.5 million ($6.62 million) per annum for the RNZAF, with a follow-on purchase option.

Pakistan was still owed $501 million of $658 million paid from FMS funding for these aircraft, which flew fewer than 10 hours on initial acceptance and ferrying sorties before being held in flyable and then long-term AMARC storage. The US retained their ownership, plus responsibility for their disposal and refunding to Pakistan the balance, less $34 million in service charges.

The proposed contract, which includes $NZ200 million ($106 million) for reactivation, training and support, should save the New Zealand government at least $NZ431 million ($228.5 million) over the cost of new combat aircraft. It can also apparently be accommodated within the RNZAF's NZ$435 million ($230 million) five-year capital investment budget, while further modernisation, costing some $NZ54 million ($28.6 million), would have been required to keep 13 upgraded MDC A-4K and five two-seat TA-4K Skyhawks in planned operation until about 2007.

All but two of the ex-Pakistani F-16s, due for spares cannibalisation,

plus four in reserve, will now replace the first RNZAF Skyhawks in No. 2 Squadron, deployed at Nowra, New South Wales, in Australia, and No. 75 Squadron, at Ohakea, in New Zealand, from 2001. Procurement is also planned of a targeting pod for delivering precision guided munitions, supplementing existing AGM-65 ASMs and defensive AIM-9 AAMs.

Second-phase Orion upgrade funded

Completion in November 1998 of the first of the six RNZAF Lockheed P-3K Orions being rewinged in Australia by Hawker Pacific, which is also fitting new tailplanes and nacelle skins through the Project Kestrel upgrade programme, preceded requests for proposals for their $NZ240 million ($127 million) second-phase modernisation. Known as Project Sirius, this will involve new mission systems avionics (MSA) from eight kits with new off-the-shelf radar, infra-red and electro-optical sensors, plus enhanced data processing, MAD, INS/GPS, Link 11 tactical data transfer, IFF, ESM and ECM systems.

Main competition for this contract is expected from Boeing Information & Surveillance Systems and Raytheon Systems, with additional participation from Lockheed Martin Aeronautical Systems, British Aerospace Australia, and the Safe Air subsidiary of Air New Zealand. Equipment selection was still in progress, with inputs sought from other Orion MSA upgrade programmes, including those in Australia and Spain. RNZAF P-3 roles are confined to surveillance and ASW, with no anti-surface warfare or anti-ship missile requirement.

New grading trainers

Re-equipment of the RNZAF's Flying Training Wing at Ohakea started in 1999 with delivery of the first of 13

The Prefectura Aeropolicial of the Carabineros de Chile (militarised police) received its first Eurocopter EC 135T1 on 14 January 1999. The EC 135s will replace BO 105s based mainly at Santiago.

The Brazilian navy has acquired 20 A-4KUs and three TA-4KUs from Kuwait. They are known respectively as AF-1 (below, armed with four AIM-9Hs) and AF-1A (above). The fleet, based at São Pedro da Aldeia Naval Air Base, is being repainted in a grey scheme.

CT-4/E Airtrainers from the Pacific Aerospace Corporation (PAC), for primary tuition and grading roles. Powered by 300-bhp (224-kW) Lycoming IO-540 piston engines, they are being leased from PAC through a 20-year $NZ30 million ($14.87 million) supply

and support contract signed in August 1998. Due to improved reliability, the 13 new aircraft will replace 15 older CT-4/Bs, powered by 260-bhp (194-kW) Lycoming IO-360 engines, which have been operated by the RNZAF since 1975.

South America

ARGENTINA:

UK arms restrictions eased

A British government veto on UK arms exports to Argentina, imposed during the 1982 Falklands War, was partly lifted late in 1998 to allow sales of defensive equipment, following the improvement in relations which culminated in the London visit of President Menem in November. Foreign Office Minister Tony Lloyd said that export licences would continue to be refused for any equipment likely to jeopardise Falklands security. Agreement was reached, however, on closer training links between the armed forces of the two countries.

The FAA still operates 13 of 17 FMA IA 63 Pampas originally built, but, with no further production planned, needs at least 18 more jet trainers, for which BAe's Hawk 60 series would qualify. FAA interest, however, has reportedly been directed more towards acquiring 18 surplus USN two-seat TA-4 Skyhawks from AMARC storage, and upgrading them alongside the 36 A-4Ms being similarly modernised by Lockheed Martin Aircraft Argentina.

BRAZIL:

F-5 upgrade approved

Israel's Elbit Systems Ltd was set for further successes in the lucrative Northrop F-5 upgrade market in

October 1998 from its selection as joint contractor with EMBRAER for the modernisation of some or all of Brazil's 45 or so F-5E/Fs. Details of new digital avionics and required structural upgrades were being finalised in early 1999, to precede a $180 million contract to extend FAB F-5E/F operating lives to at least 2015.

The FAB will be seeking some commonality with its new EMBRAER EMB-312H ALX light attack aircraft mission systems, for which Elbit is also supplying and/or integrating the modular avionics, including the mission computer, liquid-crystal colour multi-function cockpit and HUDs, HOTAS, stores management, and defensive aid systems. Elta's EL/M-2032 fire-control radar may face competition from the Alenia/FIAR Grifo for the FAB's F-5s, despite earlier proposals to install some of Brazil's AMX avionics and systems, including the indigenous SCP-10 radar.

Elbit is also favoured to supply similar digital avionics for Brazil's fourth batch of AMX ground-attack fighters, comprising 34 upgraded single-seat and four two-seat combat trainer versions, planned to supplement earlier deliveries of 45 and 11, respectively.

COLOMBIA:

More US anti-drug aid

Supply to the Colombian National Police of six Sikorsky UH-60 Black Hawks costing $60 million and 50 Bell

The second F-22A Raptor arrived at Edwards for tests in late 1998 (top right). In early 1999 Boeing began flight testing of the F-22 Flying Test Bed (above and right), a conversion of the prototype Boeing 757 with F-22 avionics, including a representative leading-edge section. On board is a simulated F-22 cockpit.

UH-1H Iroquois upgraded to Huey II standards and armed with 0.3-in Miniguns, for a further $70 million, were among US military aid proposals being finalised in Washington in late 1998. They were included in a $2.3 billion three-year anti-drug programme planned by the US for Latin America.

C-130 drug bust

US Customs agents at Fort Lauderdale (Florida) International Airport seized a Colombian Air Force C-130H Hercules on 9 November 1998 after finding 1,639 lb (743 kg) of cocaine beneath the floorboards of the aircraft. Agents said large metal pallets aboard the C-130H contained unusual rivets, and inspectors smelled fresh glue. A Customs Service drug-sniffing dog was brought in and alerted agents to the presence of the cocaine. The seizure led to the arrests of several Fuerza Aérea Colombiana officers and prompted recently-appointed chief of staff General Manuel Sandoval to tender his resignation. The aircraft was Lockheed 382C-42E c/n 4965, registered as N41030 when it was delivered to Colombia in June 1983 to become FAC 1005. It was the newest of 13 Hercules transports operated by the FAC at various times.

Only three weeks earlier, three FAC junior officers were sentenced in Colombia to prison terms for an incident in September 1996, when 8.8 lb (4 kg) of heroin were found aboard Colombia's presidential jet shortly before it was to fly then-President Ernesto Samper to New York for a United Nations meeting. The presidential jet in question apparently was Fokker F28L2 FAC-0001 (formerly FAC 001) c/n 11992 which Colombia has had since January 1971.

ECUADOR:

Kfir supply approved

US government approval was received late in 1998 for the supply by Israel Aircraft Industries of two surplus IAI Kfir fighter-bombers as attrition replacements to the Ecuadorian air force (FAE). State Department clearance was required for their $5.6 million resale because of their US GE J79 turbojets and some equipment. After refurbishment and minor upgrades by IAI, the Kfirs will supplement the remainder of 10 Kfir C.2s and two TC.2 two-seat combat trainers operated by Escuadrón Combate 2113 within Ala de Combate 21 (Grupo 211) from Taura air base. An upgrade agreement for the surviving FAE Kfirs was also being finalised with IAI in late 1998, within an overall $60 million package.

PERU:

MiG-29 support deal

A late 1998 Peruvian government order to MIG-MAPO for three new 'Fulcrums' finally extracted a Russian promise of spares, technical support and co-operation for the 16 surplus MiG-29s, two MiG-29UB combat trainers and 14 Sukhoi Su-25 ground-attack fighters bought by the FAP from Belarus in 1996 in a $385 million cut-price package. Due to arrive in early 1999, they are expected to be undelivered MiG-29s from former Soviet air force orders, and will include a replacement for one ex-Belarus 'Fulcrum' which has already crashed. Belarus is also reported to be offering to trade in another 36 MiG-29s to Algeria for the latter's 120 or so MiG-21s.

URUGUAY:

New Cessna U206s

Earlier Cessna U206 utility lightplanes operating with the Fuerza Aérea

Uruguaya on a range of training, air ambulance and surveillance roles were recently supplemented by 10 Cessna 206 Stationairs. With a maximum payload of 700 kg (1,543 lb), the Stationair is the third of Cessna's well-tried light aircraft to return to production, after the Model 172 and 182.

North America

UNITED STATES:

Atlantic Fleet Hornets begin relocation

The dozen Atlantic Fleet F/A-18 Hornet squadrons, which collectively form Commander Strike Fighter Wing Atlantic (COMSTRIKFIGHTWING-LANT) currently based at NAS Cecil Field, Florida, began relocating during December 1998. First to move were VFA-131 and VFA-136, which are part of Carrier Air Wing 7 and which flew to their new home station at NAS Oceana, Virginia on 4 December. They will be followed by VFA-34 during March 1999, while one month later VFA-91 and VFA-83 will move north. VFA-105 should arrive at NAS Oceana during July 1999. The final squadrons due to relocate to Oceana are VFA-15 and VFA-87, which will embark aboard CVN-71/USS *Theodore Roosevelt* from NAS Cecil Field in April 1999 and are not due back to the USA until six months later. Once the squadrons have relocated to NAS Oceana by the autumn of 1999, Cecil Field will be transferred to the city of Jacksonville. The new owner intends to lease facilities to various civilian and military organisations, including Northrop Grumman, which intends to establish an F-14 overhaul facility at the base. The Florida Army National Guard will relocate its helicopter

squadrons from Craig Municipal Airport to Cecil Field early in the next decade.

Unlike all the other squadrons which will simply relocate, VFA-106, the Atlantic Fleet Replacement Training Unit, is scheduled to decommission on 1 July 1999, but reform at NAS Oceana on 31 July. The only squadrons not planned to move to NAS Oceana are VFA-82 and VFA-86, which are both assigned to Carrier Air Wing 1. They will embark aboard CVN-73/USS *George Washington* from Cecil Field in September 1999, but will be housed at MCAS Beaufort, South Carolina following their return to the USA in March 2000.

Production Super Hornet first flight

The first production Super Hornet F/A-18E (165533) made its maiden flight from the Boeing plant at Lambert International Airport, St Louis, Missouri on 9 November 1998 during a sortie which lasted 1 hour and 18 minutes. The aircraft, designated E6, is the first of a dozen low-rate initial production Hornets, and was scheduled for delivery to the Navy in January 1999 for evaluation. Assembly of the second batch of 20 EF-18E/Fs began in December 1998. The Navy is

Military Aviation Review

due to establish VFA-122 at NAS Lemoore, California early in 1999 as the Fleet Replacement Unit to train aircrews on the new Super Hornet.

The three-year F/A-18E/F flight test programme was due to have been completed early in 1999. Seven aircraft have been devoted to flight testing, having completed almost 2,500 flights accumulating in excess of 3,800 hours by the end of 1998. Flutter testing, which began in March 1996, was successfully completed on 23 October 1998, one month ahead of schedule, verifying no limitations on carriage speeds for external weapons. The final sortie involved the carriage of two AIM-7 Sparrows, a pair of AGM-65E Mavericks, and two AGM-154 JSOW missiles. The flutter tests were conducted on aircraft E1/165164, which will now be employed testing flying qualities of the Super Hornet.

Marine Corps receives Thai Hornets

The Department of Defense has placed a $236 million contract with Boeing for four F/A-18C and four F/A-18D aircraft for the US Marine Corps. The aircraft were originally ordered by the Thai Air Force, but were cancelled due to the economic crisis affecting many Southeast Asian nations. The eight aircraft will commence delivery later in 1999, with completion due by April 2000.

Raptor goes supersonic

The F-22A Raptor established another milestone in its test programme on 10 October 1998 when test pilot Jon Beesley flew the prototype at Mach 1.1 for the first time. The aircraft achieved this significant event over Edwards AFB, California at an altitude of 29,000 ft (8840 m). The next stage is for the F-22 to demonstrate its ability to fly at supersonic speed for an extended period without the use of afterburner.

Boeing has altered the 757 aircraft it uses to test F-22 Raptor systems by adding a representative F-22 fighter wing on the crown of the aircraft above and behind the flight deck. The

VMFA-134 is one of four Marine Corps Reserve units flying the F/A-18A. Normally based at MCAS Miramar as part of MAG 46, this pair is seen off the coast of Hawaii.

aircraft flew in the new configuration in January 1999.

X-35 mock-up unveiled

A full-scale mock-up of the Lockheed Martin X-35 Joint Strike Fighter design was unveiled at Fort Worth during September 1998. The unveiling followed confirmation from the USAF of the design, and has paved the way for construction of the first prototype to begin at the Skunk Works in Palmdale, California. Executive Vice President of Lockheed Martin, Paul Martin, announced during November 1998 that the Skunk Works is to more than double the workforce to 15,000 employees within the next five years. Meanwhile, Lockheed Martin has progressed with wind tunnel tests at Arnold AFB, Tennessee using scaled-down models. Pratt & Whitney is also progressing well with test and development of the JSF119-611 engine. Calspan's research facility at Buffalo, New York has been evaluating the vehicle management system aboard the VISTA F-16. The first X-35 head-up display has been delivered by Flight Visions of Sugar Grove, Illinois, and is half the weight specified by Lockheed Martin, just 25 lb (11 kg).

Changes within USAFE

The 52nd Fighter Wing at Spangdahlem Air Base, Germany is to inactivate the 53rd Fighter Squadron following the transfer of its 22 F-15s elsewhere. Five F-15Cs and a two-seat F-15D were transferred to the 493rd FS, 48th FW at RAF Lakenheath by the end of 1998. The remaining aircraft are due to be flown back to the USA for assignment to other units. For several years the 53rd FS had been the sole USAFE representative at the annual Tiger Meet, and it is hoped the OA/A-10A-equipped 81st FS will be permitted to join during 1999. The 81st FS has a black panther as its unit

emblem, but will likely be granted membership as the Tiger Association has expanded its guidelines to admit squadrons whose badge contains any large feline species.

The two resident F-16 squadrons are to increase their complement from 18 to 24 aircraft each. The additional aircraft are from the latest orders, and include six Block 50 F-16Cs funded from the FY1996 budget. The first, serial 96-0080, was handed over to the USAF at the Lockheed Martin Fort Worth facility on 4 December 1998. A further six were ordered from the FY1997 budget, with delivery due during 2000. These latter six will be fitted with a modular mission computer and colour cockpit displays. Four more F-16s are on order, with others likely to be purchased as attrition replacements for the active duty service and to permit the reserves to gradually convert to the latest version of the Fighting Falcon. The USAF has asked Lockheed Martin for the cost of 30 additional F-16s, with funding split equally between FYs 2000 and 2001. The Air Force has stated that it needs additional F-16s to perform the suppression of enemy air defences (SEAD) role to equip the 10 planned Air Expeditionary Forces (AEF).

The USAF has received funding for an additional 18 F-15Es as attrition replacements, six being ordered in each of FYs 1996, 1997 and 1998. Among the recipients of these new aircraft will be the 48th FW at RAF Lakenheath. The new aircraft were originally due to begin emerging from the Boeing production line at St Louis in November 1998, although this has been delayed until mid-1999 to enable the Strike Eagle orders for Israel and Saudi Arabia to be completed.

Reconnaissance operations over Kosovo

Manned and unmanned reconnaissance aircraft are operating over Kosovo to assist with the verification of the Serbian compliance with United Nations Resolution 1199, which calls for the ceasefire and withdrawal of Serbian military and police forces from the area. RQ-1A Predator unmanned air vehicles (UAVs), which had previously been employed to monitor

Serbian forces in Bosnia, began operations over Kosovo on 30 October 1998. The Predators are operated by the 11th Expeditionary Reconnaissance Squadron from Taszar Air Base, Hungary. In addition, a pair of U-2Ss has been stationed at Aviano AB, Italy and placed under the operational control of the 31st Air Expeditionary Wing.

Special Operations evaluates the V-22

Two MV-22 Osprey tilt-rotor aircraft were flown to Eglin AFB, Florida on 23 October 1998 to perform a week-long series of trials by Air Force Special Operations Command (AFSOC) designed to be pre-operational testing. The two aircraft concerned were Navy test airframes borrowed from the Naval Air Test Center at NAS Patuxent River, Maryland. During their short stay the two MV-22s flew a number of sorties, including visits to nearby Hurlburt Field, which is the headquarters of AFSOC. The deployment was accompanied by 130 members of the multi-operational test team (MOTT), which included USAF and US Marine Corps pilots, maintenance personnel, engineers and contractors' staff. The MOTT examined compatibility with the special operations mission, which included air-to-air refuelling methods with MC-130P Combat Shadow tankers of the 9th SOS. No fuel was transferred during these sorties, which were all dry hook-ups. Members of the 23rd Special Tactics Squadron at Hurlburt Field staged various field exercises with the Osprey, including infiltration and extraction of special forces ground troops.

MV-22A production commences

The fuselage of the first low-rate initial production MV-22A for the US Marine Corps was delivered from Philadelphia to the new Bell Helicopter Textron facility at Arlington, Texas aboard a C-17A on 8 September 1998. The fuselage is due to be mated with the powerplants and all other components before performing its first flight early in 1999. Following completion of these manufacturer's tests, the aircraft will then be delivered to the V-22 Integrated Test Team at NAS Patuxent River, Maryland in May 1999. The aircraft will perform engineering manufacturing development during operational evaluation,

In January 1999 Naval Air Reserve squadron VF-201 gave up its F-14As (right) in favour of F/A-18s (above), becoming VFA-201 in the process. The new tail markings hark back to the days of the F-8 Crusader.

The 1998 Edwards Open House allowed an examination of the Schweizer RU-38A twin-boom surveillance aircraft under development for the USCG. The primary sensors are housed in the front of the booms.

prior to joining HMMT-204 (the Osprey Fleet Readiness Squadron) at MCAS New River, North Carolina.

AFMC reorganises Armament Test

Air Force Materiel Command (AFMC) has implemented a reorganisation of its main weapons test and evaluation facility at Eglin AFB, Florida. The Air Force Development Test Center (AFDTC) was retitled as the Air Armament Center (AAC) to more accurately reflect its responsibility of the test, development, acquisition, logistics support and disposal of all armaments for the US Air Force. The 46th Test Wing, which is the flying component of the AAC, operates a mixed complement divided between the 39th and 40th Flight Test Squadrons.

The AAC has assumed responsibility for the 377th Air Base Wing at Kirtland AFB, New Mexico, which was previously under the Space and Missile Systems Center (SAMSO) at Los Angeles AFB, California. AAC has also acquired some of the armament-related duties previously performed by the Aeronautical Systems Center at Eglin AFB. Headquarters of the Aeronautical Systems Center at Wright-Patterson AFB, Ohio has gained responsibility for the Human Systems Center at Brookes AFB, Texas which has been redesignated as the 311th Human Systems Wing.

PGMs for the A-10

The OA/A-10A Thunderbolt II is to receive modifications to enable it to deliver precision-guided munitions (PGM). The programme has received initial funding of $12 million for research and development necessary to integrate a global positioning system (GPS) into the aircraft's targeting acquisition computer. Among the PGM weapons which may be carried by the A-10 are the Joint Direct Attack Munition (JDAM) and Wind-Corrected Munitions Dispenser. It is planned for the FY 2004 budget to contain funding for the first modification kits, with an initial operational capability to be achieved two years later. The active-duty Air Force has approximately 210 A-10s, while the Air National Guard and Air Force Reserve Command have a further 100 and 50, respectively. The new capability for the A-10 will provide an operational career expansion to at least 2020,

RU-38A progress

After long delays, the US Coast Guard is putting its two Schweizer RU-38A Twin Condor surveillance aircraft into operation at CGAS Miami, Fla. Both RU-38As (8101 ex-N61428 c/n 1 and 8103 ex-N61449 c/n 2) underwent tests with the USAF's 445th Flight Test Squadron at Edwards AFB, Calif. from 10 July 1998. Although the first airframe (8101) had been rolled out in 1995, numerous aerodynamic and technical problems required solution before the aircraft could be put into service. The Twin Condor is based on the single-engined RG-8A Condor surveillance aircraft, one of which, assigned the intervening serial 8102, crashed while in service.

A unique feature of the RU-38 is the front-engine exhaust pipes positioned so that exhaust flows over the wings, allowing the wings to serve as a sound shield. This permits quiet operation when the rear engine is shut down. Testers at Edwards put the RU-38 through a complete range of flight testing, such as envelope expansion, evaluation of flying qualities and stall testing.

A news release identifies the two RU-38As as 'prototypes', hinting that further production of the type may be planned. The two current serials (8101, 8103) are the same numbers carried by the USCG RG-8As before they were remanufactured as RU-38s. Another RG-8A (8102) was lost in an air accident near Puerto Rico in early 1996.

The RU-38A's push/pull engine system uses one Teledyne Continental GIO-550A flat-six engine at each end of the fuselage. The dual-engine design increases overwater safety compared to the RG-8. Normal operating procedure is to operate with only a single engine during normal cruise operations. The Twin Condor makes effective use of its twin-boom configuration, the forward end of each boom having a pod containing various instruments. The port pod contains the AN/APN-215(V) colour radar which has search and mapping capabilities; the starboard pod contains an AN/AAQ-15 FLIR system, as well as an LLLTV system. This equipment is optimised for the RU-38A's primary mission of night-time surveillance. In addition to the above equipment, the RU-38A is fitted with OMEGA and

GPS receivers, and HF/VHF/UHF clear voice and communications encryption systems.

AGM-130 range increase

The US Air Force and Boeing are working to increase the range of the AGM-130 air-to-surface missile which is now carried by USAF F-15E Strike Eagles; the missile made its combat debut in Iraq in January 1999 when about 10 AGM-130s were expended in post-Operation Desert Fox operations against Iraqi air defences. Unfortunately, one apparently went astray and struck the city of Basra, where Iraqi officials claimed 11 civilians were killed.

The AGM-130 is a powered derivative of the modular GBU-15 guided bomb and has a developmental history that dates to September 1984. Low-rate production began in 1990 and the first production delivery was in 1992. Boeing says that it does not currently expect sales of a lightweight version of the AGM-130, which dispenses with the missile's solid-fuel rocket motor in favour of a turbojet engine manufactured by Microturbo USA, a subsidiary of France's Labinal Group. The combination of the new engine and a lighter-weight warhead reduced the AGM-130's weight from 3,000 lb (1360 kg) to 2,365 lb (1072 kg) and has doubled the missile's previous range of about 40 miles (64 km). This version is known unofficially as the AGM-130TJ.

An F-15E fired the AGM-130TJ variant at the Eglin, Fla. range on 21 September 1998 at an altitude of 15,000 ft (4571 m). The AGM-130TJ proceeded at Mach 0.85 for more than 11 minutes before reaching predetermined GPS co-ordinates over the Gulf of Mexico. Boeing developed the lighter and farther-reaching AGM-130TJ for use with the USAF's large F-16 Fighting Falcon fleet, which is not currently validated for the standard AGM-130. In 1997, tests were conducted with another lightweight version which used a rocket motor.

89th AW modernisation

The 89th Airlift Wing at Andrews AFB, Maryland recently took delivery of the first of two C-37A Gulfstream Vs. 97-0400 was handed over on 14 October 1998, and is due to be followed by 97-0401. An option for an additional pair was partially exercised when the USAF confirmed one of

The 'AGM-130TJ' mates a lightweight version of the EO-guided missile with a Microturbo turbofan engine for increased range.

them from FY99 funds. The C-37 is based on the Gulfstream V, but with the addition of mission avionics including a Tactical Air Navigation equipment and a military IFF transponder. The cockpit features a Honeywell flight management system linked to an integrated head-up display. An enhanced ground proximity warning system is also installed, along with a microwave landing system and FADEC for the two BMW/Rolls-Royce BR710-48 powerplants.

The wing also received its third C-32A (99-0003) during November, while the fourth and final aircraft from the order – 99-0004 – made its first flight at Boeing Field, Renton, Washington on 5 November. The C-32As and C-37As have joined the 1st Airlift Squadron operating alongside three VC-9Cs, five C-20Bs and two C-20Hs ferrying senior politicians and high-ranking military and government personnel. The arrival of the first two C-32As earlier in 1998 enabled C-137B 58-6971 to be retired for storage with AMARC. 58-6970 has been preserved with the Museum of Flight at Boeing Field, Seattle, while 58-6972 and C-137Cs 85-6973 and 85-6974 will be retired from service early in 1999.

Pacer Crag KC-135

The Air Force has received the first examples of the KC-135Rs which have been modified under the Pacer Crag programme. Two multi-function colour display consoles have been installed, an inertial navigation system (INS) has been coupled to a global positioning system (GPS), and other upgrades enable operations to be performed by a two-man flight deck crew. The first unit to receive the modified aircraft is the 905th Air Refueling Squadron, which is part of the 319th ARW based at Grand Forks

Military Aviation Review

AFB, North Dakota. By December 1998 the squadron had received five modified aircraft, and is performing upgrade training for aircrew and maintenance personnel. Apart from eliminating the navigator position from the crew, projected studies have indicated there should be fewer component failures, with repair times and maintenance costs reduced accordingly.

T-3s remain grounded

Following 66 cases of unexplained engine stoppages in flight, Air Education and Training Command (AETC) grounded the T-3A Firefly to investigate the cause. The 412th Test Wing at Edwards AFB, California conducted extensive evaluation with three aircraft at Colorado Springs, Colorado under the supervision of the Federal Aviation Agency, but was unable to determine the reason. The 412th TW recommended that AETC resume flight operations. However, the Command has instigated a modification programme which will take two years to complete. The loss of the T-3 fleet has contributed to a rise in pilot training attrition rates, with many students beginning their Air Force career without completing pilot screening. AETC has redressed this problem by screening candidates through civilian training schools located across the USA. In the meantime, the T-3As of the 557th FTS at the USAF Academy, Colorado Springs, Colorado and the 557th FTS at Hondo Municipal Airport, Texas have been placed in minimal maintenance status whereby they are kept ready to return to service.

Special Operations Little Bird SLEP

The 160th Special Operations Aviation Regiment based at Fort Campbell, Kentucky is to undertake a Mission Enhanced Little Bird (MELB) programme for its 20 AH-6Js and 20 MH-6Js. The two versions of the H-6, known as Little Birds, will be fitted with the more powerful Allison T703 engine rated at 650 shp (485 kW), similar to that installed in the OH-58D Kiowa Warrior. In addition, the H-6s will have a six-bladed rotor fitted. The conversion programme is due for com-

pletion by the end of 1999, enabling the helicopters to remain in service for at least another 15 to 20 years.

YRAH-66 Comanche ongoing tests

The prototype Boeing Sikorsky YRAH-66A Comanche helicopter, which had been grounded since July 1998, recommenced flight testing at West Palm Beach, Florida on 24 October. The resumption of flying duties followed a comprehensive 100-hour inspection and installation of various system improvements. The helicopter is due to continue flight assessment trials of the modifications, before receiving new co-ordinated software for flight control and engine management, as well as a mission equipment package. The installation of the new software will be the first such addition for almost a year. Once this has been installed, the Comanche will begin an expanded flight test programme which will involve higher load factors, a new main rotor pylon, and development of the flight operations involving the weapon door-open. In the meantime, the second prototype YRAH-66A, which made its public debut on static display at Farnborough International '98, is being readied for its first flight in March 1999.

Special Operations C-17?

The US Defense Department has concluded in its review of air, sea and ground transportation that additional Boeing C-17s should be acquired to meet the requirements of US Special Operations Command. The forces currently utilise 13 C-141B StarLifters which have been modified with upgraded communications and navigation equipment, along with defensive countermeasures. Beneath the nose has been installed a FLIR turret, while electronic countermeasures are housed in small fairings beneath the cockpit aft of the radar nosecone. Defensive systems include ALR-69 radar warning receivers mounted on the nose and rear fuselage, along with an AAQ-17 IR detection system. An AAR-44 missile approach warning system is also installed, as are chaff and flare dispensers. The cockpit has been modified to enable the crew to utilise night vision goggles. The aircraft are known as Special Operations Low Level II (SOLL II) and are assigned to the 16th AS, 437th AW at Charleston AFB, South Carolina. The SOLL II C-141Bs

serve the Army and Navy special forces as well as those of the US Air Force, and perform normal airlift duties when not required for their clandestine role.

The aircraft are all more than 30 years old and are in need of replacement early in the next decade. The DoD review, entitled Mobility Requirements Study 2005, has recommended 15 additional C-17s be purchased sometime around 2003 after the existing multi-year purchase for AMC has been completed.

USAF retires C-27 Spartan

The US Air Force retired the last seven examples of the C-27A Spartan during January 1999. Ten C-27As were purchased from Alenia during FYs 1990 and 1991, all assigned to the 310th Airlift Squadron, 24th Wing based at Howard AFB, Panama. Three were withdrawn during 1998 and flown to Davis-Monthan AFB, Arizona for storage with AMARC. The remainder had been retired by the end of 1998, with four departing for storage on 8 January 1999 followed four days later by the remaining three. One of the final missions for the C-27A fleet was to airlift aid to remote locations in Central America following the devastation caused by Hurricane Mitch during the autumn of 1998. The C-27As will be followed by the withdrawal of the handful of C-130s operated by the 310th AS later in 1999 prior to the complete removal of US forces from Panama. All US military installations are to be vacated by the end of 1999 in accordance with the terms of the Panama Canal Treaty of 1977.

Conventional warfare role upgrade for the B-1B

The first B-1B Lancer upgraded for improved lethal operations in conventional warfare commenced flying with the 28th BW at Ellsworth AFB, South Dakota on 3 December 1998. The sortie involved the aircraft flying to the Utah Test Range to deliver Joint Direct Attack Munitions (JDAMs) to a number of targets. The combination of the B-1B's speed and vast range, together with the precision accuracy of the JDAM and its adverse weather capability, are expected to greatly improve the effectiveness of the Lancer bomber. The JDAM provides the B-1B with a substantial increase in bombing accuracy, with the aircraft

Suitably painted, this Kaman K-MAX undertook a series of trials for the USMC, including simulated pilotless operations. Here the aircraft carries the Magic Lantern mine detection equipment.

capable of carrying 24 of these weapons. The 28th BW was due to have seven modified aircraft in service by early 1999.

The B-1B has also received an upgrade to the defensive suite which includes the installation of a towed decoy designed to increase survivability. A new communications/navigation system is also being fitted to provide crews with updated, real-time battle zone information. Collectively, these upgrades form Block D, which is part of the B-1B Conventional Mission Upgrade Programme (CMUP), a multi-year plan to increase the Lancer's capabilities for conventional warfare. The seven aircraft with the 28th BW were placed in operational service on an accelerated schedule two years ahead of the original date. The current plan is for all 93 B-1Bs to have the communications/navigation and JDAM upgrade completed by 2001. The towed decoy should be installed fleet-wide by 2003.

US Coast Guard C-130Js?

The Norwegian government has decided not to proceed with the purchase of six new C-130Js intended to replace a similar number of C-130Hs which are now around 30 years old. They may instead be obtained for the US Coast Guard, which has a requirement for the C-130J, although the service has not yet had funding made available for new aircraft. Several of the USCG C-130Hs are now more than 25 years old and are beginning to approach the end of their service careers.

Pending a decision on the new aircraft, the US Coast Guard has awarded a $15.6 million contract to Canadian company Westcam of Flamborough, Ontario to upgrade sensors aboard seven C-130Hs. The upgrade will involve the fitting of a forward looking infrared/electro-optical device (FLIR/EO), an airborne tactical workstation and a military satellite communications link. Collectively, the new features will aid night and long-range identification of surface vessels, as well as providing the sensor operators with centralised work stations to gather and process data. The satellite link will provide near real-time transmission of

A recent type taken on charge by the US Army is the Cessna UC-35A Citation Ultra. This example serves with the 78th Aviation Battalion, headquartered at Camp Zama, Japan, but flying from NAF Atsugi.

Seen on a visit to Port Melbourne in Australia, this SH-60B is from HSL-43 Det 1 aboard USS Elliott (DD-967, 'Spruance'-class). Of note are the FLIR turret and the AGM-114 Hellfire carried on the weapons pylon.

Below: US Embassy Flight aircraft rarely stray far from their home bases. This Beech C-12C is from the Canberra flight, seen at the Avalon show.

information to other US Coast Guard aircraft and ships. Structural modifications will be contracted to Boeing at Shreveport, Louisiana, while Lockheed Martin at Eagan, Minnesota will integrate the new sensor package with existing workstations. The first completed aircraft is due to be returned to the Coast Guard by spring 1999, with the remainder modified by the autumn. The Coast Guard has an option for an additional eight aircraft to be modified, which will involve exactly half of the 30 HC-130Hs currently in service.

F-15E developments

The US Air Force has completed a programme to evaluate the 24,000-lb (106.73-kN) afterburning thrust General Electric F110-GE-129 IPE (Improved Performance Engine) as a powerplant for the F-15E Strike Eagle. The USAF has long wondered whether the GE engine would improve reliability rates, compared with the F100 powerplant built by arch rival Pratt & Whitney. Reliability issues were revived in June 1998 when General John Jumper, commander of USAFE, ordered a study of a possible engine substitute after problems with Pratt & Whitney powerplants grounded Strike Eagles at RAF Lakenheath, England, in January 1998. Jumper complained of problems which include compressor stalls and faster-than-expected deterioration of a variety of engine parts, attributed to harder-than-usual use of the F-15Es based in England.

A Field Service Evaluation (FSE) of the General Electric powerplant – begun before Jumper expressed concern about problems at Lakenheath – was conducted by the 422nd Test and Evaluation Squadron at Nellis AFB, Nev., beginning in April 1997. The FSE followed a 1996 qualification flight test of the engine in an F-15E (87-0180) at Edwards AFB, Calif., which involved 19 flights and 44 flight hours. The Nellis FSE involved two Strike Eagles (86-0189 and 88-1678) and surpassed 1,600 flight hours (600 more than originally envisioned) before ending in January 1999.

In a separate development, on 15 January 1999 Boeing announced plans to almost halve its monthly F-15 production and to dismiss workers – about 1,000, of 5,000 who work on the programme, according to an outside source – at its St Louis, Mo. plant. Boeing will reduce the Eagle/Strike

Eagle production rate from 3.5 aircraft per month to one.

K-MAX operations

Although the US armed forces have yet to purchase any examples, a Kaman K-MAX heavy-lift helicopter (N3182T) has been employed in several recent military demonstrations. The US Marine Corps leased a K-MAX and has evaluated the helicopter in missions which include sea-based aerial resupply, communications relay, and airborne surveillance.

In one application, the K-MAX operated with the Kaman-built Magic Lantern Adaptation (ML(A)) pod for blue-green laser detection of mines in shallow water and the surf zone. The Marine-leased K-MAX was employed in tests near Green Beach at Stephenville, Newfoundland – during a NATO exercise in August 1998 – where Magic Lantern detected a number of mines, including several types of anti-tank land mines that were 8-13 in (20-33 cm) in diameter. Magic Lantern uses the laser and a camera array to scan water below the helicopter from the surface down to depths below a ship's keel. The system correlates multiple scans to identify mines, with outstanding reliability. In the Newfoundland exercise, the ML(A) system was designed to operate at shallow depths near the shoreline where amphibious operations occur.

The K-MAX also acted as a surrogate drone in the Newfoundland demonstration. ONR believes that the use of an airborne mine countermeasures system in very shallow waters and in a hostile environment could benefit from the use of a pilotless aircraft, which is one well-publicised application for the K-MAX. Kaman claims that K-MAX would offer considerable loiter time for this mission and be capable of carrying medium to large payloads.

A separate mission by the K-MAX demonstrated sea-based aerial resupply of small troop units ashore. In late August 1998, the K-MAX took part in a limited technical assessment of the

BURRO (Broad-area Unmanned Responsive Resupply Operations) concept in Hawaii. The Marine Corps Warfighting Lab conducted the exercise to demonstrate that an unmanned aerial vehicle could provide logistic support from the sea. Using GPS navigation, the K-MAX simulated flight as a UAV to accurately locate the pre-assigned drop areas. The BURRO effort included simulated supply missions flown to a SWATH ship (Small WAter plane Twin Hull), a specially-configured catamaran. Supporters say the demonstration offers proof that the helicopter could be used as a UAV in direct support of fluid, fast-moving littoral and amphibious operations.

First upgraded EA-6B Prowler delivered

Northrop Grumman delivered the first of 20 upgraded EA-6B Prowler electronic warfare aircraft to the US Navy on 13 January 1999. The Block 89A upgraded aircraft was flown from the manufacturer's facility in St Augustine, Fla. to Whidbey Island Naval Air Station, Wash., home of the Prowler fleet. The first upgraded aircraft, known as ML-1, is BuNo. 160035. The upgraded Prowlers, which are receiving a new wing centre-section and standard depot-level maintenance under the Block 89 configuration, will be delivered at the rate of one aircraft per month well into 2000.

Northrop Grumman is operating two major upgrade programmes to keep the system ahead of the threats. The first is the Block 89A, under which all fleet aircraft are converted to an enhanced configuration that ensures

interoperability with other US forces. The second upgrade is the development of the next-generation EA-6B system known as Improved Capability-III (ICAP-III). Northrop Grumman was awarded this competitively bid contract, valued at approximately $150 million for initial development, in early 1998. ICAP-III will provide a reactive tactical jamming system, as well as new displays, controls and associated software to counter advanced threat radars. Initial operating capability is planned for early 2004.

ES-3 retirement concerns

The two current detachments of Lockheed ES-3 Viking (Shadow) aircraft (one from VQ-5 aboard USS *Vinson* (CVN-71) and one from VQ-6 aboard USS *Enterprise* (CVN-65)) will be the last to operate at sea. VQ-5 'Sea Shadows' ('SS' tailcode), established at NAS Agana, Guam on 15 April 1991 as the US Navy's first squadron to operate the ES-3A, is scheduled to be disestablished in July 1999. VQ-6 'Black Ravens' ('ET' tailcode), established 8 August 1991 at NAS Cecil Field, Florida, is scheduled to be disestablished in September 1999. The US Navy's decision to retire its fleet of ES-3As to avoid upgrade costs may have been based on incomplete analysis. The Navy decided in early 1998 to retire the Vikings rather than upgrade their Sigint systems using the Joint Airborne Sigint Family of high- and low-band systems, but a key admiral has suggested that the retirement was "not thought out completely". Advocates of keeping the ES-3A in service appear to have lost their case.

In June 1998 the 114th Fighter Squadron, 173rd Fighter Wing at Klamath Falls, Oregon, transitioned from the F-16 to the F-15A/B. The bald eagle tail marking has been retained.

BRIEFING

MiG 1.44

Russia's Raptor?

For the last four years the aviation community has been tantalised by the impending debut of Russia's first 'fifth-generation' fighter, the Mikoyan MFI (*mnogofunktseeon-ahl'nyy frontovoy istrebeetel'* – multi-role tactical fighter). Originally, the public debut of Mikoyan's then-latest creation was to have taken place at the MAKS-95 air show in Zhukovskiy on 22-27 August 1995. However, the Russian Defence Ministry refused to declassify the fighter and the prototype stayed behind firmly shut doors in a hangar. The scenario was repeated two years later, at MAKS-97 (19-24 August 1997); Mikoyan had wanted to show the fighter, and the military had said no.

The 1.42's appearance was highly classified; still, titbits of information were leaked to the West and artists set to work. However, apart from the twin-engined, double-tailed canard layout, the resulting drawings were largely fiction, showing either an analogue of ongoing Western next-generation fighter designs or an incongruous combination of MiG-29 bits and pieces; some artists even went so far as to show a straight-winged aircraft. The only available evidence of the real 1.42 was a photo of a forward fuselage installed on a rocket-powered trolley for ejection system trials at the State Research and Test Range for Aircraft Systems (GosNIPAS) in Faustovo near Moscow.

Aviation experts the world over kept guessing what stage the development programme had reached and

The lines of the 1.44 clearly show their Mikoyan heritage, but also display a curious mix of design approaches. The heavy riveting apparent across the fuselage is just one of these surprising aspects.

if Mikoyan could make the 1.42 fly at all, given Russia's financial complications. Eventually, tired of waiting for the fighter to be unveiled, Western experts began speculating that it was more of a proof-of-concept aircraft than a 'real' fighter and, finally, presumed that the programme was dead and buried because of defence budget cuts. The latest developments show that the sceptics were wrong – up to a point.

In the final weeks of December 1998 ANPK MiG managed at last to break through the walls of secrecy and red tape imposed upon it. In an unprecedented step, the company allowed the *Nezavisimaya Gazeta* newspaper to publish several photos and a brief news item about the fighter. Then, on 12 January 1999, a public showing of the aircraft occurred at the Zhukovskiy Flight Test Centre.

The aircraft is the MiG 1.44, that being the official designation released by ANPK MiG and applied to this (single?) prototype; the widely-used 1.42 designation refers to the programme only. Great claims have been made for the 1.44 and it is worth recording some of them. Senior Mikoyan staff and engineers, as well as Russian MoD officials, describe the MFI as a fighter at least equal to – and in some respects, better than – the Lockheed Martin F-22A Raptor incorporating the latest advances of the 'US defence industry'. For example, the Russian fighter has thrust-vectoring control (TVC) in both pitch and yaw planes, whereas the F-22A has pitch-only TVC. This is probably because the MFI has been designed with dogfights in mind – a traditional strength of Mikoyan fighters – while the

The boxy, squared-off main engine intakes of the 1.44 and the underwing weapons pylons – two of its most noticeable 'anti-stealth' features – are clear in this view. Also obvious is the unusual 'double-dogtooth' canard arrangement.

Raptor is intended primarily for beyond visual range (BVR) air-to-air combat.

The MFI was designed to counter the threat posed by the ATF programme under which the F-22 was created. As early as 1986, the Soviet Council of Ministers issued a classified directive ordering Soviet fighter makers – Mikoyan, Sukhoi and Yakovlev – to develop the concept and general arrangement of a 'fifth-generation' fighter in close co-operation with Ministry of Aircraft Industry (MAP) and Soviet Air Force (VVS) research establishments. A general operational requirement (GOR) was drawn up, and several years later Mikoyan presented a number of preliminary development projects. Most were rejected, leaving two contenders bearing the in-house designations Product 1.41 and Product 1.43. After lengthy consultations and debates with the VVS, the two evolved into an advanced development project designated Product 1.42, which was approved by the State commission.

The MFI was developed under the leadership of General Designer Rostislav A. Belyakov and chief project engineer Grigoriy Sedov (succeeded at a later stage of the

programme by Yuriy Vorotnikov). Mikoyan engineers made large-scale use of computer-aided design. So great was Mikoyan's faith in the new fighter and the technical features it incorporated that a complete set of manufacturing documents was completed at this early stage.

Prototype construction began in 1989 at Mikoyan's experimental shop. In early 1994 the first prototype, also referred to as Product 1.44, was delivered to the company's flight test facility at the Gromov Flight Test Institute (LII) in Zhukovskiy. The 1.44 is a demonstrator intended for handling, performance and powerplant testing and differs from the 'real' 1.42; the two aircraft have about 80 per cent commonality. The 1.42 differs in having cranked-delta wings (though Mikoyan says that flight tests will show if this change needs to be made), a slightly different air intake design and an internal weapons bay which is faired over on the demonstrator.

On 12 January 1999 the veil of secrecy was finally withdrawn from the 1.44 when it was shown to a group of high-level military officials and Russian politicians at Zhukovskiy (above). For this demonstration the aircraft was taxied on the airfield, with Mikoyan's new chief test pilot Vladimir Gorbunov at the controls (right). A first flight date remained unknown.

After lengthy ground tests the aircraft commenced taxiing trials and made its first high-speed run in late December 1994 with Roman Taskayev (then Mikoyan chief test pilot) at the controls. Unfortunately, however, the programme had to be suspended before the 1.44 could become airborne because ANPK MiG was in dire financial straits in the mid-1990s. The company petitioned numerous government agencies, seeking support, but to no avail. Only when Mikhail Korzhuev was appointed as Mikoyan General Director and General Designer did the situation begin to improve.

The 1.44 is a single-seat heavy fighter utilising, for the first time in Russia, the 'tail-first' layout. While resembling both the F-22A and the Eurofighter in certain respects, 1.44 still has characteristic Mikoyan traits. The aircraft has mid-set cropped-delta wings and no leading-edge root extensions (LERXes); the wings have about 45° leading-edge sweep and feature almost full-span leading-edge flaps and large two-section elevons – powered by ventral actuators enclosed in prominent fairings.

The large dogtoothed canards are mounted immediately aft of the cockpit so as not to impair visibility. Previously, dogtoothed canards have been associated (on a MiG design) only with early artist's impressions of the so-called MiG-35, a speculative version of the

MiG-29M, which came to nothing. The canards have been described as 'double-dogtooth' because the 1.44 demonstrator is fitted with canards designed for the 1.42, which (for reasons unknown) do not mate smoothly with the demonstrator's airframe.

The twin fins are spaced wide apart and canted outwards in a manner reminiscent of the F-22. The fins are attached to long slender oval-section booms outboard of the engines and augmented by ventral fins (which, unlike the fins, are not canted). A unique feature of the 1.44 is that the aft portions of the ventral fins are movable and can be deflected left and right to augment the conventional rudders. Small control surfaces, also with prominent actuator fairings, are incorporated between the fins and engine nozzles aft of the wing trailing edge to assist the canards; these 'elevatorettes' have cut-outs on the inboard sides, allowing the nozzles to deflect horizontally.

It is noteworthy that the tailfins are relatively small (in comparison to the MiG-29, for example) and the ventral fins quite large, as if to compensate. A possible explanation is that, apart from their obvious purpose, they assist in reducing the aircraft's heat and radar signature, thereby adding stealth. With 'fourth-generation' (in Russian terms) fighters – the MiG-29 and Su-27 – Sukhoi used ventral fins and Mikoyan deleted them after using them for a while. With 'fifth-generation' fighters, it is the other way: Mikoyan used ventral fins and Sukhoi did not.

The fuselage is area-ruled at the wing/fuselage joint; the forward portion is of quasi-triangular section and the underside is very flat. The aft-hinged canopy is outwardly similar to that of the MiG-29 but opens in a different way, moving up and back on four straight arms. It is followed by a shallow fuselage spine which terminates in a large brake parachute housing. The spine

can be readily enlarged later to accommodate additional fuel and/or avionics.

The MFI is powered by two Lyul'ka-Saturn AL-41F afterburning turbofans. As noted earlier, the engines have axisymmetrical nozzles with thrust vectoring in both pitch and yaw planes. The AL-41F, which recently entered production at the Rybinsk engine plant, has a weight/thrust ratio of 0.09 (compared with 0.125 for the AL-31F which powers the Su-27) and will give the aircraft both ultra-manoeuvrability and extended supersonic cruise capability. The engine was tested on a modified MiG-25. According to M. Korzhuev, the MFI will be capable of supersonic cruise at full military power (without engaging the afterburners). A maximum speed of Mach 2.6 has been claimed for the MFI, with a supercruise capability of M1.6/1.8.

The engines are located very close together and breathe through a boxy, Eurofighter-style (but

BRIEFING

unsmiling) common intake under the forward fuselage, with a lower lip to improve high-Alpha performance. Farther aft the intake is divided into two S-ducts. Here, Mikoyan engineers have succeeded in making a virtue out of necessity: while introduced primarily to circumvent the internal weapons bay, the S-ducts also aid stealth, and are coated with radar-absorbent material. An unusual feature of the AL-41F is that the inner petals of the axisymmetrical nozzle are covered with a heat-resistant ceramic coating, hence their light tan colour.

Air-to-air and air-to-ground weapons are mostly carried in a bay in the centre fuselage (which, as already mentioned, is missing on the demonstrator). Additional stores may be carried on underwing pylons, to the detriment of any stealth capability. Surprisingly, the 1.44 was shown with pylons in place under each wing – defeating any suggestions that the design was already optimised for stealth. The demonstrator has two pylons under the flaperon actuator fairings and showed provisions for two more pylons each side inboard of them. The principal armament will consist of long-range fire-and-forget AAMs and AGMs; these unidentified 'fifth-generation' weapons are said to have been specially developed for the MFI. For close-in fighting, the aircraft is armed with a 30-mm internal cannon, probably the proven Gryazev/Shipunov GSh-301. Although not obvious at first sight, this weapon appears to be housed in the port upper fuselage, level with the wing leading edge, and hidden under a flush 'door' – as in the F-22 design.

Landing gear design is straightforward, with a twin-wheel nose unit (similar to that of the MiG-29, though much shorter) retracting aft into the air intake splitter and levered-suspension main units retracting forward into the fuselage sides. The Mikoyan MFI appears to sit somewhat lower over the ground than its Sukhoi competitor, the S-37. The reason is probably that the latter's nose gear unit is positioned ahead of the air intakes and the danger of foreign object damage (FOD) must be greater, forcing Sukhoi engineers to take preventive measures. Mikoyan claims that the MFI will have better field performance than current fighters; the tough landing gear typical of Russian fighters will undoubtedly contribute to this.

The MFI airframe makes large-scale use of carbon-fibre and polymeric composites and does incorporate some degree of stealth technology. ANPK MiG states that the shape of the forward fuselage has been optimised to minimise radar cross-section (RCS) and that the airframe is coated with RAM (though the rough-finished fuselage of the demonstrator clearly lacks this coating). Mikoyan claims that the MFI has an RCS comparable to that of the Raptor. If this is true, Mikoyan will have scored a major point, since the Russian fighter is larger than the F-22A. However, while there may be some truth in the company's claims – taking into consideration Mikoyan's considerable experience of working with RAM – the 1.44 as it stands today is

clearly not a stealth aircraft, though it may serve to trial many design concepts. The MFI's exact dimensions were not known at time of writing, but overall length has been quoted as approximately 20 m (65 ft 7.4 in) and wingspan as more than 15 m (49 ft 2.5 in). In comparison, the F-22A is 18.92 m (62 ft 1 in) long and has a 13.56-m (44-ft 6-in) wingspan. The airframe is understood to comprise aluminium-lithium alloys (35 per cent), steel alloys (30 per cent), composites (30 per cent) and other materials (five per cent).

The MFI is (or will be) equipped with a 'fifth-generation' (again, in Russian terms) pulse-Doppler fire control radar persistently referred to as NO-14. The aircraft's designers have refused to officially identify the radar. This phased-array radar is designed for BVR combat and has the ability to attack six targets at a time (Korzhuev has also been quoted as saying that the radar can "simultaneously attack more than 20 targets"). The radome of the 1.44 demonstrator, however, is remarkably small, suggesting that no radar is fitted. It also terminates in an unusual forked pitot which is probably part of the test instrumentation and may be replaced by a single pitot later. The real MFI (1.42) will certainly have a much larger radome, but the forward fuselage cross-section will remain unchanged.

The aircraft features a comprehensive EW/ESM suite, part of which is located in the tailfin booms, which are both tipped by dielectric fairings. More communications, navigation and ECM aerials are housed in the dielectric wingtips, fin caps and front portions of the ventral fins. (Once again, the equipment proper is almost certainly missing on the demonstrator.)

The appearance of the MFI is far from revolutionary from a Western point of view and, surprisingly, lacks the refinement and subtlety of line that were apparent in the briefly-sighted ejection seat mock-up. Russian aviation experts point out that that aircraft has been carefully designed and should meet the designers' expectations – but quite what this means is open to question. Mikoyan states that the entire airframe (in particular the flat-bottomed fuselage which generates substantial lift), coupled with TVC and the fighter's integrated control system, will give the MFI 'ultra-manoeuvrability' – the ability to fly stably at extreme angles of attack and enter and exit this mode quickly – which in turn allows it to use its weapons more effectively (e.g., firing 'over the shoulder' at a pursuing enemy fighter).

The fighter's control system was the subject of a bitter debate. Two

This view exaggerates the proportions of the 1.44's nose, which is far longer and more slender than this angle suggests. In fact, the nose seems to be too small to house the advanced pulse-Doppler radar intended for the MFI.

configurations were proposed and the Central Aero- and Hydrodynamics Institute (TsAGI) which authored one of them was adamant that its configuration be selected, threatening to give a thumbs-down to the whole project.

According to a Mikoyan press release, the MFI has all the characteristics of a 'fifth-generation' fighter: long range (including supersonic cruise at full military power), a low IR and radar signature, internal weapons stowage, high maintainability and low operating costs. Mikoyan claims that the MFI's combination of aerodynamic properties, armament and avionics render it superior to any contemporary fighter, including the F-22A. Like all other such claims made time and time again by the Russian fighter design bureaux, a combination of dire funding shortfalls, little political or industrial support and a fundamental lack of understanding of sales, marketing and basic advertising means that such actual capabilities for the MFI are far in the future.

As noted earlier, the MFI demonstrator was almost complete in late 1994 and construction was halted because the Ministry of Defence had no funds to deliver some equipment items (frequently reported as the hydraulic actuators for the canard foreplanes, which were still reported not to be fitted at the time of the 1.44's unveiling). Mikoyan's arch-rival, the Sukhoi company, seized the chance to beat the opponent. At the time, Sukhoi was better off financially than Mikoyan, having sold Su-27SK/Su-27UBKs to China and Vietnam, along with delivering Su-30Ks to

the Indian Air Force. Part of these proceeds was diverted to the completion of the Sukhoi 'fifth-generation' fighter originally referred to as S-32 but since redesignated S-37 and named Berkut (Royal Eagle).

The first prototype S-37 entered flight test on 25 September 1997 (see *World Air Power Journal*, Volume 34) and several modifications have been made in the course of the flight test programme. Unlike the Mikoyan MFI, the S-37 has forward-swept wings with large LERXes, conventional tailerons in addition to canards (which has caused it to be called, somewhat misleadingly, a 'triplane' in the Russian media) and twin lateral air intakes. This aircraft was designed to take the AL-41F engine but, since the MFI (unlike the S-37) was officially selected by the MoD and enjoyed government support, prototype AL-41F engines were secured for the Mikoyan aircraft.

The pilot of the 1.44 sits on a standard Russian Air Force K-36 ejection seat (right). The canopy is raised by four hydraulic arms inside the cockpit, and slides back slightly over the spine when opened. The rough surface finish of the 1.44 is particularly apparent in this view. The wing (below) is encumbered first by pylons and then by the large housings for the flaperon actuators. The pylons, as seen here, are of a simple design and unable to carry weapons. The engines (below right) have a complex nozzle arrangement and promise to be one of the 1.44's most advanced features.

Sukhoi had to make do with Solovyov D-30F6 afterburning turbofans borrowed from the MiG-31, albeit uprated to some 196.08 kN (44,090 lb st).

Despite its attempts to attract attention to the S-37, Sukhoi has not succeeded in capturing the public imagination, while Mikoyan's MFI remains a popular subject, for several reasons. It is the Russian air force's officially selected 'fifth-generation' fighter. Unlike the MiG-29 and Su-27, which were developed to complement, rather than compete with, each other, the Russian military is now seeking a single 'fifth-generation' multi-role aircraft simply because there is not enough money to field two aircraft developed by two competing bureaux. Sukhoi is not yet completely out in the cold, as it has been contracted to develop the

T-60 next-generation strike aircraft, but the status of this project, which has a history as confused as the MFI, is a complete unknown. Russian Air Force spokesmen have gone on record to state that the Mikoyan MFI suits the Air Force's needs better than the S-37. Last, but not least, the MFI has been playing cat and mouse with the aviation community for several years, while the S-37 was developed quietly and then unveiled as a *fait accompli*.

Yakovlev's MFI contender was even less lucky, being terminated at the advanced development project stage. In appearance it was quite similar to the Mikoyan MFI, having cropped-delta wings and large canards, but also incorporated some features of the current F-22A, such as the pronounced chines on the forward fuselage, the shape of the canopy and the sharply canted trapezoidal fins. Interestingly, both wings and canards had a double-kinked (S-shaped) trailing edge with forward/backward/forward sweep. The main difference, however, lay in the powerplant – a single large afterburning turbofan with pitch-only TVC, and it was probably this that killed the project, for the Air Force demanded twin-engine reliability.

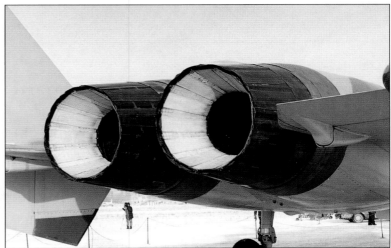

BRIEFING

On 12 January 1999 the MFI prototype ('Blue 01'), painted in air superiority grey with light blue undersurfaces, was demonstrated to top-ranking Russian officials, foreign military attachés and the press along with other new Mikoyan products. Guests at the ceremony included Army General Igor Sergeyev (Defence Minister), Colonel General Anatoliy Kornukov (Air Force/Air Defence Force C-in-C), Lieutenant General Yuriy Klishin (deputy C-in-C) and Yevgeniy Shaposhnikov (presidential advisor on aviation matters). Before the guests were allowed to examine the MFI, the aircraft was shown taxiing with Mikoyan chief test pilot Vladimir Gorbunov at the controls. The AL-41F engines sounded unusually quiet.

Kornukov was very impressed, stating that "the aircraft can do everything you want it to". Sergeyev was more reserved, saying "we shall see [what the aircraft can do] when flight tests begin". The first flight date was stated as "somewhere in February". Korzhuev was later quoted as saying that flight tests were "a point of honour for the company", with a March 1999 first flight date mentioned.

However, soon after its widely-publicised debut, the 1.44-*cum*-1.42

became the subject of a major media 'scandal'. On 17 January 1999 the *Moscow News* ran a two-page feature headlined "Bluff". The essence of it was that the 1.44 demonstrator shown in Zhukovskiy had absolutely nothing in common with the real MFI (1.42), which allegedly did not exist at all, and that the whole affair was a spectacular hoax intended to cover large-scale embezzlement of state money by MAPO-MiG. The author stated that Mikoyan representatives were reluctant salesmen, telling Sergeyev that "the MFI is all very well but way too expensive and it's better to upgrade the good old MiG-29." He also urged Russian authorities to look into the matter and take legal action, though expressing strong doubt that measures would be taken.

The article, which has now been widely circulated on the Internet, appears to have been based on a misconception of the difference between the 1.44 and 1.42. It is clearly no secret that prototypes differ from the finished product. For example, Sukhoi's flawed T-10 'Flanker-A' underwent a major redesign before becoming the production Su-27 'Flanker-B'. It is also clear that expensive RAM coatings do not need to be applied

to a first prototype intended for aerodynamic and powerplant testing – which is what the 1.44 has become. On 19 January Yevgeniy Fedosov, General Director of the State Research Institute of Aircraft Systems (GosNIIAS), discounted the *Moscow News* report as "absolutely unprofessional". That same day Mikhail Korzhuev stated to the *Nezavisimaya Gazeta* newspaper that the MFI would enter flight test between 5 and 10 March. The *Moscow News* article had claimed that the aircraft was incapable of flight. Vladimir Gorbunov is project test pilot but it is possible that Anatoliy Kvochur will also fly the 1.44. One claim by *Moscow News*, that MiG's long-serving chief test pilot Roman Taskayev had been replaced for refusing to co-operate with the 1.44 'disinformation' campaign, remains unexplained. Taskayev's expected place at the head of the 1.44 flight test programme certainly appears to have been taken by Gorbunov.

The future of the MFI remains unclear and the line between it and the 1.44 remains equally blurred. Given Russia's current economic situation, no aircraft will enter production for the Russian Air Force in the next few years, and it will

The MiG 1.44 has emerged as a curious collection of contradictions. Billed as 'Russia's F-22', it is viewed in the West as (almost) an antique collection of 'next-generation' technology. It remains to be seen whether 1.44 will serve as a stepping stone to a true MFI or become a museum curio – and an epitaph for ANPK MiG.

cost two to three times as much as the current 'fourth-generation' fighters. A unit price of $70 million has been quoted for the definitive MFI, a cost which is unsupportable in today's Russia. Neither can the promise of the MFI preclude essential upgrading to Russia's existing fighters. The pace of 1.44 flight testing and system development remains a complete unknown, and substantial progress in these fields is absolutely essential if the definitive MFI is ever to make an appearance. The technology embodied in the 1.44 demonstrator is already ageing and if Russia's 'fifth-generation' fighter aspirations are to have any future, then ANPK MiG must transform the 1.44 into a viable aircraft – and soon. Still, the appearance of actual hardware after so many years of rumour and counter-claim is at least a step in the right direction, and no-one should write off the MFI just yet.
Yefim Gordon, Dmitriy Komissarov

Xian JH-7/FBC-1

The nine lives of the Flying Leopard

The star of the November 1998 Zhuhai Air Show was the JH-7 fighter-bomber, appearing under its export designation FBC-1 Flying Leopard. In development since the mid-1970s by the Xian Aircraft Design Institute, and manufactured by the Xian Aircraft Co., the JH-7 first flew on 14 December 1988. Its first supersonic flight took place on 17 November 1989, but for most

of the last decade the programme has been troubled. Problems included difficulty in producing satisfactory engines and a reported inability to meet performance goals. These flaws were seemingly confirmed by the lack of substantial orders from the Air Force of China's People's Liberation Army (PLAAF). The PLA Air Force and Navy have had a long-standing

The FBC-1/JH-7 programme may have almost as many lives as its feline appellation suggests and its emergance as a seemingly serious export prospect, at Zhuhai, came as a surprise.

Xian FBC-1 Flying Leopard (JH-7)
SPECIFICATION
Length: 22.23 m (72.93 ft)
Wing span: 12.71 m (41.70 ft)
Height: 6.58 m (21.59 ft)
Max take-off weight: 28475 kg (62,775 lb)
Max fuel weight: 10050 kg (22,156 lb)
Max external stores: 6500 kg (14,330 lb)
Max operational speed: 1210 km/h (752 miles)
Ferry range: 3650 km (2,268 miles)
Combat radius: 1650 km (1,025 miles)
Take-off run: 800 m (2,625 ft)
Landing: 1100 m (3,609 ft)
Stress: 7g

Above: Xian publicity material released at Zhuhai showed several other JH-7/FBC-1 aircraft in construction and under test. This example was shown with a range of Chinese air-to-air and air-to-ground weapons.

Above right: The white-painted FBC-1 displayed at Zhuhai had its PLA roundels painted over, but not quite concealed.

need for an all-weather low-level attack fighter, the intended role for the JH-7. In PLA service the JH-7 should replace the completely obsolete B-5 (Il-28), which still serves in some numbers. Perhaps as many as 150 B-5s still serve in the Navy in a combat role, providing at least one potential indicator of the number of JH-7s that might eventually enter service. The JH-7 resembles a bulky Jaguar, with a high-mounted, low-aspect wing, ideal for low-altitude attack. Its projected performance is closer to the Tornado IDS, carrying less, but with a longer unrefuelled range.

By the early 1990s, the failure of the JH-7 to reach operational status led the PLA to consider a Russian alternative. The 1991 decision to buy the Sukhoi Su-27, followed by the 1996 decision to co-produce 200 more, has logically led to PLA negotiations to buy the Su-30 dedicated strike aircraft.

Surprisingly, the acquisition of the Sukhois has not ended the JH-7 programme. During China's 1995/96 'exercises' near Taiwan, the world was given a brief glimpse, through Chinese television coverage, of a JH-7 dropping bombs. It is likely that the PLA's desire to modernise its air forces and to be able to offer more modern fighters for export helped revive JH-7. The decision to feature the aircraft very prominently at the 1998 Zhuhai show has also been accompanied by a PLA decision to buy a modest number.

At Zhuhai, Xian officials noted that the key reason for the programme's survival is China's requirement for an indigenous fighter-bomber. Despite ongoing negotiations for the Su-30, which offers combat performance superior to the JH-7, self-sufficiency arguments have apparently succeeded in

sustaining the JH-7. The degree to which the JH-7 remains an indigenous product continues to cause some debate. A Xian official claims that the company has mastered the construction of the aircraft's WS-9 engines, a slightly enhanced version of the Rolls-Royce Spey Mk 202 turbofan. In 1975 Rolls-Royce sold a small number of Speys to China and entered into a co-production deal that did not quite give China what it wanted, i.e., self-sufficiency in Spey production. Now, Xian officials claim to have had the ability to produce the WS-9 for about two years. Other sources interviewed in Taiwan claim that Xian still relies on critical imported components to complete the WS-9, and may even be negotiating to purchase up to 84 new Spey engines. The Spey Mk 202 is said to have a maximum thrust with

reheat of 20,515 lb (91.29 kN), and Xian officials credit the WS-9 engine as having 20,900 lb (92.95 kN) of thrust, with reheat.

Chinese self-sufficiency is also advanced by other JH-7 components. It is not clear that the China Leihua Electronic Technology Research Institute's (CLETRI) JL-10A multi-mode radar will be the JH-7's intended radar, but the aircraft has been used as a testbed for it. The radar has a search range of 80 km (50 miles), a tracking range of 40 km (25 miles), and the ability to track up to 15 targets and engage between four and six. It also has a ground-mapping mode. The radar will likely be tied to an inertial/GPS navigation system.

Another CLETRI product associated with the JH-7 is the Blue Sky low-altitude radar/FLIR

navigation pod, which closely resembles the US LANTIRN (radar) pod. Blue Sky is effective from altitudes of 60 to 400 m (197 to 1,312 ft), the radar has a range of 15 km (9 miles) in forward view and the FLIR a 10-km (6-mile) range. Also advertised at the Zhuhai show was a FLIR/laser targeting pod, which resembles the second half of the LANTIRN system. Chinese officials indicated that the navigation and targeting pods would be attached to the forward fuselage under the air intakes.

The service version of the JH-7 may have nine hardpoints, instead of the seven seen on the FBC-1 prototype, and carry a maximum load of 6500 kg (14,330 lb). In naval service the JH-7 is likely to be armed with the 40-km (25-mile) range C-801 anti-ship missile.

Video footage released at the show recorded this aircraft (081, right) engaged in flight trials. The white-painted display aircraft at Zhuhai (below) wore spurious 'CFTE' titles, which Xian representatives stated stood for 'China Flight Test Establishment'. On the few days that it flew, the FBC-1 display was brief and restrained.

Xian video footage shows JH-7s 081, 083 and 085 conducting various weapons trials and stores drop tests. These included NORINCO 250-kg GP bombs (far left, above and below), the YJ-1 (C-801) air-to-surface missile (above left) and unidentified wingtip AAMs (left and above), possibly dummy PL-3s. Also shown were centreline drop tank release tests.

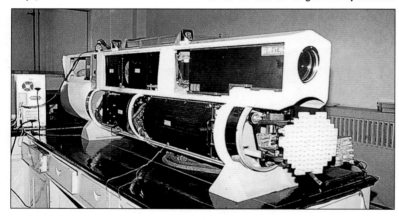

机载多功能脉冲
多普勒火控雷达
Airborne pulse Doppler Radar

Below: The unveiling at Zhuhai of the Blue Sky low-altitude navigation pod – which combines a terrain-following radar and a FLIR – was one of the quiet surprises of the show and represents a major step forward in avionics.

Above, right and far right: The JH-7's CLETRI JL-10A is a multi-mode pulse-Doppler radar that functions in the X-band. It has Doppler beam sharpening for ground mapping functions and a claimed 11 modes of air-to-air and air-to-ground operation.

With external cueing, it could also use the 120-km (75-mile) range turbojet-powered C-802. Another future weapon is the KR-1, a reported anti-radiation version of the Russian Zvezda Kh-31, which will be co-produced in China. This formidable Mach 2.5-capable missile is credited with ranges of 150 to 200 km (93 to 124 miles). For ground-attack missions the JH-7 can carry free-fall bombs and a range of TV- or laser-guided PGMs under development by China. The PLA has (at least) developed a laser-guided bomb that resembles the GBU-10. There is also the possibility that the JH-7 could be used to deliver an air-launched version of the YJ-22, a GPS-guided land-attack version of

the C-802, with a reported range of 400 km (249 miles).

For self-defence the JH-7 will have a twin 23-mm cannon, mounted to starboard, and wingtip IR AAMs. Pictures released at Zhuhai show a JH-7 prototype armed with the 84.5-kg (186-lb), 16-km (9.9-mile) range PL-5 AAM. It is not clear if the wingtip mounts can accommodate the heavier 115-kg (254-lb) PL-9, which is based on the Israeli Python-3 and has an all-aspect guidance system and a longer 21-km (13-mile) range. The PL-9 can be cued by a CLETRI version of the Ukrainian Arsenel helmet sight for high off-boresight shots.

The JH-7 will also carry an ECM suite of warning receivers

with active and passive counter-measures. They could include the Southwest China Research Institute of Electronic Equipment (SWIEE) KJ8602 radar warning receiver and KG8605A ECM jammer. Also revealed for the first time at Zhuhai were the SWIEE KG300G jamming pod and the KZ900 tactical Elint pod. A Xian official said that a dedicated electronic warfare variant of the JH-7 is in development.

So far, the number of JH-7s said to have been produced by Xian ranges between seven and nine, with Taipei sources suggesting one or more has crashed during development. A Xian official said that China's air force would buy a number of JH-7s, but would not reveal just how many, or how soon they would enter service. Sources in Taiwan believe that most new

JH-7s will go to the PLA Naval Air Force, with some left over for training and experimental purposes. Its concentration on obtaining the Su-30 explains PLA Air Force disinterest in the JH-7. If the figure of 84 new engines to be purchased is factual, that acquisition would support about 35 aircraft, given the normal PLA practice of allocating 12 engines for every five twin-engined aircraft. This would only support one PLA regiment, normally 25 to 32 aircraft.

Even if initially purchased in such small numbers, the JH-7 would have a decided effect on the balance of power in the Taiwan Strait. Taiwan's air defence calculations would have to account for an effective naval attack aircraft armed with subsonic or supersonic cruise missiles, cued by airborne radar platforms like the Racal Searchwater radar-equipped Y-8 or the Russian/Israeli IAI Phalcon radar-equipped Il-76. With its commendable range, the JH-7 would have an even greater impact on the simmering conflict over the South China Sea. The better-armed air forces of Malaysia or Vietnam would be hard-pressed to provide

Left: JH-7/FBC-1 development aircraft 083 is seen here at a Chinese test airfield taxiing behind a J-8II which is carrying an unidentified medium-range AAM. This missile appears to be the new PL-10 AAM which is under development for the J-8.

the constant air cover needed to ward off low-level attacks by JH-7s; the Philippine Air Force, which only has a few serviceable F-5A/Bs, would find it impossible. The JH-7 could reach targets in the Philippines and cover the major sea-lanes of the northern South China Sea, from the PLA air base in Paracel Island group on Woody Island, which has an 8,500-ft (2590-m) runway. Armed with the supersonic KR-1 missile, the JH-7 could even pose a threat

to the better-defended navies of the US or Japan. Such high-speed missiles require either long-range air cover or an AEGIS radar/missile system for adequate defence.

At Zhuhai there was a clear emphasis on marketing the JH-7. China's combat aircraft sales in recent years have been paltry, due largely to its inability to offer aircraft comparable to Russian or Western designs. The JH-7 may have already featured in one attempt to reverse this situation. In 1996 it

was reportedly included in a Chinese arms package offered to Iran that floundered due to financing disagreements and Iran's apparent preference for the MiG-29. Now that there is cause to place greater confidence in the JH-7 programme, and it is clear that it can be armed with a range of reasonably effective electronic systems and modern weapons, sales prospects may improve. For the right (low) price, a country like Iran or Pakistan may be attracted by its potential.

While it is possible to scoff at the JH-7 as being already long in the tooth, and bringing only a modest improved attack capability, that would miss the point. For China, the JH-7 represents growing success by its indigenous military aircraft and electronics sector to develop the essential range of systems necessary to construct an all-weather attack aircraft; for China's neighbours, even an old leopard can have sharp teeth.
Richard Fisher

TY-90 and C-701
New missiles for the Z-9

At the 1998 Zhuhai Air Show, China revealed two brand new helicopter-launched missiles that are being offered for export. The TY-90 is a 6-km (3.6-mile) range IR-guided air-to-air missile. Unlike several Western helicopter AAMs derived from shoulder-launched SAMs, like the US Stinger, the TY-90 is a purpose-built AAM. While not yet in PLA service, the TY-90 may be used initially to arm the Harbin Z-9, a licence-produced copy of the SA 365 Dauphin. At the show, a Z-9 was shown armed with four TY-90s. In addition, it is possible this missile could arm the SA 342L Gazelle already in PLA service, or the Changhe Z-11, a copy of the smaller AS 350 Ecureuil. Chinese officials indicated that the TY-90 could in the future be slaved to a helmet sight. A new Chinese dedicated attack helicopter is reportedly in development.

The second new helicopter-launched missile revealed at Zhuhai was the C-701 anti-ship missile, marketed by the China National Precision Machinery Import and Export Corporation. Weighing 100 kg (220 lb), the C-701 is powered by a solid rocket motor to a speed of Mach 0.8 and has a maximum range of 15 km (9 miles). It has a TV guidance system and a 29-kg (64-lb) warhead. In PLA service it will very likely initially arm the naval version of the Harbin Z-9. The C-701 will give an over-the-horizon attack capability to PLA frigates and destroyers. In addition, the PLA has the option of placing C-701-armed Z-9s on some its larger bases in the Spratly Island chain, like the large facility on Fiery Cross, to bolster its claim to that disputed area. The C-701 is the first Chinese TV-guided missile to be revealed, raising the possibility that other TV-guided PGMs are in development. **Richard Fisher**

China's new TY-90 air-to-air missile (below right) has been shown on a Harbin Z-9, fitted with a pair of twin launchers (right). The TY-90 is not believed to be in service yet and this Z-9 doubtless carries inert 'shapes'. A second new missile type unveiled at Zhuhai was the C-701 anti-tank missile (below), another weapon most likely destined for the Z-9. A single Z-9 fitted with rocket pods was displayed (bottom).

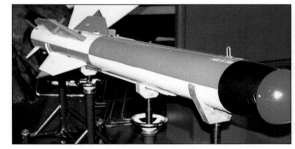

Seoul International Air Show '98

Surviving the crash

The second biennial Seoul International Air Show took place at Sungnam Air Base located just south of the capital, between 26 October and 1 November 1998. Due to the financial difficulties in South Korea and the surrounding region, the organisers were concerned about the success of the air show. The 84 per cent drop in value of the South Korean wan against the US dollar during 1998 has had a devastating effect on the whole nation, and it was anticipated that many foreign companies would not attend. Nonetheless, with 60 per cent of the budget of the 1996 show and substantial cooperation from the host, the Republic of Korea Air Force (RoKAF) – which was celebrating its 50th anniversary – the organising committee was able to attract 155 exhibitors from 17 countries and set up an impressive static display that included most of the aircraft currently serving in the Republic of Korea Armed Forces.

The seven-day air show was divided into four trade days from Monday to Thursday, and three public days from Friday to Sunday. To house the indoor exhibition, four giant 'aero-tents' were set up,

hosting the Korean, American and two International pavilions. Next to these tents an outdoor static display boasted nearly 50 aircraft. On trade days flight demonstrations were held from 14.00 to 15.30, and on public days they started at 11.00 and ran until 16.00.

For the opening ceremony on the morning of 26 October, a giant stage was set up to accommodate the 600 invited guests including Korea's Prime Minister, the RoKAF Chief of Staff and many foreign defence-/commerce-related VIPs and diplomats. The show was then opened by revealing the fifth prototype of the KTX-1 Woong-Bee (great flight) trainer. The Daewoo Heavy Industries (DHI) KTX-1 is the first modern aircraft to be designed and developed in South Korea and this latest prototype is representative of the final production configuration. Since a first flight on 12 December 1990, the five prototypes have recorded approximately 1,200 flights and 1,500 flying hours. Prior to its first public appearance at the show, the No. 5 prototype had clocked up about 150 flying hours. Featuring a conventional all-metal construction, the KTX-1 is powered by the Pratt

& Whitney Canada PT6A-62 turboprop (from third prototype onwards; previously a PT6A-25A) rated at 950 shp (708 kW), and has a digital cockpit. The two crew members are seated on Martin-Baker Mk 16L zero/zero ejection seats. Students will transition from the Woong-Bee to the RoKAF's Hawk 100 advanced jet trainers.

The RoKAF has completed its operational evaluation testing programme and a go-ahead was expected by the end of 1998 for an initial 85 aircraft to replace the ageing T-37s and T-41s, to be followed by another 20 equipped with four underwing weapon pylons, mission computer and HUD for forward air control roles. Production is planned to start at the new Daewoo plant at Sachon in August 1999, with the first deliveries to the RoKAF scheduled for 2000. Four of the five prototypes built were present at the show, including one in the daily flying display. DHI is now seeking export customers for the production KT-1.

On the opening day a special flypast of 38 RoKAF aircraft was conducted, consisting of four- and

six-ship formations of F-4Es, F-5E/Fs and F-16C/Ds – the latter aircraft carrying smoke pods trailing South Korea's national colours of red, white and blue. Daily demonstration flights were performed by the Dassault Rafale, a USAF 35th FW F-16C and the Daewoo KTX-1. There were also rescue demonstrations by a Korean Coast Guard AS 365 Dauphin, fire-fighting demonstrations by a Kamov Ka-32T and an AS 350 (both from the Korean Forest Department), an Mi-26 lifting a crane, and a presentation by Eurocopter featuring the BO 105 in Korean Army markings and roundels, just for this show. Twelve BO 105s have been ordered by the RoK Army and the first aircraft will be assembled from kits by Daewoo in late 1999. The daily flying was rounded off by the RoKAF's 'Black Eagles' display which conducted an aerobatic routine with their six A-37B Dragonflies.

The 10 per cent cut imposed on South Korea's 1998 defence budget due to the economic crises has slowed the progress of some important projects, including the RoKAF's F-X new combat fighter programme. About 120 new multi-role combat aircraft are needed, with a production goal of 2003/04. For the F-X requirement the RoKAF is still looking at the Dassault Rafale, the Boeing F-15E, the Eurofighter Typhoon and the Sukhoi Su-35; although the final decision has been delayed, it was expected that the Korean Defence Ministry would shorten the list to just two contenders after the Seoul show. With this in mind, all the competing manufacturers were keen to show off their aircraft. The Rafale B and F-15E were offering daily backseat rides to senior RoKAF pilots, in the hope of winning their favour. Absent from the show were the Su-35 and the Typhoon, although a full-scale mock-up of the Eurofighter cockpit was provided by CASA.

Sukhoi's expected participation with an Su-27UB and an Su-29, which was supposed to give inflight demonstrations of its

The KTX-2, one of the two highly ambitious advanced supersonic jet trainer projects now underway in South Korea, was unveiled in its finalised mock-up form at Seoul '98.

Left: Korea's KTX-1 Woong-Bee primary trainer, built by Daewoo, is now well into its flight test programme and the fifth prototype was on show at Seoul.

Below: Korea's high-tech aviation industry aspirations are built largely on the back of its F-16 licence-production programme. This LANTIRN-equipped Block 52 F-16C is a 123 TFS aircraft and was built entirely in Korea.

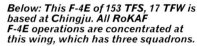

Above: The Block 52D F-16Cs of 155 TFS, 19 TFW are normally based at Yungwon. This wing has four component F-16 squadrons.

Below: This F-4E of 153 TFS, 17 TFW is based at Chingju. All RoKAF F-4E operations are concentrated at this wing, which has three squadrons.

Above: 11 TFW, normally based at Taegu, still operates two squadrons of the elderly F-4D; this is from 151 TFS.

Below: This RF-4C is from 131 TRS, 39 TRG. Korea's squadron of RF-4s is attached to Strike Command (all other Phantoms serve with Fighter Command).

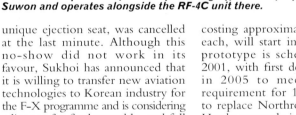

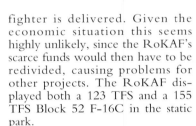

F-5 operations are split between four wings and 11 squadrons. They include the F-5As of 101 TFS (above) and the F-5Es of 102 TFS, 10 TFW at Suwon. A dedicated squadron of RF-5As (below right), 125 TRS, is part of 39 TRG at Suwon and operates alongside the RF-4C unit there.

unique ejection seat, was cancelled at the last minute. Although this no-show did not work in its favour, Sukhoi has announced that it is willing to transfer new aviation technologies to Korean industry for the F-X programme and is considering a licence for final assembly, and full maintenance, of the Su-35 by a South Korean company if chosen.

Another project that has been delayed was presented in the Korean pavilion by Samsung Aerospace and Lockheed Martin. They were displaying a full-scale model of the KTX-2, a supersonic advanced jet trainer/light attack aircraft, initially intended for the RoKAF but now squarely aimed at international markets. Resembling an F-16 with lateral fuselage intakes, the KTX-2 features tandem seats, has a 'glass' cockpit and is designed for Mach 1.4 performance on a single General Electric F-404-GE-402 turbofan, with seven hardpoints for air-to-air and air-to-surface missiles. Pending approval by the Korean government, which is funding 70 per cent of the $2 billion development programme, full-scale development of two static and four flight-test prototypes,

costing approximately $15 million each, will start in 1999. The first prototype is scheduled to fly in 2001, with first delivery scheduled in 2005 to meet the RoKAF requirement for 100-150 KTX-2s to replace Northrop F-5s and BAe Hawks currently in RoKAF service. Interim needs for an advanced trainer will be met by a lease-agreement for 30 ex-USAF T-38As.

Another major ongoing programme for Samsung Aerospace and Lockheed Martin is the delivery of the 120 Block 52 F-16C/Ds ordered by the RoKAF as part of the $5.2 billion Korean Fighter Programme (KFP). These aircraft will replace part of the 150 F-4D/E Phantoms, 25 RF-4Cs, 55 Northrop F-5A/Bs and 170 F-5E/Fs which remain in RoKAF service. Up to 60 F-5Es may be upgraded, pending the finalisation of the F-X requirement for at least 100 new fighters for service by 2010. To fill the gap between the last F-16 delivery in 2000 and the start of the production of KTX-2 in 2005, Samsung hopes for a follow-on order of more F-16s as interim fighters until the new F-X

fighter is delivered. Given the economic situation this seems highly unlikely, since the RoKAF's scarce funds would then have to be redivided, causing problems for other projects. The RoKAF displayed both a 123 TFS and a 155 TFS Block 52 F-16C in the static park.

Beside the KTX-2, Samsung Aerospace displayed a camouflaged full-scale mock-up of the SB 427 helicopter, developed together with Bell. So far 75 examples have been ordered, and Samsung holds another 25 letters of intent from China and Korea. The SB 427 is capable of carrying eight people and is powered by two Pratt & Whitney Canada 600-shp (448-kW) PW206D turboshaft engines. Military versions are planned which were due for certification at the end of 1998.

Another future project on display in the Korean pavilion was a full-scale mock-up of the AT-2000 Mako presented by Hyundai Space & Aircraft and DASA. At the show both companies signed a memorandum of understanding to jointly develop the AT-2000 supersonic jet trainer, which is a direct competitor to the KTX-2. A go/no-go decision for this still-to-be launched $2 billion development programme is expected in early 1999. AT-200 was one of the aircraft under consideration in the 1998 South African next-generation advanced trainer/attack aircraft competition. The decision to opt for the BAe Hawk and Saab/BAe Gripen in South Africa was a heavy blow to the Mako's future. The Mako has a length of 45.1 ft (13.75 m) and a wingspan of 26.2 ft (7.99 m), a tandem digital cockpit and fly-by-

Above: This BAe Hawk Mk 67 of 216 TCS is normally based at Wongju as part of the 8th TCW. This wing is Korea's attack training unit.

Below: This Cessna A-37B is from 238 TCS, 8th TCW. Dragonflies are used for weapons training and serve with some ex-USAF OA-37Bs.

Above: The RoKAF has two squadrons of Cessna T-37B/Cs. This T-37C is from 236 FTS, Training Command, at Chongju.

Below: This C-130H-30 is from 255 TAS, Transport Command, at Pusan-Kim Hae. Korea has two squadrons of stretched Hercules.

Above: This CN.235M is from 236 TAS, based at Pusan-Kim Hae. The type replaced Korea's long-serving Fairchild C-123s during 1994.

Above: This Cessna O-2A is from 237 TCS, 12 TCW, normally at Kangnun. The O-2As operate with OV-10D Broncos in the FAC role.

Left: 212 FTS, Training Command operates this Cessna T-41B. The T-41 is the RoKAF's primary trainer, after which students transition to the Lockheed T-33.

wire flight control systems, and will have Mach 1.5 performance provided by the EJ200 engine of the Eurofighter. With participation in both the Mako and the KTX-2 programmes, Korean industries hope to be well-placed to capture the worldwide market of up to 3,000 trainers and light fighters anticipated in the next century.

To celebrate the 50th anniversary of Armed Forces Day, the RoKAF had a large number of its aircraft on static display. Parked parallel to the runway, the line-up started with trainers/light attack aircraft including a 208 FTS CAARP CAP-10B, a 212 FTS T-41B Mescalero, a 237 TCS Cessna O-2A Skymaster followed by a 236 FTS Cessna T-37C, a 238 TCS Cessna A-37B Dragonfly and a 216 TCS T-59 Hawk Mk 67. Next came the fighters, a 132 TRS RF-5A and a 102 TFS F-5A Freedom Fighter, a 101 TFS F-5E Tiger, a 131 TRS RF-4C, a 151 TFS F-4D and a 153 TFS F-4E Phantom. Most RoKAF F-5s seem to have two large tiger heads painted on the fuselage under the cockpit next to the squadron badge, while the F-4s have a lion head on the intake. The

line-up ended with a 235 Squadron CH-47D Chinook and a 255 TAS C-130H Hercules. Also on display was a 256 TAS CN.235, one of the 12 delivered by CASA. The delivery of another eight CN.235s, ordered directly from Indonesia's IPTN, is now under question due to payment difficulties.

Also on show were two UH-60P Black Hawk helicopters, a dark blue RoKAF aircraft and a green-camouflaged RoK Army version, produced under licence by the Aerospace Division of Korean Air. After building more than 200 Hughes 500MDs for the RoK Army, Korean Air has now produced over 100 of the 138 UH-60Ps on order for the RoK Armed Forces and is planning upgraded versions for the future. The RoK Army wishes to place an order for a third batch of 60-80

UH-60Ps, but is still short of funding. Another project being delayed due to a shortage of funds is the Army's $500 million AHX programme for 18 attack helicopters to replace its AH-1S Cobras. With seven contestants in the race (Agusta A 129 International, Bell AH-1Z Super Cobra, Boeing AH-64D Longbow Apache, Denel CSH-2 Rooivalk, Eurocopter Tiger, Kamov Ka-50 Werewolf and Sikorsky S-70 Black Hawk), the Army hopes to get the final selection funding in 1999.

The RoK Navy had a 621 Squadron SA 319B Alouette III, a 627 Squadron Lynx Mk 99 and a 613 Squadron P-3C Orion on static display. The Navy's 1997 orders for 13 Super Lynxes and five Cessna F406 Caravans are still continuing on schedule, but the option for another eight P-3C Orions is reported to have been cancelled.

The US military contingent at the show included two 44th FS F-15Cs, two 90th FS F-15Es, two 35th FW F-16Cs, a 909th ARS KC-135R and, the highlight, a 5th RS U-2S. The US Navy flew two of its CVW-5 'CAG birds' in from the USS *Kitty Hawk* – an F-14A from VF-154 and an F/A-18C from VFA-195. A US Marine Corps AV-8B of VMA-311 also featured colourful tail markings. Next to an OH-58D, the US Army presented the Avenger and Patriot air defence missile systems. Raytheon is proposing the Patriot to meet South Korea's need for a new air defence missile system to counter the aircraft, tactical ballistic missile and cruise missile threats facing the country. The Patriot is interoperable with the Raytheon Hawk air defence missile currently used by South Korea. Raytheon was also promoting the Hawker 800XP special mission aircraft, of which eight have been ordered by the RoKAF. Four 800SIG versions

Above: RoKAF CAP 10s provide primary flight screening and aerobatic experience; this CAP 10B is from 208 FTS.

Below: This Boeing-Vertol HH-47D Chinook belongs to 235 Sqn. A single squadron of Chinooks is operated by Transport Command.

A total of 138 UH-60Ps is being built by Korean Air for the Korean Army, with the prospect of substantial follow-on orders. A black-painted HSS-equipped aircraft was exhibited at Seoul '98 (above), contrasting with the camouflaged and armed example seen at Seoul '96 (below).

The appearance of a Korean Navy Alouette III (above) at Seoul '98 came as a surprise to most observers, who believed the type had long since been withdrawn. This aircraft is an SA 319B Alouette III, of 621 Squadron. The Alouettes were understood to have been replaced by the Westland Lynx Mk 99 (below), which serve with 627 Squadron.

Below left: This is a TOW-armed Hughes 500MD. Well over 150 remain in ROK Army service, most assembled under licence.

Above: This Lockheed P-3C Orion is from 613 Sqn, RoK Navy. Korea's P-3Cs can carry the AGM-84A Harpoon, as seen here.

will be fitted with E-Systems' remote control surveillance signals intelligence avionics installations, while four 800RAs will carry other sensors, including Lockheed Martin's Loral advanced imaging radar system. Delivery is planned from 1999 to replace US Army-operated RC-12/RU-21 Guardrails. A notable absentee from the show was the Apache, which is a strong contestant in the AHX programme.

The requirement for four airborne early warning aircraft still receives RoKAF priority even though the $3 billion programme has been delayed by the economic reforms. The Boeing 767AEW with Northrop Grumman APY-2 radar is named as the leading contender, ahead of the IAI/Elta Phalcon radar in a Boeing 767/Airbus A310 or the Saab 2000 with Ericsson Erieye. A final decision is expected in 1999, but a lack of funding may well force Korea to lower its sights and settle for a smaller aircraft.

With the current economic depression and hard-hitting monetary reforms, it is unlikely that South Korea's ambitious attempt to have one of the world's leading aerospace industries by 2000 will now materialise. One of the great talking points of the 1996 show was the Samsung-led efforts to rescue Fokker from collapse, in the Netherlands. In 1998 the tables had turned, with Korea desperately searching for outside investors.

To abide by the conditions set by the International Monetary Fund and to strengthen their position in the future international market, Samsung Aerospace, Daewoo Heavy Industries and Hyundai Space & Aircraft have signed a memorandum of understanding to consolidate their aircraft businesses by merging into a new company – Korean Aerospace Industries (KAI) – but the timescale for this is still unclear. This will force major job losses and plant closures. Korean Air, which does not have anything like the massive debts of the other big firms, has opted out of the partnership. By enticing foreign investors to take a joint stake of up to 40-50 per cent in KAI, they hope to redevelop a competitive industry.

With an eye on the future markets and industry, and given a total attendance of about 500,000 over the week, the organisers announced Seoul Air Show '98 a success and plans for the next show are already underway.

Roland van Maarseveen and **Cees-Jan van der Ende**

VMA-513 Night Attack AV-8Bs deploy with NVGs

'Flying Nightmares' go around the clock

In December 1997 nine pilots and six US Marine Corps AV-8B Night Attack Harrier IIs, from VMA-513 'Flying Nightmares', based at MCAS Yuma, Arizona, began their work-ups for deployment aboard the USS *Essex* (LHD-2). Acting as part of the USMC's 15th MEU (SOC) – Marine Expeditionary Unit (Special Operations Capable) – this 1998 deployment would be the first fleet use of the third-generation AN/AVS-9 night vision goggles (NVGs) and the first ever fleet squadron carrier qualification with night vision goggles.

The '513 Det' was able to undertake these ground-breaking operations chiefly through the influence of the Det OIC (Officer-In-Command), Major Dale Willey. An experienced LSO (Landing Signal Officer) and AV-8 test pilot, Major Willey presented a strong case for NVG operations 'on the boat'. He lobbied the MAG-13 (Marine Air Group 13, which

'owns' the four Harrier squadrons at MCAS Yuma) CO for permission, which was granted. NVG capability on the AV-8B had been explored at the Naval Strike Aircraft Test Squadron, NAS Patuxent River, for several years but has not been fully incorporated at an operational unit level. The USMC West Coast Harrier detachments have deployed aboard ship many times in Night Attack Harriers and flown NVG missions, but the pilots had to take off and land unaided (without goggles). One fatal AV-8B crash was attributed to a pilot flying into the water while trying to 'goggle up' after an unaided take-off. A night unaided recovery is not an easy one, but nevertheless there was some opposition to the full introduction of NVGs simply because it 'hadn't been done before'. Most pilots felt that aided recoveries would be a great benefit to the Harrier community and to Marine aviation operations in general.

During their six-month work-up period the VMA-513 Harrier pilots trained primarily for large force exercises, with 40 per cent of the training accomplished after sunset, using what the Marines refer to as night vision devices (NVDs) – more commonly known as night vision goggles. The chief significance of NVDs to AV-8B operations is that they allow deck landings with almost no lights on the ship, coupled with the expansion of helicopter operations. For years, Marine Corps helicopters have landed aboard ship using NVDs with the deck lit only at very low light levels. However, for the Harriers to land the deck had to be reconfigured (with standard bright lighting) for their recovery. This reconfiguration process takes up to five minutes; while it is going on, the deck is unable to accommodate any aided or unaided recoveries. With the Harriers now recovering using the uniform decreased deck lighting, all ACE night operations are faster and safer – and less obvious.

The Harrier pilot has several sensors and systems available to manage so-called 'night system' sorties, including the onboard FLIR, GPS, multi-scale colour

Left: This dramatic view of an AV-8B landing on the darkened deck of the USS Essex clearly shows the IR 'hotspots' of the Harrier airframe and its NVG-compatible lighting strips.

Below: VMA-513 deployed as part of HMM-163(+) with six Night Attack AV-8Bs. These Harriers, all carrying prominent Operation Southern Watch mission marks, are armed with AIM-9M Sidewinders and Mk 7 CBUs, filled with Mk 20 Rockeye bomblets. Note also the full flare packs on each aircraft.

moving map and NVDs. During high light periods the NVDs are the primary sensor, while the FLIR is the low-light sensor of choice. The NVDs used by VMA-513 during this work-up period were the older GEC-Marconi Avionics Cats Eyes goggles. Cats Eyes functions relatively well during periods of high illumination (when skies are clear and the moon is bright) but they are less effective in restricted light or 'low illum' conditions. Cats Eyes' field of view (FoV) is 30°. Field carrier landing practice sessions were accomplished using these goggles by three of the VMA-513 pilots.

NVDs are just another sensor, like radar or FLIR, to help the pilot and make his job easier. The NVDs make night tactical flying easier but are not without their limitations. One of the problems encountered with the NVDs is that closure rates are hard to determine. A pilot can get very comfortable flying with NVDs and may not appreciate the rapid approach of other aircraft or terrain. As a result, the pilot must continuously cross-check other instruments and the radar. For NVD carrier evolutions, the most difficult skill is judging closure with the boat and, in a vertical landing, avoiding excessive rates of descent due to the lack of visual clues. NVDs are universally seen as a great tool, though not a perfect one. NVDs do not turn night into day and a pilot can quickly get disorientated if relying exclusively on the goggles. Even on the very latest ANVIS-9 goggles, the FoV (field of view) is only 40° so the pilot gets few of the peripheral vision cues that that are so important – and taken for granted – during normal flying. The use of NVGs (NVDs) among all aircraft communities has resulted in numerous

cases of pilots flying into terrain, or other aircraft.

VMA-513 took its new-found NVD capability to sea as part of the 15th MEU (SOC) – Marine Expeditionary Unit (Special Operations Capable). The MEU (SOC) concept was adopted and refined by the Marine Corps in the mid-1980s. Each MEU (SOC) – of which the Corps currently has seven – is a self-contained, rapid-deployment combat unit, capable of undertaking a range of crisis response and warfighting roles. The 'special operations' tag of the MEU (SOC) does not equate to textbook special operations as conducted by dedicated special forces units. Rather, the MEU (SOC) is capable of undertaking a wide range of specialist missions, with no external support, far from friendly bases and lines of supply. The MEU is forward-deployed and can sustain itself for several weeks, giving time for combat power from the US to deploy, if necessary.

Each MEU (SOC) is based around an amphibious squadron (PHIBRON) with three amphibious assault vessels, which make up the Amphibious Ready Group (ARG). Deployed aboard those ships is the MEU, which comprises a Ground Combat Element (GCE, or BLT – Battalion Landing Team), Air Combat Element (ACE), Force Service Support Group (FSSG) and the Command Element (CE). The GCE is a battalion-sized Marine Corps unit with its own tanks, armoured reconnaissance, amphibious transport, artillery, heavy weapons and ground troops. It is the heavy combat element of the MEU. The GCE is put ashore by the assault landing craft of the PHIBRON or by the assault helicopters of the ACE. Each ACE is a composite unit, based around a single Marine Medium Helicopter Squadron (HMM), which is reinforced with assets from other Marine aviation units. Typically this will include eight CH-53Es, eight AH-1Ws, three UH-1Ns, and six AV-8Bs (with an MACG – Marine Aviation Control Group – that provides air control and Stinger air defence teams). The HMM is the only element of the ACE to deploy as a complete squadron, the other units providing detachments from their home squadron. The detachments join the HMM squadron for the

Taxiing out during a pre-deployment work-up (still wearing VMA-513 codes), the lead AV-8B in this group is carrying live Mk 82 500-lb bombs, while the second aircraft is carrying blue BDU-45 dummy bomb shapes.

By the time VMA-513 was departing the Gulf, its pilots were undertaking Case 1 landing procedures using their NVDs. The aircraft could enter the break at 800 ft (244 m), with a downwind leg at 600 ft (183 m), followed by a 'sidestep' landing. Before this, the AV-8Bs had to fly a much slower Case 3 (IFR) recovery, which involves a rigid approach pattern to the stern of the ship. Case 1 ops allowed concurrent flying with the helicopters, on a low-light deck, with no wasted time.

six-month deployment and are commanded by the HMM's commanding officer. Each aircraft is remodexed to the HMM unit designation and the HMM squadron becomes an HMM (Reinforced) squadron, or HMM(+). Although the detachments remain in contact with their respective home squadrons, the HMM is responsible for all personnel and equipment for the duration of the deployment. Maintenance and administrative help does not come from the home squadron, nor can it dictate how its aircraft are employed. If an aircraft is lost, that mishap is attributed to the HMM rather than the home squadron. On the boat, all pilots and crews act as one team and all wear the HMM(+) patch.

The 15th MEU (SOC)'s ARG consisted of the USS *Essex* (LHD-2), USS *Duluth* (LPD-6) and USS *Anchorage* (LSD-36) – PHIBRON 5. The ACE squadron was HMM-163 'Evil Eyes' (Reinforced), or HMM-163(+), normally based at MCAS El Toro, California, and commanded by Lieutenant Colonel Ray Fox. On this deployment HMM-163(+) had 12 CH-46Es,

four CH-53Es, four AH-1Ws, three UH-1Ns and six AV-8Bs.

In late March 1998 VMA-513 joined the rest of the MEU's Air Combat Element (ACE) aboard the USS *Essex* as all elements of the MEU embarked on a FLEETEX, including live-fire missions, on San Clemente Island. In April the 15th MEU conducted a 15-day at-sea training period followed by a major exercise, the 12-day Joint Task Force Exercise 98-1 (JTFX 98-1), which tested its ability to undertake a wide range of missions such as humanitarian assistance, airfield

seizures, non-combatant evacuations and tactical recovery of aircraft and personnel (TRAP, the Marine Corps' term for combat search and rescue). Only after the successful completion of JTFX 98-1 did the 15th MEU get its SOC qualification. The MEU and its ARG also exercised with the carrier battle group of the USS *Abraham Lincoln*, with each preparing the ground for joint operations during their upcoming Persian Gulf deployments. The task of the *Essex* ARG (and the *Lincoln*'s battlegroup) would be to support Operation Southern Watch (OSW),

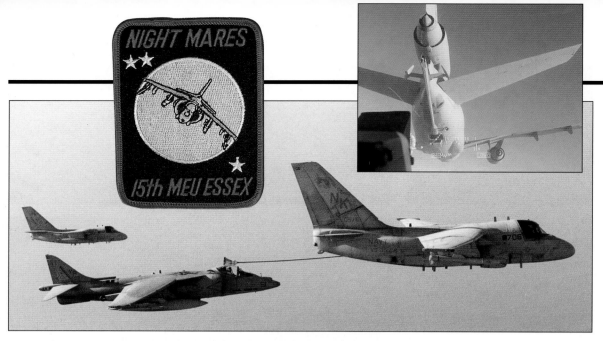

Left: Some tanker support was provided by the S-3Bs of VS-35 deployed aboard the USS Lincoln. Note the AGM-84 Harpoon also carried by this Viking. All operational OSW tanking was undertaken with USAF KC-10As (inset).

On arrival in Kuwait, VMA-513 pilots conducted familiarisation sorties over the area. This aircraft (left) is seen passing over the landmark of 'CNN Bridge' (made famous by LGB footage during the Gulf War). The two-ship formation (below left) is en route to a Kuwaiti bombing range armed with AGM-65Fs and inert BDU-45 500-lb bombs.

which would essentially be a 'Harrier-only show'. The rest of the MEU would conduct training ashore in Kuwait while VMA-513 augmented OSW strike packages. While the AV-8s flew OSW sorties and were available for strike taskings, their primary mission would always be to provide CAS for the Marine assault force if the MEU was ordered to go ashore.

Two weeks prior to the final sailing date, VMA-513 was informed that it would receive the improved, third-generation AN/AVS-9 NVDs, which offer superior low-light performance. They also offer an 80 per cent hardware compatibility with the ANVIS-6 NVDs used by Marine helicopter pilots. Thus, VMA-513 became the first Marine detachment

cleared to wear the goggles in fleet operations. On 22 June 1998 the 15th MEU (SOC) and the *Essex* ARG sailed from San Diego on the first leg of their six-month deployment. After a sustainment training stop at Oahu and a brief stay at Pearl Harbor, the ARG departed for Hong Kong on 2 July 1998.

In transit across the Pacific, VMA-513 conducted air-to-air and air-to-ground training, in conjunction with night system operations to include NVD carrier qualifications (CQ) for the three majors attached to the unit, using the AVS-9s for the first time. These CQ periods were held in high-illumination conditions and were very successful. All three pilots completed the requisite eight 'bounces' and became the first fleet AV-8B aviators

to be successfully carrier qualified on night-vision goggles.

VMA-513's NVD take-off and landing operations were put briefly in jeopardy when the pilots discovered that all the procedure manuals for NVD operations were for the old Cats Eyes goggles only, and did not cover the use of AN/AVS-9. In effect, this meant that once airborne a Harrier pilot could don 'the 9s', but he still had to use the inferior NVGs for the critical take-off and landing phase. Major Willey immediately tried to obtain clearance for the use of the AN/AVS-9 goggles. It was decided, finally, that since he was an AV-8B test pilot he could conduct the necessary testing during high- and low-light periods aboard the *Essex*, and submit the data to the Patuxent River Maryland Test Facility for analysis. Clearance was obtained for high-light period use of the '9s', but (initially) further testing was pending low light-level use.

From Hong Kong, the ARG sailed to Singapore, departing there on 29 July. Next stop was Phuket, Thailand followed by Port Kelang, Malaysia. By 4 August the *Essex* ARG was in the Indian Ocean, but on 7 August the US embassies in Kenya and Tanzania were bombed by Muslim extremists in response to the US cruise missile strikes on alleged terrorist facilities in Afghanistan and Sudan. At one point, it looked as if the 15th MEU (SOC) would be despatched to recover US nationals from Kenya and Tanzania – a perfect illustration of the rapid-response capability of an MEU (SOC) – but

this was not required. Instead the *Essex* arrived at Muscat, Oman, on 15 August for a four-day port call. The *Essex* ARG finally arrived at its modloc (modified location) in the Persian Gulf – Kuwait City – on 20 September 1998.

The MEU was deployed to Kuwait to support the ongoing Southern Watch operations over Iraq, but, along with the rest of the MEU, the Harriers participated in a large force MEU-Exercise utilising all the ACE assets to support the GCE as it practised its primary assault mission. About 1,500 sailors and Marines of the GCE (BLT 3/1) came ashore in an amphibious assault and live-fire exercise. Numerous three/four-hour night system tank-CAS (Close Air Support) missions were flown into Kuwait's Udari range. CAS was the primary focus for the ACE, with forward air controllers (FACs) – on the ground and airborne – co-ordinating mortars, artillery, and rotary- and fixed-wing fires. The Harriers expended tons of Mk 82 500-lb bombs during the MEU-EX, and some MEU-EX missions were actually carried out as an extension of regular OSW (Operation Southern Watch) patrol sorties.

VMA-513 received its OSW mission briefs from the USS *Lincoln*. The Harriers routinely operated with packages of Navy aircraft including F/A-18s, F-14s, E-2s and EA-6Bs. In mid-September they started flying as part of large force packages into southern Iraq on air interdiction missions. Initially, VMA-513 aircraft flew missions outside the known Iraqi Missile Engagement Zones (MEZ) – these sorties were termed familiarisation (FAM) flights until all pilots had flown at least one mission. After the FAM flights were completed, several OSW missions were conducted as MEZ penetration sorties (as far as 250 nm into Iraqi territory). After more than a week working with Navy units, VMA-513 transitioned to the command of the USAF, and its element of OSW.

Inbound packages would form up near a tanker track, and refuel from a KC-10A before proceeding. Aircraft such as the F-14 and F/A-18 would have different targets to the Harriers, and so would split to execute their assigned 'attack' profiles on their specific targets. Most of the Harrier's assigned 'targets' were in the Basra area. All patrol opera-

Above: This AV-8B is seen during the Essex ARG's transit to Kuwait. Unfortunately, on the return trip, HMM-163(+) lost one of the VMA-513 Harriers after a reaction control system failure on 3 December 1998. The pilot ejected and was rescued safely by an HC-11 HH-46D.

Right: A 'yellowshirt' clears a Harrier to go – note the sharkmouth applied to this AV-8B.

tions were conducted under the protection of HARM-armed EA-6Bs and F-14 CAPs. After running their assigned missions the Harriers would transition back to the tanker at approximately 20,000 ft (6096 m) and 480 kt (888 km/h; 552 mph), refuel, and then proceed to the Kuwaiti ranges to conduct CAS missions for the MEU.

On the last few days of Harrier 'play' in OSW, VMA-513 was assigned CAS boxes, working with A-10s as forward air controller-airborne (FAC-As). Air interdiction missions with the USAF demanded much longer legs, meaning that the AV-8Bs became fuel-critical on several occasions. All of the OSW missions were flown from the ship. This caused problems, as the Harriers would be too heavy for take-off carrying a full load of ordnance, drop tanks, and air-to-air missiles. The solution to this problem was to take off lightly loaded (at 7,000 lb/ 3175 kg weight compared to a possible 11,500 lb/5216 kg with drop tanks), then immediately fly to a KC-10 tanker, fly the mission and return to the tanker at its conclusion, prior to ship recovery.

Another problem tackled was that of recovering for vertical landings while still carrying unexpended ordnance, which could amount to an extra 1,500 lb (680 kg) with two CBU-89s or Mk 82s and two AIM-9s. This called for a vertical deck landing right on the numbers, using little or no excess power. All OSW sorties were day sorties, but

VMA-513 aircraft often recovered at night, with the three qualified majors executing many NVD vertical landings. The imagery and intelligence provided for the OSW mission briefs was excellent, and detailed target (area of interest) co-ordinates could be downloaded directly into the AV-8's mission computer. The encrypted GPS that the Harrier boasts was an essential tool. Most pilots found that with the GPS information supplied, the 'designation diamond' in the HUD displays would be overlaid exactly on the target – so with a flick of a switch the optics in the nose of the aircraft (with their 6:1 magnification) would be looking directly at the target with little or no slewing.

A deployment to Ali Al Salem Air Base, Kuwait provided the opportunity to conduct full operational clearance with the AN/AVS-9s for four other pilots who were previously night system qualified. These CQs with the AN/AVS-9 began under high-light conditions, followed by Major Willey's low-light testing and certification of the NVDs as the moon waned.

Most NVD sorties were carried out in section and VMA-513 was ultimately capable of undertaking at night on the goggles all AV-8B day missions. The pilots flew armed reconnaissance, CAS, aerial interdiction (strike) and air-to-air intercepts (but no ACM, at that point). Excellent results were achieved when working with the ACE's AH-1Ws running CAS missions in Kuwait ranges. The Whisky Cobras would laser desig-nate a target and the Harriers could roll in and confirm the target using the goggles/FLIR. VMA-513 pilots also ran low-level strike missions with either a low- or medium-altitude pop to target, all with NVDs. One aircraft always provided top cover as the other attacked the target. The two would then switch and the 'cover' attacked, while the first 'shooter' covered. It was sometimes a challenge using the goggles in Kuwait, as blowing sand degraded their performance, in which case the pilots had to fall back on the FLIR as their primary sensor. NVG reconnaissance missions were carried out from medium

altitude, usually a little lower than a daytime reconnaissance, to facilitate target acquisition and identification.

On 1 November 1998 the *Essex* ARG left station and began the transit home, but this was halted on 5 November when the vessels were ordered back to the Gulf against a background of mounting tension as Iraq continued to flout its responsibilities to the UNSCOM monitoring mission. Withdrawal of the UNSCOM teams due to Iraqi interference and intransigence was followed by the Operation Desert Fox strikes, in which VMA-513 did not take participate. On 18 November the 15th MEU (SOC) sailed through the Straits of Hormuz and left the Gulf behind, to return to San Diego on 21 December 1998. It is VMA-513's hope that, after its very positive experience, NVD-aided evolutions will now become standard in the Harrier community. In January 1999 the Harriers of VMA-214 'Blacksheep' arrived on station with the 13th MEU (SOC), and full ANVIS-9 clearance, to follow in VMA-513's footsteps **John Rahe**

Venezuela
Fuerza Aérea Venezolana

The FAV headquarters is based at La Carlota in Caracas. The air force has six main operating bases, all situated in the northern part of the country. Base Aérea El Libertador, Palo Negro, situated south of Maracay, is the FAV's main base. It has four flying Grupos, and a large logistic facility which takes care of all aircraft maintenance and modification programmes.

The pride of the air force is Grupo Aéreo de Caza No 16 'Dragones', formed on 31 August 1983 equipped with 18 F-16As and four F-16Bs. The Grupo parents Escuadrón 161 'Caribes' and Escuadrón 162 'Gavilanes' and operates F-16A/B Block 15 OCU aircraft powered by the F-100-PW-200. Currently, the FAV is considering seeking funds to upgrade its F-16s to Mid-Life Update standard and adding -220E engines. Twenty-four F-16s were delivered from 1983 onwards but Grupo 16 lost one two-seater (9581) on 20 April 1994 to a bird strike and another (2179) on 22 November 1995 at El Libertador. The FAV is looking for attrition replacements for these two F-16Bs.

The other fighter unit is Grupo Aéreo de Caza No 11 'Diablos', currently equipped with 11 Mirage 50EVs and three 50DVs. The unit was activated on 26 July 1973 to fly with the 10 Mirage IIIEs, four Mirage 5Vs and two 5Ds ordered in 1971 as F-86K replacements. No 11 formed Escuadrón 33 'Halcones' for the fighter role and Escuadrón 34 'Caciques' for the air-to-ground role. In recent years more aircraft have been bought in France as attrition replacements.

In 1989 a major refurbishment programme began, to upgrade the surviving Mirages with a new SNECMA ATAR 9K-50 engine, new avionics, chaff and flare dispensers, and canards; also, some surplus airframes were bought in France. On 30 October 1990 the first upgraded Mirage re-entered service, able to use more potent weapons like the Exocet anti-ship missile. This capability gives more weight to the Grupo's motto 'Vencer o Morir' (Defeat or Die).

On 27 July 1961 Grupo Aéreo de Transporte No 6 'Pegasos' was formed with the C-47 Dakota and the C-123B Provider. The C-47s of Escuadrón T1 were replaced by four Lockheed C-130H Hercules in early 1971, augmented by four more. Two Hercules have been lost in accidents: 7772 crashed on landing at Lajes on 27 August 1976 and 3556 crashed on take-off from Caracas on 4 November 1980. The Escuadrón's strength was augmented by two Boeing 707-346C tanker/transport aircraft in 1990. In 1982 six Aeritalia (now Alenia) G222s were ordered to replace the 18 C-123s origi-nally delivered to Escuadrón T2. More G222s were added to the inventory in 1989 with the acquisition of two aircraft originally delivered to the Venezuelan Army; one suffered an accident shortly after the take-over and is used now as a cockpit trainer. Currently, only one G222 (4402) is serviceable and the FAV is looking for funds to get 3526 operational. All others have been put into storage at El Libertador.

The fourth flying unit at El Libertador is Grupo Aéreo de Operaciones Especiales No 10 'Cobras', which undertakes transport, COIN, liaison, SAR and medevac duties. The Grupo was formed on 12 March 1948 and has flown a variety of helicopters such as the Bell 47G and 47J, Sikorsky UH-19, Bell 212 and 412. One UH-1B in a special colour scheme and about eight UH-1H Hueys form Escuadrón 101 'Guerreros'. Sister unit Escuadrón 102 'Piaras' flies with the surviving six of more than 20 Aérospatiale Alouette IIIs delivered in 1968 and eight Eurocopter AS 332B-1 Super Pumas delivered in 1989. In 1999 the unit will take delivery of two VIP-, two SAR- and six trans-port-configured Cougar Mk 1s.

Base Aérea Teniente Vicente Landaeta near Barquisimeto is home of the surviving F-5s of Escuadrón 36 'Grifos' of the Grupo de Caza No 12. This Grupo was formed on 28 July 1968 and originally comprised Escuadrón 34 with

Top and above: The FAV's Mirage force comprises 11 Mirage 50EVs (top), and three two-seat Mirage 50DVs. All are operated by Grupo 11, at Palo Negro. From 1990 the Mirages were upgraded with canards, refuelling probes, Atar 9K-50 engines, Cyrano IVM3 radar and a Uliss 81 INS. Armament options include the Magic 2 and Exocet.

Left and above left: Venezuela has long been the only South American nation to operate modern US-built combat jets. With the recent change in US export policies towards the region, this may soon change as Chile and Brazil line up for the F-16 also. The FAV's Block 15 F-16A/Bs are all based at Palo Negro (BA El Libertador) with Grupo 16. This freshly-painted single-seater (left) taxis out for a training mission carrying a load of BDU-33 practice bombs. The F-16B is one of four remaining in service.

Above and below: The F-5 is the only FAV fast jet type not based at Palo Negro. Instead, Grupo 12's mix of VF-5s and ex-Dutch NF-5 aircraft are all based at Barquisimeto, as part of Escuadrón 36. The single-seat F-5s (above) have been upgraded, with help from Singapore Aerospace, and now sport refuelling probes and improved avionics. This two-seater (below) is the last operational VF-5D – all other trainers are NF-5Bs.

Above and below: The OV-10A/E Broncos of Escuadrón 151, Grupo 15, based at Maracaibo, are routinely called on to deal with insurgent forces crossing the border from Colombia. This OV-10A (above) is seen on alert at its home base, armed with a LAU-131 rocket pod, for just such a mission. Another, ex-USAF, OV-10A (below) is armed with a LAU-10/A pod and is one of the few Broncos that do not wear the three-tone green/brown scheme.

Venoms, Escuadrón 35 with Vampires and Escuadrón 36 with North American F-86 Sabres. During 1972 the FAV received a total of 16 CF-5As and two CF-5Ds from the Canadian Armed Forces. In addition, two new-build two-seaters were received on 27 January 1974. In Venezuelan use the aircraft were redesignated VF-5A and 5D. Seven aircraft had been lost by 1990 and the remainder were put into storage.

When funds became available, a contract was signed with Singapore Aerospace in June 1990 to upgrade two aircraft with new avionics (GPS) and a refuelling probe. After a two-year maintenance programme, these aircraft re-entered service in May 1993. Funding has been found to

upgrade seven more aircraft. The work is carried out in Venezuela with the assistance of Singapore Aerospace technicians. The second stage of the F-5 update programme was the purchase of seven ex-KLu Canadair NF-5s – one F-5A and six F-5Bs – plus five spare J-85 engines for $5.6 million. They were all delivered by 1993. Only three NF-5Bs are still in service and they have been equipped with GPS like the eight VF-5As and the sole VF-5D.

Twice a year, the unit goes on a two-week deployment to Isla Margarita, where they act as DART-tugs. On one week they tow for the F-16s of Grupo 16 and on the other for the Mirages of Grupo 11, so they can practise air-

to-air gunnery. For liaison duties, Grupo 12 still has a Be 65 Queen Air.

As part of a modernisation programme the FAV ordered 16 OV-10E Broncos as a B-25J Mitchell replacement. Delivery started on 10 December 1973 to Escuadrón 151 'Los Linces' of the Grupo Aéreo de Operaciones Especiales No 15 at Base Aérea General en Jefe Rafael Urdaneta, near Maracaibo. In April 1991 the Grupo received 10 ex-USAF OV-10A Broncos as to supplement in the unit's counter-insurgency role. Armament routinely carried by the 15 Broncos still in service includes rocket pods (LAU 10/A and LAU 131), 500-lb bombs (Mk 82) and the four onboard M-60 machine-guns.

Above: Venezuela operates a combination of silver Tucano trainers and camouflaged AT-27s, with four hardpoints, which undertake weapons training at the GAE's Escuadrón Secundario.

Below: This is the sole Aeritalia (Alenia) G222 that remains operational with Escuadrón T2, Grupo 6, based at Palo Negro.

Above: Venezuela plans to replace the six T-2D Buckeye primary jet trainers of Grupo 13 with digital cockpit-equipped Aermacchi MB.339FDs in 2000.

Below: This well-weathered C-130H is one of those attached to Escuadrón T1, Grupo 6, Palo Negro. Venezuela would be an ideal customer for the C-130J/C-27J combination, if funds were available.

Left: The arrival of two HDU-equipped Boeing 707-346Cs in 1990 gave the FAV air-to-air refuelling capability for the first time.

Below left: Grupo 12 at Barquisimeto operates a Beech 65 Queen Air on liaison duties.

Below: This camera-equipped Falcon 20DC is currently withdrawn from use, but the FAV is seeking funds to have it reinstated to active duty.

Base Aérea Generalísimo Francisco de Miranda at La Carlota in downtown Caracas is home of the two VIP Grupos. Grupo Aéreo de Transporte No 4 was formed on 10 October 1980 and started flying with a mix of types including DC-9, HS.748, Be 200, Mu 2 and two Beech 90s, and acts as the presidential unit. Helicopter support came with UH-1H Hueys from Grupo 10. In 1981 a Gulfstream II and two Bell 412s were added to the inventory, while the HS.748 and Mu 2 left. They were followed by the acquisition of a Gulfstream III and three Bell 214STs in 1984, and a Boeing 737 and Learjet 24Ds in 1989. Grupo 4 currently consists of Escuadrón 41 with a Boeing 737-2N1 and two Gulfstreams, and Escuadrón 42 with three Bell 214STs.

Co-located at La Carlota is Grupo Aéreo de Transporte No 5, which has undertaken VIP and medevac duties since its activation on 14 April 1975. Escuadrón 51 operates five Beech 200

Super King Airs and Escuadrón 52 flies a mix of four Cessna Citations, four Dassault Falcon 20s and a Learjet 35A. One of the Citation 550s (YV-2338P) is equipped with cameras for mapping duties. Two Falcon 20DC jets (0442 and 5480) can also be used for photographic duties and utilised in the communications/ECM training role; however, these two aircraft have not flown for eight years and the FAV is waiting for funds to return them to flying status. They are both stationed at El Libertador due to their heavy take-off weight and are maintained by the Mirage maintenance unit (Escuadrón de Mantenimiento No 117) of Grupo 11.

The FAV training base is at Base Aérea Mariscal Sucre, Boca del Rio located west of Maracay. Escuadrón Primario with VT-34A Mentors and Escuadrón Secundario with two types of the EMBRAER Tucano form the Grupo de Entrenamiento Aéreo. The 14 surviving Mentors, of which delivery started in

1959, will be gradually replaced by SIAI Marchetti SF.260s. Students fly 60 hours before they move on to Escuadrón Secundario, with which they fly 100-120 hours on the T-27 Tucano. The FAV ordered originally 30 of these Brazilian trainers in 1985, a mix of trainers and small attack versions.

The attack versions of the Tucano (A-27) were delivered to Escuadrón 152 'Zorros' to augment the Broncos of Grupo 15 in the COIN role. In April 1992 that squadron was disbanded because the FAV had received additional Broncos, and the Tucanos were then moved to Barcelona where they undertook the advanced tactical training role with Grupo 13. For logistic reasons, they were relocated again to Mariscal Sucre in August 1996, when the Grupo adopted its current name.

Pilots who are going to fly transports or helicopters undergo conversion training with these units, while others do the tactical course for 45

Above: The three Bell 214STs in service with Escuadrón 42, Grupo 4 largely undertake Presidential transport taskings.

Below: Grupo 10, which is charged with special operations duties, has one UH-1B which has recently been painted in this special scheme.

Above: Over the years the FAV took delivery of 20 Sud-Est Alouette IIIs. Today, six of these veteran helicopters remain in service with Escuadrón 102, Grupo 10.

Below: The backbone of the air force's helicopter fleet is the Bell UH-1H. Approximately eight UH-1Hs, plus the single UH-1B, make up Escuadrón 101, of Grupo 10.

hours. After finishing this course the would-be OV-10 pilot goes to Grupo 15, and the others move to Barcelona for lessons at the combat school. The GEA also has five Cessna 182s on strength and is considering using these trainers for a different approach to the flying training programme.

The six remaining Rockwell T-2D Buckeyes are used as tactical combat trainers with Escuadrón 131 'Los Avispones' of the Grupo de Entrenamiento de Combate at Base Aérea Teniente Luis de Valle Garcia, Barcelona since August 1996. Pilots fly about 100 hours with this Venezuelan 'Topgun' before they move to the fighter unit where they will be posted. Originally, 24 Buckeyes were delivered to the FAV training school at Mariscal Sucre in the mid-1970s. The T-2s were relocated to Escuadrón 36 at Barquisimeto, which has acted as the Escuela de Combate since 26 May 1986, but due to unsuitable weather conditions they were relocated again to Barcelona. In 2000 the T-2D Buckeye will be replaced by 12

Aermacchi MB.339FDs fitted with glass cockpits and refuelling probes. The FAV has an option on 12 more of these Italian trainers.

Fuerza Aérea Venezolana

Base Aérea El Libertador, Palo Negro

Grupo Aéreo de Transporte No 6 'Pegasos'
Escuadrón T-1   C-130H, B.707
Escuadrón T-2   G222

Grupo Aéreo de Operaciones Especiales No 10 'Cobras'
Escuadrón 101 'Guerreros'   UH-1B/H
Escuadrón 102 'Piaroas'   AS 332B-1, Alouette III

Grupo Aéreo de Caza No 11 'Diablos'
Escuadrón 33 'Halcones'   Mirage 50DV/EV
Escuadrón 34 'Caciques'   Mirage 50DV/EV

Grupo de Caza No 16 'Dragones'
Escuadrón 161 'Caribes'   F-16A/B
Escuadrón 162 'Gavilanes'   F-16A/B

Base Aérea Teniente Vicente Landaeta, Barquisimeto

Grupo Aéreo de Caza No 12
Escuadrón 36 'Grifos'   VF-5A/D, NF-5B, Be 65

Base Aérea General en Jefe Rafael Urdaneta, Maracaibo

Grupo Aéreo de Operaciones Especiales No 15
Escuadrón 151 'Los Linces'   OV-10A/E

Base Aérea Generalísimo Francisco de Miranda, La Carlota-Caracas

Grupo Aéreo de Transporte No 4
Escuadrón 41   B.737, G.1159, G.1159A
Escuadrón 42   B.214ST

Grupo Aéreo de Transporte No 5
Escuadrón 51   Be 200
Escuadrón 52   Ce 500, Ce 550, Da 20, LJ-35A

Base Aérea Mariscal Sucre, Boca del Rio

Grupo de Entrenamiento Aéreo
Escuadrón Primario   VT-34A, Ce 182N
Escuadrón Secundario   A/T-27

Base Aérea Teniente Luis de Valle Garcia, Barcelona

Grupo Aéreo de Entrenamiento de Combate No 13
Escuadrón 131 'Los Avispones'   T-2D

Comando Aéreo del Ejército

The small but expanding Comando Aéreo del Ejército, headquartered at La Carlota-Caracas, is largely a helicopter force, with some fixed-wing aircraft used mainly for transport. The air department of the Army was formed in 1970 with the purchase of a Beech 65 Queen Air, as Sección de Ala Fija of the Departamento Aéreo del Ejército. Until 1984 all the Grupos were numbered, but as part of a recent reorganisation this system has been abandoned.

The service currently has a helicopter and transport unit and a maintenance and logistic command. The Comando Logístico at La Carlota is responsible for the maintenance of the fleet; due to insufficient funds there is a shortage

of spare parts, so many aircraft await attention. Flight operations are based at three airfields, and army aviation is charged with reconnaissance, liaison, transport and casevac roles.

Individual aircraft serials begin with the prefix EV for Ejército Venezolana, followed by the year of acquisition and then two digits in sequential order. Basic colours are wrap-round olive green/brown.

About 10 pilots are trained each year at the Centro de Instrucción Aeronáutica 'General Juan Gomez' at San Felipe, part of the Comando Logístico. For fixed-wing pilots the training requires 60 hours on the two Cessna 182Rs delivered in May 1982 and a sole Cessna 172L

which was acquired two years earlier. Helicopter pilots are trained over a 40-hour course on a single Bell 206B JetRanger (in service since 1977) and a Bell 206L LongRanger (since 1981).

Centro de Instrucción Aeronáutica

Type	Serial	Construction number
B.206B	EV7703	2176
Ce 172L	EV8013	59914
B.206L	EV8120	45736
Ce 182R	EV8221	68216
Ce 182R	EV8222	68221

San Felipe is also home to the Grupo Aéreo de Apoyo y Asalto 'General F. Jimenez', the

Above: Army aviation acquired two Bell 412SPs in 1988 which have since been joined by four Model 412EPs.

Below: The primary transport type attached to the Ejército's Grupo Aéreo de Transporte is the IAI Arava. A mix of IAI 201 and wingletted 201 Aravas is based at La Carlota.

Above and below: The Agusta A 109 is numerically the most important type in Ejército service, and also the most potent. In addition to the five VIP-configured A 109As (above) the Grupo Aéreo de Apoyo y Asalto has four gunship-capable A 109A-2s (below), armed with machine-gun pods.

Above: The Centro de Instrucción Aeronáutica undertakes aviator training on Bell 206L LongRangers (as seen here) and 206B JetRangers.

Below: Venezuela is one of the few Sea King operators to use its aircraft in an entirely land-based role. Four AS-61Ds fly with the GAAA.

Above: The three Bell 205As in service with the GAA – which also operates six similar UH-1Hs – will soon be augmented by six UH-60L Black Hawks.

Below: Two Cessna 182Rs are used for fixed-wing primary training at San Felipe, with the Centro de Instrucción Aeronáutica.

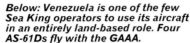

Army's helicopter unit. For a variety of tasks the GAAA uses six Bell UH-1Hs, three Bell Model 205As and nine (of 10 delivered) Agusta A 109s. Four of these Agustas can be armed with 7.62-mm or 0.50-in machine-guns and 70-mm rocket pods for offensive use. Utility services are provided by four Augusta-Sikorsky AS-61D Sea Kings received in 1984, which are usually based at La Carlota due to space problems at San Felipe. Throughout the year helicopters are deployed around Venezuela for Army support duties. In 1997 the two Bell 412SPs delivered in 1988 were augmented by four of the 412EP model. In 1999 six Sikorsky UH-60L Black Hawks will enter service.

Grupo Aéreo de Apoyo y Asalto

Type	Serial	Construction number	Remarks
UH-1H	EV7704	13869	ex 76-22651
UH-1H	EV7705	13870	ex 76-22652
UH-1H	EV7706	13871	ex 76-22653
UH-1H	EV7707	13872	ex 76-22654
UH-1H	EV7708	13873	ex 76-22655
UH-1H	EV7709	13874	ex 76-22656
Bell 205A-1	EV8015	30301	
Bell 205A-1	EV8016	30305	
Bell 205A-1	EV8017	30300	
A 109A	EV8329		
A 109A	EV8330	0017	
A 109A	EV8331	0016	
A 109A	EV8332	0019	
A 109A	EV8333	0020	
A 109A	EV8334		preserved at San Felipe
AS-61D	EV8437	6057	
AS-61D	EV8438	6058	
AS-61D	EV8439	6059	
AS-61D	EV8440	6060	
Bell 412SP	EV8841	33155	
Bell 412SP	EV8842	33157	
A 109A-2	EV8943		
A 109A-2	EV8944	7446	
A 109A-2	EV8945	7447	
A 109A-2	EV8946	7448	
Bell 412EP	EV9749		
Bell 412EP	EV9750		
Bell 412EP	EV9751	36181	
Bell 412EP	EV9752	36182	

The 812 Grupo de Transporte was formed as a combination of the Departamento Aéreo del Ejército and the Regimiento Aéreo del Ejército at La Carlota on 21 July 1982. In the same year the Grupo received two Aeritalia (now Alenia) G222 medium transport aircraft but in 1989 it passed them to the air force, on which it now depends for heavy lift. A reorganisation of the Army in 1984 gave the Grupo its present name. As flying activity increased, the government forbade piston-powered aircraft at La Carlota, so the Grupo Aéreo de Transporte moved to 'Dr Oscar Machado Zuloaga' Aeropuerto, Caracas on 5 November 1985, where it still resides. The main aircraft of the GAT is the IAI Arava, of which five are in use. For VIP use there is a Beech 90 King Air and a Beech 200 Super King Air, which can usually be found at La Carlota. Three Cessna 206s and a sole Cessna 207 all taken on service in 1982 are in use for small transport and liaison duties. As part of cost reduction, two Beech 65s and the Britten Norman BN-2A Islander were withdrawn from use and stored at Aeropuerto Caracas and put up for sale.

Grupo Aéreo de Transporte

Type	Serial	Construction number	remarks
Be 65-B80	EV7001	LD-441	for sale
Be 90	EV7702	LW-229	
Be 200	EV7910	BB-489	
BN-2A-6	EV7911	851	for sale
IAI 201	EV8012	0062	ex 4X-ICI
IAI 201	EV8014	0063	ex 4X-ICJ
IAI 202	EV8118	0102	ex 4X-CVC
IAI 202	EV8119	0103	ex 4X-CVD
Ce TU.206G	EV8223	06655	ex N9778Z
Ce TU.206G	EV8224	06642	ex N9748Z
Ce TU.206G	EV8225		
Ce T.207A	EV8226	00755	ex N9941M
IAI 201	EV9047	0087	ex 4X-CUG
Be A65	EV9048	LC-272	for sale

With the delivery of more helicopters, the Comando Aéreo del Ejército has put increased emphasis on mobility and expanding its general services to the state, especially near the Colombian border. The army has a requirement for an unspecified number of dedicated attack helicopters, but there is currently no timetable (or funding) for their acquisition.

Comando Aéreo del Ejército

Grupo Aéreo de Transporte 'General Tomas Montilla', Aeropuerto Caracas
Be 90, Be 200, Ce 206, Ce 207, IAI 201, IAI 202

Grupo Aéreo de Apoyo y Asalto 'General F. Jimenez', San Felipe
A 109A, B.205A, UH-1H, AS-61D

Centro de Instrucción Aeronáutica 'General Juan Gomez', San Felipe
B.206B/L, Ce 172L, Ce 182R

A number of Beech twins including this Model 65 Queen Air (far left, the very first Ejército aircraft, delivered in 1970), E90 King Air (left) and 200 Super King Air (above) serve with the GAT.

Comando de la Aviación Naval

The smallest air arm is the Comando de la Aviación Naval which, although only established in the mid-1970s as an organisation in its own right, traces its history to November 1922. A Centro de Aviación Naval (Naval Aviation Centre) was inaugurated at Palmita on the Laguna Valencia, with two float biplanes, a Caudron G.IV and a Farman F.40, under control of the Army. In 1962 a Cessna 310 was taken on service. followed in 1967 by an ex-LAV Douglas DC-3. These aircraft formed the Sección de Aviación Naval in 1970. Due to reorganisations, the service got its present name on 11 May 1983 as one of five Comandos in the Comando Naval de Operaciones.

The service is still very small, with the primary task of ASW, supported by a mix of light transport and communication aircraft. For this purpose, four flying Escuadrones operate from three airfields. The headquarters is in Caracas and the main base is Aeropuerto 'General Bartelomé Salom' at Puerto Cabello, some 100 km (62 miles) north of Maracay on the Caribbean coast. Aircraft used to wear a serial system of two letters indicating the role, followed by four numbers of which the first two represented the Escuadrón, but this system has been abandoned and all carry ARV titles for 'Armada Republica Venezolana'.

The Escuadrón Aeronaval de Adiestramiento at Puerto Cabello was formed at 2 November 1988 and is responsible for flying training. Elementary training takes place in a single Cessna 210. Fixed-wing pilots will then continue on the Cessna 310 or Cessna 402 (two of each in service) for twin-engine training.

These aircraft are also used for small transport and liaison tasks. Helicopter training is conducted on a Bell 206B Jet Ranger. In 1998 the service bought two ex-US Navy TH-57As from storage at AMARC; the tight budget means these helicopters are not in flying status, but they will be made so in due time.

Escuadrón Aeronaval de Adiestramiento

Type	Serial	Construction number	Remarks
Ce 402C	ARV-0202	00352	
Ce 310	ARV-0205	062	
Ce 310R	ARV-0207	2120	sold
Ce 310R	ARV-0208	2124	
Ce 402B	ARV-0215	00311	
Ce 210E	ARV-0501	58664	
B.206B	ARV-0502	2611	
TH-57A	ARV-0503	5027	ex 157381
TH-57A	ARV-0504	5011	ex 157365

Above: A single Bell 206B JetRanger is tasked with helicopter pilot training at Puerto Cabella. The navy also has ex-US Navy TH-57A Sea Rangers, which are awaiting funds to make them serviceable.

Below: The navy has eight (of nine delivered) AB 212AS ship-borne ASW helicopters in service. When at sea they have a secondary SAR role.

Top: The two Cessna 402s operated by the navy's Escuadrón Aeronaval de Adiestramiento have a dual utility transport and training role.

Above, centre: In 1998 the Maiquetia-based Grupo de Transporte Táctico took delivery of three CASA 212-400s. The -400 has the winglets of the improved CASA 212-300, but also an EFIS cockpit and uprated TPE331 engines.

Above: This VIP-configured Rockwell Aero Commander 980 serves with the transport unit based at La Carlota.

Right: This camouflaged Bell 212 is one of two transferred from the air force now in service with the Escuadrón Aeronaval de Helicópteros.

Above left: Like Venezuela's other armed forces, the naval air arm has several Beech turboprop twins tasked with VIP and priority transport duties. This Model 200 Super King Air is in use with the Escuadrón Aeronaval de Transporte.

Above: Operating alongside the Super King Air, this Model 90 King Air has been in service with the navy since 1981.

Left: In 1974-75 Venezuela took delivery of eight Grumman S-2E Trackers from the US Navy. The Trackers, which were land-based, were used to establish Escuadrón Aeronaval Antisubmarino 2, but by 1987 spares shortages had forced their retirement. The role of the Trackers was taken over by four Grumman HU-16As, which in turn were replaced by CASA 212s. Today, seven Trackers are in open storage at Puerto Cabello.

In July 1980, the first two of nine Italian-built Agusta-Bell 212ASs were delivered for anti-submarine operations. The helicopters can embark on 'Sucre-'class frigates, armed with a pair of Mk 26 or A244/S torpedoes. For a secondary anti-shipping role they can use the Marte missile, and can provide mid-course guidance to Oto-Melara anti-shipping missiles, which are launched from the frigates. Some AB 212s are also fitted with a hoist for SAR missions. In 1992 a contract was signed with Israel Aircraft Industry to upgrade the AB 212s with new avionics and electronic warfare/ESM equipment.

A pair of Bell 212s was taken over from the Fuerza Aérea Venezolana and will be used on land operations over the rivers for anti-guerrilla missions. Only one is in service at the moment; the other is in need of repair, since both helicopters were in storage for some years at El Libertador. All helicopters are part of the Escuadrón Aeronaval de Helicópteros, which was created on 11 June 1980, and are based at Puerto Cabello.

Escuadrón Aeronaval de Helicópteros

Type	registration	construction number	remarks
AB 212AS	ARV-0301	5162	
AB 212AS	ARV-0302	5164	
AB 212AS	ARV-0303	5167	
AB 212AS	ARV-0304	5171	
AB 212AS	ARV-0305	5176	
AB 212AS	ARV-0306	5177	
AB 212AS	ARV-0307		crashed 1991 at Puerto Cabello
AB 212AS	ARV-0308	5210	
AB 212AS	ARV-0309	5211	
B.212	ARV-0310	30538	ex FAV 0929
B.212		30770	ex FAV 1972

In mid-1986 the Navy took delivery of four CASA 212 aircraft for shore-based ASW and maritime patrol missions as replacement for eight ex-US Navy Grumman S-2E Trackers. The Trackers, taken on charge on 22 November 1974 for the newly formed Escuadrón Aeronaval Antisubmarinos, were put into storage in 1987 and remain at Puerto Cabello, where one (AS-0105) has been 'promoted' to gate guard. The three remaining S-43s, as the CASA 212ASW is called, of the Escuadrón Aeronaval de Patrulla at Puerto Cabello are equipped with an APS-128 search radar and are currently in Spain for avionics update as part of the deal for buying three new CASA 212-400s.

Escuadrón Aeronaval de Patrulla

Type	Serial	Construction number	Remarks
C.212-200ASW	ARV-0401	S43-1-351	
C.212-200ASW	ARV-0402	S43-1-352	crashed on 25 3 1987
C.212-200ASW	ARV-0403	S43-1-353	
C.212-200ASW	ARV-0404	S43-1-354	

For transport, the Escuadrón Aeronaval de Transporte can use a variety of aircraft and is divided into two Grupos. The Grupo de Apoyo is based at Base Aérea 'Generalísimo Francisco de Miranda' at La Carlota, flying VIP missions with a Beech 90 King Air delivered in 1981, a Beech 200 Super King Air and a Rockwell 980 Turbo Commander. The Grupo de Transporte Táctico operates two types of the CASA 212 and a sole de Havilland Canada DHC-7 and is based at the eastern part of 'Simon Bolivar' international airport at Maiquetia. Four CASA 212-200s were delivered in 1981 to replace four Douglas C-47 Dakotas, but two aircraft are lost in accidents in the early 1990s. To boost the transport capacity, three CASA 212-400s were taken on charge in 1998.

Escuadrón Aeronaval de Transporte

Type	Serial	Construction number	Remarks
Be E.90	ARV-0201	LW-264	
DHC-7-102	ARV-0203	68	
C.212-200	ARV-0204	A27-1-177	
C.212-200	ARV-0206	AV27-1-183	
C.212-200	ARV-0209	A27-2-264	crashed 10 1 1991 south of Mérida
C.212-200	ARV-0210	A27-3-268	crashed 23 January 1990 at Avila Park
AC 980	ARV-0211	95007	
Be 200	ARV-0212	BB-906	
C.212-400	ARV-0216	462	
C.212-400	ARV-0217	463	
C.212-400	ARV-0218	464	

The Comando de la Aviación Naval also suffers from a lack of funds but tries to get the most out of what it has by updating current material, like the AB 212AS and the C.212ASWs, or buying low-cost projects like the TH-57s and obsolete Bell 212s from the Air Force. To free the Agusta AB 212s for the SAR and utility task, there is an order for four Bell 412EPs, with an option on two.

Comando de la Aviación Naval

Escuadrón Aeronaval de Transporte
Grupo A, La Carlota-Caracas
Be 90, Be 200, AC 980
Grupo B, Maiquetia-Caracas
C.212-200, C-212-400, DHC-7

Escuadrón Aeronaval de Helicópteros, Puerto Cabello
AB 212AS, B.212

Escuadrón Aeronaval de Patrulla, Puerto Cabello
C.212-200ASW

Escuadrón Aeronaval de Adiestramiento, Puerto Cabello
Ce 210E, Ce 310R, Ce 402B/C, B.206B, TH-57A

Guardia Nacional

Venezuela's National Guard is a paramilitary organisation, which operates a diverse aviation arm. The Guardia Nacional is charged with aid to the civil power duties, including border security, anti-smuggling and anti-narcotics operations. Many of its aircraft have been acquired through military channels, while others have been direct purchases from manufac-turers and yet more have been seized from criminals. While little is known of the GA's day-to-day operations, its structure and inventory, is listed here for the first time. **Dick Lohuis**

Guardia Nacional

DAA-1 — Santa Barbara de Barinas

B.206B	GN-7840	2373
Ce U206G	GN-7954	20605019
B.412EP	GN-97118	36188
Pa 34-200T	YV-2090P	34-7970393

The Pa 34 is an impounded drugrunner and a GN code will be allocated later.

DAA-2 — Santa Barbara del Zulia

A 109A	GN-7947	7169
B.206B	GN-7958	2764
A 109A	GN-7962	7176
Ce U206G	GN-8063	20605402
B.412EP	GN-94102	36083

DAA-3 — Maracaibo

Be 58	GN-7428	TH-418
B.206B	GN-7959	
AS 355F-2	GN-8885	5389
AS 355F-2	GN-8887	5395
B.412EP	GN-94100	36078
PZL M-28 Skytruck	GN-96106	AJE001-04
B.412EP	GN-97115	36185

DAA-4 — Barquisimeto

Be E.90	GN-7593	LW-154
B.206L	GN-7842	46614
Ce 402	GN-7948	0104
B.412SP	GN-8273	
AS 355F-2	GN-8888	5403

DAA-5 — Caracas

B.206B	GN-7638	2100
Be E.90	GN-7839	LW-260
A 109A	GN-7946	7119
IAI 201	GN-8168	071
Be B.200C	GN-8270	BL-051
Be B.200	GN-8274	BB-980
IAI 201	GN-8576	089
AS 355F-2	GN-8882	5379
AS 355F-2	GN-8889	5404
AS 355F-2	GN-8890	5407
AS 355F-2	GN-8892	5410
PZL M-28 Skytruck	GN-96107	AJE001-05
PZL M-28 Skytruck	GN-96108	AJE001-06
PZL M-28 Skytruck	GN-96109	AJE001-07
PZL M-28 Skytruck	GN-96110	AJE001-08
B.412EP	GN-97113	36168
B.412EP	GN-97117	36187

DAA-6 — San Fernando de Apure

IAI 201	GN-8575	088
AS 355F-2	GN-8883	5385
AS 355F-2	GN-8891	5408
B.412EP	GN-94101	36084
B.412EP	GN-97114	36169

DAA-7 — Porlamar, Isla Margarita

B.206B	GN-7429	1303
B.206B	GN-7430	1304
B.206B	GN-7841	2376
B.206B	GN-7957	2760
Ce U206G	GN-8197	20606156

DAA-8 — Tucupita

Ce U206F	GN-7224	20601819
Be 65-B.80	GN-7325	LD-466
B.206B	GN-7955	2723
Ce 206	GN-8199	
IAI 201	GN-8595	099
B.412EP	GN-94103	36085

DAA-9 — Puerto Ayacucho

B.412SP	GN-94104	33086
PZL M-28 Skytruck	GN-96105	AJE001-03

SAA-11 — Santa Barbara de Barinas

B.412EP	GN-97116	36186

CAAGN Porlamar, Isla Margarita

F28C	GN-7950	483
F28C	GN-7951	481
Ce 152	GN-7994	15283196
Ce 152	GN-8065	15283969
Ce 152	GN-8066	15284489
F-280C	GN-8096	1207
B.206B	GN-97111	4449
B.206B	GN-97112	4450
PZL M-26 Iskierka	GN-98125	
PZL M-26 Iskierka	GN-98126	
Ce 182	YV-1014P	

The Ce 182 is an impounded drugrunner and a code will be allocated.

DAA = Destacamento de Apoyo Aéreo
SAA = Sección de Apoyo Aéreo
CAAGN = Centro de Adiestramiento Aéreo Guardia Nacional

Above: This smartly-painted Bell 206B JetRanger is one of the Guardia Nacional aircraft based at La Carlota, Caracas, with Destacamento de Apoyo Aéreo 5 (DAA-5). DAA-5 is the largest of the GA's aviation units.

Above right: Every GA aviation detachment has a Bell 412 allocated to it. This example is a radar-equipped Bell 412EP.

Right: An unusual type in GA service is the PZL M-28 Skytruck, a developed version of the original PZL-built Antonov An-28. Four Skytrucks are based at Caracas, with two others deployed to Maracaibo and Puerto Avachucho.

Mil Mi-24 'Hind'
Combat Crocodile

Mikhail Leontyevich Mil's Mi-24 design was a revolutionary one, a 'flying IFV' that combined heavy firepower with the ability to carry squads of fully-equipped troops to the front of the battlefield. There has never been a combat helicopter quite like the 'Hind', and it is still feared and respected. The Mi-24 earned the nickname 'devil's chariot' from the Mujahideen, in Afghanistan – though to its Soviet crews it was always the 'krokodil'. Since then the Mi-24 has gone on to see more combat worldwide than virtually any other military aircraft in service today.

ESKADRA 3 SZTURMOWA

Mil Mi-24 'Hind'

Above and right: The appropriately coded Mil V-24 mock-up bore a striking resemblance to the Bell 'Huey', but also incorporated all the basic elements of Mil's 'flying IFV' concept – cabin space for troops and onboard weapons with which to protect them. The V-24 was clearly far too small and fragile to be a practicable assault helicopter and Mil's subsequent 10.5-tonne, twin-engined 'Hind' designs bore no resemblance to this early contraption. The wooden V-24 model is seen here outside the OKB's experimental workshop at Panki. Features of note include the split folding cabin doors, the GSh-23L cannon attached to the starboard skid and dummy missiles canted at an angle that seems sure to fire straight through the main rotor disc. When Mil was ready to take its final Mi-24 design forward for approval, it faced competition from the rival design bureau led by Nikolay Il'yich Kamov, the Soviet Union's other major helicopter designer. Kamov suggested a cheaper solution – an army CAS version of the proven Ka-25 Hormone ASW helicopter with two FFAR pods on outrigger pylons, which was actually built and tested. This later evolved into the Ka-25F (frontovoy – tactical) project of 1966 featuring a totally redesigned streamlined fuselage with two double doors on each side, a GSh-23 cannon in a chin barbette and skid landing gear. Mil's idea to build an all-new, heavily-armed assault helicopter prevailed and Kamov's low-cost option was dropped.

The father of the Mi-24 and the man who brought about a revolution in Soviet battlefield tactics was General Designer Mikhail Leontyevich Mil. As Soviet forces became more mechanised during the 1960s, Mil saw that the next logical step would be to create 'flying IFVs' (infantry fighting vehicles) which could deliver a squad of troops and provide close air support (CAS). The first tangible form of Mil's concept came in 1966 when the full-scale mock-up of a new combat helicopter designated V-24 (V, *vertolyot* = helicopter) was rolled out at the experimental shop at the Ministry of Aircraft Industry's factory No. 329 in Panki, a suburb of Moscow. This factory is now known as MVZ (*Moskovskiy vertolyotnii zavod* = the Moscow Helicopter Plant named after M. L. Mil).

Outwardly, the original mock-up had nothing in common with the prototype which took to the air several years later; in fact, it looked strikingly similar to the Bell 204 (UH-1A Huey). Yet, it incorporated all the main features of the helicopter which was to gain fame (and notoriety) as the Mi-24 'Hind'. It had two crew – a pilot and the weapons systems operator (WSO) – and accommodation for seven or eight fully-armed troops. The armament comprised a Gryazev/Shipunov GSh-23 double-barrelled 23-mm (0.90-in) cannon, four or six anti-tank guided missiles (ATGMs) and two or four UB-16-57 rocket pods, each holding 16 57-mm (2.24-in) S-5 folding-fin aircraft rockets (FFARs). (UB, *unifitseerovannii blok* = standardised [FFAR] pod, and the designation UV-16-57 sometimes found in Western literature is wrong; S, *snaryad* = in this case, unguided rocket.) The cockpit, troop cabin and vital systems had armour protection.

Mikhail L. Mil proposed his 'flying IFV' to the leaders of the Soviet Armed Forces. He won the support of some young strategists, but many high-ranking MoD officials, notably the then-Defence Minister Marshal Roman Yakovlevich Malinovskiy, opposed the idea.

Luckily, by 1967 Mil persuaded the minister's first deputy, Marshal A. A. Grechko, who was always in favour of assault helicopters, to establish a special expert panel and look deeper into the matter. The opinions of military experts ranged from open support to blunt rejection, but

the supporters won and Mil received a go-ahead. On 29 March 1967 the Defence Industry Commission of the Soviet Council of Ministers issued what might be called a request for proposals – a directive ordering the Mil OKB to prepare and submit its plans for a battlefield support helicopter.

The engineers soon had two preliminary design (PD) projects ready. One envisaged a 7-tonne (15,430-lb) helicopter powered by a single 1,700-eshp (1268-kW) Isotov TV3-117A turboshaft, the other was a 10.5-tonne (23,150-lb) helicopter powered by two TV3-117As. The OKB's experimental shop completed three different mock-ups plus five versions of the helicopter's forward fuselage so that the best placement of pilot and WSO could be chosen.

The twin-engined PD project was accepted, but the military demanded that the fixed cannon be replaced by a fast-firing heavy machine-gun in a powered chin turret. Importantly, they also specified the 9M114 Shturm-V (Assault) ATGM (known to NATO as the AT-6 'Spiral'), which was still under development at the time. The helicopter was to have a new weapons control system comprising a stabilised WSO's sight, an automatic pilot's sight and a laser rangefinder. Advanced day/night targeting systems and defensive electronics were to be incorporated as they came along.

Mi-24 'Hind-B' (Izdelye 240)

Work on the advanced development project (ADP) of the future Mi-24 began immediately after the Central Committee of the Communist Party and the Council of Ministers issued a joint directive to this effect on 6 May 1968. The Mi-24 programme progressed under the overall supervision of General Designer Mikhail L. Mil (succeeded after his death in 1970 by Marat Nikolayevich Tischchenko). The design effort was led by chief project engineer V. A. Kuznetsov, Tischchenko's deputy, and the team included project engineer V. M. Olshevets, and V. D. Zernov and B. V. Smyslov who were in charge of the flight test programme, etc.

Detail design work commenced in August. Appropriately coded '24 White', the full-scale mock-up passed the so-called mock-up inspection commission of the VVS (Voyenno-vozdushniie seely = [Soviet] Air Force) in February 1969. Prototype construction got under way soon after and progressed quickly, the first prototype being completed in June 1969.

The pace of development and construction was increased by Mil's decision to borrow the main dynamic components (engines, main and tail rotors, swashplate and parts of the power train) from the proven Mi-8 – or, rather, its naval derivative, the Mi-14, which was undergoing trials at the time. Its main rotor was not identical to that of the Mi-8, being somewhat smaller (17.3 m/56 ft 9.1 in versus 21.3 m/69 ft 10.58 in). The new TV3-117 turboshaft of the Mi-14 was then one of the world's best helicopter engines. It had a nominal rating of 1,700 eshp (1268 kW) and a take-off/contingency rating of 2,200 eshp (1641 kW); if one engine failed, the other automatically went to full take-off power. The Mi-24's engines were started pneumatically by an Ivchenko AI-9V APU located dorsally behind the main gearbox. The oft-repeated notion that early versions of the Mi-24 were powered by the Mi-8's 1,500-eshp (1119-kW) Isotov TV2-117As is wrong. Firstly, the TV2-117A has electric starting and does not need an APU (as shown by the first-generation Mi-8), whereas all Mi-24s and the second-generation Mi-8MT have an APU. Secondly, the TV2-117 has a circular-section jetpipe with several thin pipes running along it; the 'Hind' has clean oval-section jetpipes characteristic of the TV3-117.

Design features

The Mi-24, or Izdelye 240 as it was known in-house, employed the classic layout, featuring a five-bladed main rotor and a three-bladed tail rotor. Here, the similarity to the 'Hip' ended. The relatively slender fuselage was carefully streamlined and the tricycle landing gear was fully retractable. All three units retracted aft into the fuselage, the main units turning so that the wheels remained vertical but at 90° to the direction of flight. The relatively narrow aft fuselage meant that the fat low-pressure mainwheels could not be stowed completely, resulting in characteristically bulged gear doors.

The small stub wings with marked incidence (19°), which were one of the helicopter's main recognition features, not only carried weapons pylons but reduced rotor disc loading in forward flight by 19 to 25 per cent, depending on speed; the Mil OKB had clearly benefited from its experience with the Mi-6. On the original Mi-24 the wings had zero anhedral and two BD3-57Kr-V (BD, *bahlochnii derzhahteli* = beam-type [weapons] rack; Kr, *krylíyevoy* = wing-mounted; V, *vertolyotnii* = for helicopters) pylons each side for FFAR pods and bombs; the ATGMs were carried in pairs on detachable racks on the lower fuselage sides ahead of the wings. To offload the tail rotor in forward flight, the tailboom, which was faired into the fuselage, had a relatively large area and the large tail rotor pylon had an asymmetrical cross-section.

The crew sat in tandem under a common angular 'greenhouse' canopy with optically-flat glass panels. The pilot sat behind the WSO, offset to port. The WSO detected and identified the targets, fired and guided the anti-tank missiles, worked the chin turret and dropped bombs. The pilot could fire unguided rockets (FFARs) or podded guns on the wing stations and the machine-gun, providing the latter was pointing in the direction of flight. In service, a third crew member, the aircraft's technician, was also carried. The cockpit was accessed via a forward-opening car-type door for the pilot and a large upward-opening window for the WSO on the port side.

The centre fuselage was occupied by a troop/cargo cabin accommodating up to eight fully armed troops back to back and accessed via horizontally-split doors on either side. The upper and lower halves of each door opened simultaneously by means of mechanical linkages, and the lower half incorporated boarding steps. The cabin windows could be

This (inset) is how the US DoD presented the Mi-24 'threat' in the 1986 edition of Soviet Military Power – the great Reagan-era bible of the 'Red Menace'. The Mi-24 was rightly seen as a major asset to Warsaw Pact theatre forces in Europe, and one which would lead an anticipated chemical warfare assault against NATO. This artist's impression shows a pair of 'Hinds' spraying chemical agents on a European battlefield – a deadly task that the 'Hind' had already fulfilled in Afghanistan. Today, the 'Hind' is much less of a threat to a modern army and no longer such a mystery. The US Army now has its own Mi-24s (above) – three aircraft quietly acquired through friends and allies. They are used to play the part of OPFOR 'Red Air' in US military exercises, to train units in threat recognition and to develop new air defence systems.

The A-10 – Mil's record breaker

In 1975 the Mil OKB modified one of the uncoded 'Hind-Bs' built in 1970 (c/n 0200204, possibly the last-but-one pre-production aircraft) for an attempt on the Class E (helicopters) world speed and time-to-height records. In keeping with the usual Soviet practice of allocating untrue designations to military aircraft used for such record attempts, the helicopter was called A-10 in the documents submitted to the

International Aeronautical Federation. Every possible step had been taken to cut weight. The stub wings were removed and their mountings covered by shallow fairings to reduce drag. The main rotor head featured inertia-type vibration dampers later fitted to some Mi-8s (notably passenger and VIP versions). For some reason the rearmost cabin window on each side was faired over. Like most 'Hind-Bs',

the A-10 had no tactical code.

On 16 July 1975 a female crew consisting of pilot Galina Rastorguyeva and navigator Lyudmila Polyanskaya reached 341 km/h (184.3 kt) on a 15/25-km (9.3/15.5-mile) course. Interestingly, both crew members were civilian, representing the Central Aero Club named after Valeriy P. Chkalov (Tushino airfield, Moscow). Two days later, flown by the same crew, the A-10

attained 334 km/h (180.54 kt) over a 100-km (62.11-mile) course. On 1 August 1975 the helicopter clocked 331 km/h (178.9 kt) over a 500-km (310.55-mile) course with Lyudmila Polyanskaya in the driver's seat. A week later the A-10 reached 3000 m (9,843 ft) in 2 minutes 3⅗ seconds. On 13 August, defying superstition, Rastorguyeva set another speed record, reaching 333 km/h (180.0 kt) over a 1000-km (621.12-mile) course. Another time-to-height record was set on 26 August – 6000 m (19,685 ft) in 7 minutes 43 seconds. All of these records stand as of early 1999.

On 21 September 1978 company test pilot Gourguen R. Karapetyan set an absolute world helicopter speed record of 368.4 km/h (228.82 mph/199.13 kt). This stood until 1986 when it was broken by a Westland Lynx with the then-experimental BERP main rotor.

Above: This is the second V-24 prototype, seen on an early test flight. It has not yet been fitted with ATGM launch rails and the nose turret is lacking its gun. The two initial prototypes were built with straight (no anhedral) stub wings. Also of note is the original position of the tail rotor, to starboard.

Right: This is the V-24 prototype, seen before its first flight. The V-24 mock-up was coded 'Yellow 24', but the real aircraft appears to have gone unmarked.

Right: This mixed-up aircraft is either one of the V-24 prototypes, or one of the 10 pre-production 'Hind-B' 'dogships'. It has straight stub wings but the production standard lengthened nose and a port-side tail rotor. The white stripes on the fin are probably for icing detection tests.

opened and featured flexible mounts for the troopers' assault rifles. The cabin could also carry four casualties or up to 1500 kg (3,306 lb) of cargo. Outsized loads weighing up to 2000 kg (4,409 lb) could be carried externally slung.

Much attention had been given to survivability and crew protection. The cockpit and cabin were combined into a single pressurised cell to prevent chemical or biological agents getting in. The cockpit had a bullet-proof windscreen and armoured pilot's seat; the sides of the cockpit and cabin were armour-plated, as were the engine cowlings.

The aft fuselage incorporated an electrics and avionics bay. The avionics suite comprised the SAU-V24 automatic control system (SAU, *sistema avtomateecheskovo upravleniya*) including the VUAP-1 autopilot (VUAP, *vertolyotnii unifit-seerovanny avtopeelot* = standardised helicopter autopilot), a compact gyro and automatic approach system, a DISS-15 Doppler speed and drift indicator (DISS, *dopplerovskiy izmereetel skorosti i snosa*), an automatic navigation map, a short-range radio navigation system etc.

Fuel was carried in five self-sealing bladder tanks holding 2130 litres (469 Imp gal). Two cylindrical metal tanks holding 1630 litres (359 Imp gal) could be installed in the cabin for ferry flights. The control system featured four hydraulic boosters mounted on a massive plate attached to the main gearbox; stabiliser incidence was adjusted in concert with collective pitch. The Mi-24 had three separate hydraulic systems – main, back-up and auxiliary.

Interim weapons fit for the Mi-24

The Mi-24 was completed well ahead of its intended armament and, thus, Mil had to make do with what was available at the moment. He opted for the K-4V weapons system (or 'armament complex' in Soviet parlance) which had achieved a good service record on the Mi-4AV and Mi-8TV. It included four 9M17M Falanga-M (AT-2 'Swatter') ATGMs. The missiles were carried in pairs on removable launchers and manually guided by the WSO, using radio control and a sight originating from a tank.

The nose incorporated a 12.7-mm (0.50-in) Afanasyev A-12.7 (TKB-481) single-barrelled machine-gun on an NUV-1 flexible mount borrowed from the Mi-4AV (NUV, *nosovaya ustanovka vertolyotnaya* = nose-mounted helicopter [gun] installation). The pilot could fire it using a primitive PKV collimator gunsight. However, it was not until the first production version appeared that the gun was fitted. The wing pylons carried four UB-32 pods with 32 S-5 rockets each or four 100-kg (221-lb) and 250-kg (551-lb) bombs. Two 500-kg (1,102-lb) bombs or napalm tanks could also be carried.

Flight tests began on 15 September 1969, when the first tethered hover was made. Four days later the uncoded prototype made its first free flight with G. V. Alfyorov at the

controls. The second prototype joined the test programme soon after, followed by a pre-production batch of 10 helicopters, five of which were built at MVZ (plant No. 329) and the rest at the Progress Aircraft Factory (plant No. 116) in Arsenyev in the Far East. These aircraft were the workhorses of the manufacturer's trials programme, later finding extensive use in testing the improvements introduced on later versions of the Mi-24. Other pilots involved in the trials included G. R. Karapetyan and M. A. Materialnii.

Trials and troubles

State acceptance trials began in June 1970, proceeded intensively for the next 18 months, and showed that the new helicopter generally met project specifications. Mil engineers had successfully addressed the Mi-24's structural strength and fatigue life problems and designed excessive vibration out of the helicopter. Vibration levels were comparable to the Mi-8, despite a higher cruising speed.

However, some trouble areas requiring major structural changes were discovered. In turbulent conditions the helicopter was prone to Dutch roll at speeds in excess of 200 km/h (108 kt) IAS with the autopilot disengaged, forcing the pilot to take constant corrective action. To improve lateral stability the engineers introduced 12° anhedral on the stub wings; this was not associated with the 'unfavourable interaction of the main rotor downwash with the wings', as some Western authors claimed.

Immediately, another problem arose: the removable ATGM launchers on the lower fuselage sides were incompatible with the FFAR pods on the stub wing pylons, as the rockets coming out of the pods could strike the missiles. Additionally, the launchers were located in line with the cabin doors, which meant the latter could not be opened when the launchers were fitted. Therefore, the detachable launchers were deleted and downward-angled vertical endplates were added to the stub wings, terminating in horizontal frames with 2P32M (K-4V) missile launch rails inboard and outboard of the endplate. The Mi-24 received its unmistakable wing/pylon arrangement.

NATO got wind of the Mi-24's existence in 1972, shortly after the helicopter had entered service with the VVS, and allocated it the ASCC codename 'Hind'. Curiously, the pre-production version with no wing anhedral became known in the West after the first production version, the Mi-24A; thus, the Mi-24A was codenamed 'Hind-A' and the pre-production Mi-24 became the 'Hind-B'.

Mi-24A 'Hind-A' (Izdelye 245)

More changes were required before the helicopter was cleared for full-scale production. Flight tests showed that the forward fuselage of the 'Hind-B' was too cramped to accommodate the Raduga-F (Rainbow) semi-automatic command line of sight (SACLOS) guidance system for the anti-tank missiles and the fast-firing machine-gun installation. The two prototypes were converted at Mil's experimental shop in Panki by cutting off the cockpit section and grafting on a new forward fuselage. While being basically

similar to the original version, the new nose was slightly longer and had a more pointed profile, with more sharply raked upper windshield segments to reduce drag. The car-type pilot's door was replaced by a sliding bubble window to give the pilot some downward vision (incidentally, the Mi-8 had undergone the same evolution earlier when the flight deck doors of the V-8 prototypes were replaced by sliding windows and a common flight deck/cabin port-side entry door), and the A-12,7 machine-gun was fitted.

Another external recognition feature was the small teardrop fairing of the command link transmitter antenna immediately forward of the nose gear. Other changes included rudimentary flight controls for the WSO (cyclic and collective pitch and pedals) so that he could fly the helicopter home should the pilot be disabled.

In this form (with extended nose, anhedral wings, and modified controls and mission avionics), the helicopter entered production in Arsenyev in 1970 as the Mi-24A (Izdelye 245). Attaining initial operational capability the next year, the 'Hind-A' was officially accepted into the VVS inventory in 1972 after passing its State acceptance trials. Initially, the Mi-24A was operated by independent helicopter regiments within mechanised infantry or tank armies and air assault brigades. Later, the helicopter equipped independent combat control helicopter regiments; when the Army Aviation was formed within the Soviet armed forces, Mi-24s equipped independent helicopter squadrons within mechanised infantry divisions.

Early operational experience

Mi-24A deliveries to the Soviet Air Force commenced in 1970. The Voronezh detachment of the 4th TsBPiPLS (Tsentr boyevoy podgotovki i pereuchivaniya lyotnovo sostahva = Combat and Conversion Training Centre), the main facility of which is in Lipetsk, was the first to master the new helicopter. It was soon followed by VVS units located in Chernigovka (Far East Defence District), Brody (Carpathian DD), Parchim and Stendal (Group of Soviet Forces in Germany, later renamed Western Group of Forces). Later, the Mi-24 equipped units based in Prouzhany (Belorussian DD), Mogocha (Transbaikalian DD), Raukhovka (Odessa DD), Berdichev (Carpathian DD), etc.

One of the Mi-24A's major deficiencies was its propensity to rotate uncontrollably around the vertical axis when hovering in a crosswind. Often, this uncommanded rotation could not be countered even by applying full opposite 'rudder' because of insufficient tail rotor authority, and resulted in accidents. Early-production Mi-24As had the tail rotor on the starboard side, as on the Mi-8; the rotor turned clockwise when seen from the hub so that the forward blade went with the main rotor downwash. However, the helicopter had poor directional control in some flight modes, and service pilots were quick to point this out. In 1972 the tail rotor was relocated to port,

Above left: This view of 'Red 77', an early production Mi-24A 'Hind-A', shows the 'Hind' looking far more warlike – as its designers intended. The stub wings have been remodelled with 19° anhedral, giving the aircraft its distinctive hunched look. Launchers for the Falanga-M (AT-2 'Swatter') ATGMs have been fitted and the gunner's position is armed with an Afanasyev A-12,7 machine-gun. Confusion and a lack of information on the part of NATO intelligence operatives led to the follow-on model Mi-24A receiving the 'Hind-A' codename.

Above: This alternative view of 'Red 77' clearly shows its starboard tail rotor, which would soon be changed. The pilots of early 'Hind-As' were generally pleased with the type's handling and agility, which was surprising for a helicopter of this size and weight: the Mi-24A could climb at up to 50° Alpha, make turns at over 60° bank, and perform stall turns and other vigorous manoeuvres. Nonetheless, the Mi-24 had its fair share of teething troubles. The TV3-117 engines were the chief source of annoyance, as their service life initially was only 50 hours. Poor visibility from the driver's seat was another problem area; to make matters worse, the optically-flat glazing panels reflected lights on the ground during low-level night flying, which could cause pilot disorientation.

Above: 'Red 50' (2201201) was an Mi-24A used to test the revised tail rotor configuration. Today it is part of the Monino museum collection.

Left: This strangely camouflaged Mi-24A is preserved at the Akhtubinsk test centre museum.

Left: 'Red 33' (3201902), a late-model Mi-24A, is preserved at Khodynka, alongside an Mi-24V, 'White 60'.

Right: This freshly repainted and uncoded late-model Mi-24A (3202109) is preserved at the Armed Forces Museum, in Moscow.

Above and left: This Mi-24A is on display at the Vietnamese People's Air Force Museum, in Hanoi. Vietnam's 'Hind-As' entered service in the mid-1980s and saw combat in Cambodia.

As the Mi-24A became operational, the VVS began demonstrating it to various VIPs. One of the first displays was at Kubinka air base west of Moscow, where 4th TsBPP pilots put on a show of force for the defence ministers of Warsaw Pact nations, impressing them with the agility of the 'Hind'. Later, the helicopter was demonstrated to the then-Defence Minister Marshal Gheorgiy M. Grechko at the Alabino range near Naro-Fominsk, southwest of Moscow. A flight of Mi-24As, again flown by 4th TsBPP crews, spectacularly destroyed the targets with 'Swatter' ATGMs, S-5 FFARs, 100-kg (220-lb) bombs and machine-gun fire. The demonstration was a success – not least because the organisers had strategically placed fuel drums beside the tanks and APCs used as targets to create huge fireballs, adding to the effect of the show. When the explosions had subsided the marshal said with satisfaction, addressing his retinue: "The enemy will sure have to keep their heads down on a battlefield like this!"

switching from pusher to tractor configuration, as on the Mi-14 and Mi-8MT/Mi-17 'Hip-H'. The rotor still turned clockwise, so that now the forward blade went against the main rotor downwash; this increased tail rotor efficiency dramatically. According to OKB sources, the new arrangement was introduced on production 'Hinds' in 1974; however, there are several known Mi-24As built in 1973 with the port-side tail rotor.

About the same time, seven reinforcement ribs were added on the port fuselage side aft of the wings, the APU exhaust was extended and angled downwards to prevent rain from getting in, and the characteristic triple aerial of the SRO-2M Khrom (Chromium)/'Odd Rods' IFF transponder (SRO, *samolyotnii rahdiolokatseeonnii otvetchik* = aircraft (-mounted) radar [IFF] responder) were moved from the canopy frame to the oil cooler atop the engine intakes.

The armament, borrowed directly from the Mi-4AV, rendered the helicopter ineffective in its intended CAS role. The early manually-guided 9M17M (AT-2 'Swatter') missiles had an appallingly low hit ratio of 30 per cent. This improved radically to over 80 per cent when the 9M17P with semi-automatic guidance and the Raduga-F guidance system were introduced on the Mi-24D; the Mi-24V's 9M114 (AT-6 'Spiral') has a kill ratio in excess of 92 per cent.

More than 240 Mi-24As had rolled off the line in Arsenyev by the time production ended in 1974. Once again, the seemingly illogical Soviet practice of launching full-scale production even before an aircraft had been officially phased-in (as had been the case with the Mi-4, for example) had paid off, allowing flight and ground crews to familiarise themselves with the helicopter by the time approval came from the Air Force.

Getting the 'Hind' up to scratch took some time, and the learning curve was steep; it was not until the Mi-24V entered service that the Soviet Army Aviation got a dependable tank-buster. Over the years, engine life and reliability were much improved. There have been cases

when the TV3-117 turboshaft has continued to run normally after major bird strikes or ingesting foliage. During the Schchit-79 (Shield 79) WarPac exercise, one Mi-24 crew mistimed its arrival and popped up late over the target, by which time the range was already being pounded by heavy artillery. As the pilot turned the aircraft around to exit the area, one of the engines was hit by several shell fragments. On the way back to base the crew could hear that the engine had developed some knocking, but it showed no signs of catastrophic failure.

The helicopter could land in autorotation mode in the event of a double engine failure. "Test pilots in Minsk showed us what the helicopter could do," Colonel V. N. Kvashevich recalled. "The pilot shut down both engines over the runway at 250 or 280 km/h and about 30 to 50 m, then made a U-turn and landed safely."

Mi-24B 'Hind-A' (Izdelye 241)

As the Mi-24A entered production, the Mil OKB continued improving the helicopter's armament. The Mi-24B, or Izdelye 241, as the next version was designated, featured a USPU-24 powered chin turret (USPU, *universahl' naya s'yomnaya pulemyotnaya ustanovka* = versatile detachable machine-gun installation) with a 12.7-mm Yakoushev/ Borzov YakB-12,7 four-barrelled Gatling-type machine-gun (also referred to as TKB-063 and 9A624 in some sources) traversable through +20°/-40° in elevation and ±60° in azimuth. This was slaved to a KPS-53AV sighting system which made corrections for the helicopter's movement. The system featured an analog computer receiving input from the helicopter's air data sensors.

The manually-guided 9M17M Falanga-M anti-tank missiles of the Mi-24A gave way to an upgraded version, the 9M17P Falanga-P (P, *poluavtomateecheskoye navedeniye* = semi-automatic guidance). The missiles were controlled by the Raduga-F SACLOS guidance system which increased kill probability three to four times. The targeting part of the

Left: Even though they were soon replaced by more capable versions, the early-model 'Hinds' were a great leap forward for their crews – but could catch out the unwary. Unaccustomed to the retractable gear, pilots (who had transferred from the Mi-8 or Mi-4) often forgot to tuck up the wheels after take-off – or, worse still, to extend them when coming home, the helicopter suffering heavy damage in the subsequent belly landing. Another major drawback was the lack of adequate dual controls. Having only rudimentary flight controls, the WSO had to be an accomplished flyer, or very lucky, to get the helicopter down in one piece.

system comprised low-light-level television (LLLTV) and forward-looking infra-red (FLIR) sensors in a slab-sided ventral housing offset to starboard ahead of the nose gear, with twin protective metal doors covering the sensor window. The system was gyro-stabilised, enabling the helicopter to manoeuvre vigorously to avoid ground fire while targeting. The guidance command link antenna was located in a small egg-shaped fairing offset to port which could traverse as the missile manoeuvred, since the antenna dish was fixed. The Mi-24B successfully passed the manufacturer's trials in 1971-72, but was abandoned, becoming a stepping stone towards an even more radical redesign – the Mi-24V and Mi-24D.

Mi-24D/Mi-25 'Hind-D' (Izdelye 246)

Experience with the Mi-24A showed that cockpit visibility was surprisingly poor, the spacious cockpit and the relative placement of the crew creating large blind zones. The WSO obscured the right front quadrant for the pilot, who in turn impaired the WSO's visibility in the left rear quadrant. The flat glazing generated annoying reflections, and the heavy windscreen framework did not help.

This led the Mil OKB to radically redesign the forward fuselage in early 1971 – "making an already ugly helicopter truly hideous in the process," as one Western writer put it. The crew sat in separate cockpits in a stepped-tandem arrangement, the pilot sitting above and behind the WSO. The narrow cockpits had extensive armour protection and bubble canopies with large optically-flat bullet-proof windscreens which gave far better all-round visibility. The pilot entered via a rearward-opening car-type door on the starboard side, and the port half of the WSO's cockpit canopy hinged open to starboard. A long air data boom with DUAS-V pitch and yaw vanes (DUAS, *dahtchik uglah atahki i snosa* = AoA and drift sensor) was offset to starboard and the IFF aerials were mounted on the WSO's canopy frame.

The redesign improved visibility not only for the crew but also for the Raduga-F LLLTV/FLIR sensors, and enhanced operating conditions for the missile guidance antenna. However, this in turn called for more changes. To ensure adequate ground clearance for the LLLTV/FLIR sensor fairing, the nose gear unit was lengthened, giving the helicopter a pronounced nose-up attitude on the ground (unlike earlier versions). The nosewheels were semi-exposed when retracted, so the bulged twin nosewheel doors of the Mi-24A gave way to single door linked to the oleo strut. Changes were made to the fuel system: the wing pylons were 'wet', permitting the carriage of 500-litre (110-Imp gal) drop tanks and leaving the cabin free.

The up-gunned Mi-24B 'Hind-A' was an interim version that bridged the gap between the glass-nosed 'Hind-As' and the definitive Mi-24D/V. This is one of the Mi-24B prototypes (above) with its signature four-barrelled Yakoushev/ Borzov YakB-12,7 machine-gun, housed in a USPU-24 chin turret. Before the real Mi-24Bs first flew, a full-scale mock-up was produced (left). This is believed to have been rebuilt from the original 'Hind-B' mock-up, since it had no wing anhedral and featured the tested-but-failed detachable missile launchers on the fuselage sides (ahead of the main gear). The real prototypes were converted from several early-production Mi-24As with starboard-side tail rotors.

The dual-cockpit version was allocated the designation Mi-24V (this is the third letter of the Cyrillic alphabet). Unfortunately, however, its intended armament of Shturm-V ATGMs was still unavailable, forcing the Mil OKB to do the next best thing and develop a hybrid – a combination of the new airframe with the 'old' armament system as fitted to the experimental Mi-24B. This stopgap version was designated Mi-24D or Izdelye 246. Note that the fifth letter of the Cyrillic alphabet was used instead of the fourth (G); there was never an Mi-24G – possibly because G could be deciphered as *gavno* (shit).

Above and right (two): The two Mi-24D 'Hind-D' prototypes were converted from early 'Hind-As' and so came with the starboard-mounted tail rotor. For their initial flight tests the helicopters were fitted with additional pitot booms on the standard air data boom and immediately ahead of the port cabin door, and the ATGM launch rails were removed. The wing-mounted strike camera was fitted inboard of the weapons pylons (on the port side). The camera remained in this position on early-model 'Hind-Ds' but it was soon moved outboard, as the plumes from the rockets obscured its view.

The 'Hind-D' was a major step forward as it not only added new weapons and better sensors to the airframe but offered the crew far better protection in their heavily-armoured individual cockpits. This is one of the earliest Mi-24Ds delivered to Poland (actually the third aircraft, which arrived in 1978). Today it is still in service with 3 Eskadra 'Scorpions', 49 PSB (49th combat helicopter regiment), based at Pruszcz-Gdanski.

The two Mi-24D prototypes were converted in June 1972 (probably from early-production Mi-24As) and thus were unique in having a starboard-side tail rotor. State acceptance trials began the next year, continuing well into 1974, and the helicopter passed them with flying colours. In 1973 the Mi-24D entered production at the Progress Aircraft Factory and the Rostov Helicopter Factory (plant No. 168, now called Rostvertol Production Association); some 350 had been built when production ended in 1977.

The Mi-24A featured an S-13 strike camera at the port wing/inboard pylon junction. However, the smoke trail left by the FFARs streaking towards the target made recording the attack results a chancy affair, so the camera was soon moved to the port wingtip/endplate junction on the Mi-24D. An export version with slightly downgraded mission avionics, designated Mi-25, was developed for

Warsaw Pact nations and the Soviet Union's Third World allies. The ASCC codename for the Mi-24D and Mi-25 was 'Hind-D'.

Mi-24V/Mi-35 'Hind-E' (Izdelye 242)

The 9K113 weapons system based on the 9M114 Shturm-V (AT-6 'Spiral') supersonic ATGM specified by the Air Force's operational requirement finally became available in 1972, marking the appearance of the Mi-24V (Izdelye 242). This version has sometimes been referred to as Mi-24W in the Western press, a misconception caused by the German and Polish spelling of the designation (in the latter case because there is no letter V in Polish).

The new missile was not only faster than the 'Swatter' but had greater accuracy and longer range. It was also more compact thanks to folding fins, coming in a neat disposable tubular launcher/container. Like its predecessor, the 'Spiral' employed SACLOS guidance; the command link antenna 'egg' was slightly larger than the Mi-24D's and had a more rounded front end with a large dielectric dome. The new antenna was fully articulated and the pod did not need to rotate. Trials of the missile were completed in 1974.

The Mi-24V prototype was converted from an early-production Mi-24D in 1973. Apart from the 'canned missiles' replacing the rather untidy wingtip launch rails of the D, the Mi-24V differed in having TV3-117V engines (V, *vysotnii* = 'for high altitudes', i.e., for 'hot-and-high' conditions) uprated to 2,225 eshp (1660 kW) and an ASP-17V automatic gunsight for the pilot. On production Mi-24Vs the protective doors of the Raduga-F LLLTV/FLIR pod moved aft on a system of linkages to lie flat against the sides of the pod; this arrangement created less drag. A second (non-retractable) landing light was added on the port side of the nose.

New communications equipment was fitted, as indicated by two new aerials on the tailboom: a dorsal blade aerial for the R-863 VHF radio and a ventral 'towel rail' aerial for the R-828 radio used for communication with ground troops. The SRO-2M Khrom IFF was replaced by the SRO-1P Parol ('Password') transponder, aka Izdelye 62-01, with characteristic triangular blade aerials. (Some late-production Mi-24Ds also had the new avionics.)

'Hind-E' trials and improvements

The 'Hind-E', as the helicopter was codenamed by NATO, completed its State acceptance trials about a year later than the Mi-24D; however, both models were formally included in the VVS inventory by a single government directive on 29 March 1976. By then, some 400 Mi-24As and Ds had been delivered. The Mi-24V entered production in 1976, and more than 1,000 had been built in Arsenyev and Rostov by 1986. An export version with downgraded avionics was designated Mi-35.

Late Mi-24Vs received an L-006 Beryoza (Birch) radar homing and warning system (RHAWS), aka SPO-15, with characteristic protuberances on the forward fuselage sides and the tail rotor pylon's trailing edge to give 360° coverage. The forward 'horns' were usually fitted aft of the rear cockpit, but some aircraft (e.g., Polish and Hungarian Mi-35s) had them located between the two cockpits. Four ASO-2V-02 infra-red countermeasures (IRCM) flare launchers with 32 flares apiece were mounted under the tailboom for protection against heat-seeking missiles, later giving way to six identical units on the aft fuselage sides, and an L-166V-11E active IRCM jammer, aka SOEP-V1A Lipa (Linden; NATO 'Hot Brick'), was installed aft of the main rotor head. The jammer was a thimble-shaped fairing enclosing a powerful xenon lamp with a rotating reflector, in the fashion of the flashing blue light on a police car. It emitted a pulsed IR signal which darted erratically, disappearing and reappearing, causing the missile to lose track of the target. They were also fitted to some late Mi-24Ds which have sometimes been referred to as 'Hind-D Mod'.

Triple-lobe air/exhaust mixers called EVU (*ezhektorno-vykhlopnoye ustroystvo* = ejector exhaust device) could be fitted to reduce the helicopter's IR signature. After mixing the exhaust with cool outside air they directed it upwards into the main rotor downwash, reducing exhaust gas temperature by 350° to 400°C (662° to 752°F). However, the mixers could only be fitted to aircraft built from about 1984 onwards, as they had downward-angled jetpipes.

The Mi-24V is known to have carried eight 9M114 ATGMs (on the endplate racks and the outboard wing pylons), at least during trials. Multiple missile racks increasing the number of ATGMs to 16 were tested successfully in 1986. The 'Hind-E' also evolved into several experimental versions and avionics or weapons testbeds in the 1980s (Mi-24M, Mi-24N, Mi-24F, etc.), details of which are not available.

Mi-24P/Mi-35P 'Hind-F' (Izdelye 243)

Mil engineers had obviously never been happy about the Air Force's demand to substitute the Mi-24's projected cannon armament with a machine-gun. Accordingly, in 1975 the OKB commenced trials of a more heavily armed derivative of the Mi-24V designated Mi-24P, or Izdelye 243; the P stood for *pushechnii* = cannon-equipped.

The USPU-24 barbette was deleted, resulting in a smooth nose. A 30-mm (1.18-in) Gryazev/Shipunov GSh-30K double-barrelled rapid-firing cannon (also referred to as GSh-2-30) was fitted; the cannon had passed its State acceptance trials in 1976 and was fitted to the Sukhoi Su-25. The cannon was much too heavy and its recoil was too violent for it to be installed in a chin barbette, so it had to be scabbed on to the starboard side of the forward fuselage in an elongated fairing under the pilot's cockpit. The pilot was to aim the cannon by turning the whole helicopter.

The Mi-24P entered production in 1981, and more than 620 had been built when production ended in 1989. The 'big gun' 'Hind' was also offered for export as the Mi-35P; the uncoded Mi-35P prototype is said to have had construction number 3532431723858. Mi-24 construction numbers (manufacturer's serial numbers) follow several systems. Until 1973, Mi-24As had seven-digit c/ns, e.g., 3201902. The first digit denotes the year of manufacture (1973), the second is presumably an in-house product code at the Arsenyev factory (not the Mil OKB!), 019 is the batch number and 02 the number of the helicopter in the batch, with five (later 10) to a batch. The NATO codename was 'Hind-F'.

The responsibilities of the 'Hind' were fully defined after the helicopter had been officially phased in as being cover and close air support for ground forces and assault groups airlifted by Mi-8T/TVs and Mi-6s. The YakB-12,7 machine-gun or GSh-30K cannon, UPK-23-250 gun pods and 'iron' bombs of up to 500 kg (1,102 lb) were fairly effective in this role. The GUV gun pods, on the other hand, proved disappointing in both machine-gun and grenade launcher configuration. Afghan war experience showed that the 57-mm S-5 FFARs were ineffective, and they were gradually supplanted by 80-mm S-8 FFARs.

'Hind' v Cobra

Destruction of low- and slow-flying aerial targets, notably other helicopters, was another role filled by the Mi-24. Until the advent of the AH-64 Apache, the most dangerous rotary-wing adversary of the 'Hind' was the AH-1 HueyCobra. In an encounter with the HueyCobra, the Mi-24's strengths were its higher speed and rate of climb, while its main weakness was its relatively poor horizontal manoeuvrability, especially at low speed. This was important, as numerous trials had established that in a duel between two helicopters the one which could out-turn the enemy at low speeds had a better chance of making a kill.

VVS 'Hinds' met the HueyCobra when operating in the air defence role in the former East Germany. Usually, such encounters were peaceful enough – the two helicopters flew side by side along the border between East and West Germany as the crews studied each other intently. One occasion in the early 1980s, however, ended in disaster. An

Above: The 9M17 Falanga ATGM (also referred to as the Skorpion) – as fitted to the Mi-24D – was originally designed for use on light armoured vehicles. It was a short-ranged and relatively inaccurate second-generation weapon that relied on a radio guidance system prone to interference and failure. The 9M17M missile was replaced by the improved 9M17P which extended its range from 3000 m (9,842 ft) to 4000 m (13,123 ft).

Top: This late model Hungarian Mi-24D has gained the distinctive 'horned' antennas of the L-006 Beryoza radar warning system on its forward fuselage. This aircraft is also carrying a full load of live 9M17P Falanga-P missiles (with the associated Raduga-F SACLOS guidance system undernose) as it prepares to depart its base at Szabadja for a live-fire exercise.

Above: The 'Hinds' of Bulgaria's BVVS are a mix of Mi-24Ds (as seen here) and the more powerful Mi-24V. Since 1979 Bulgaria has received 38 'Hind-Ds' and only lost one, in a 1996 accident. This aircraft, one of the later Mi-24Ds to be delivered, is still an early-configuration 'Hind-D' lacking any Sirena or Beryoza RHAW antennas.

Right: Afghanistan was an early customer for the Mi-24D and its aircraft were quickly pressed into action against the Mujahideen. Though the Afghan war has been recorded largely as a Russian conflict, the Afghans had a few successful 'Hind' pilots, too, one of whom was 26-year-old Captain Sarwar. On one occasion a Stinger was fired at his aircraft as he was leading a flight of Mi-25s (export Mi-24s) on a reconnaissance sortie, but it missed. Taking note of the Mujahideen emplacement, Sarwar landed some way off while his wingmen distracted the Mujahideen. He sneaked up to their emplacement and took it out with hand grenades, capturing a few weapons, too. On another occasion, his wingman was downed by Mujahideen gunners and Sarwar landed under fire to evacuate the wounded and unconscious crew. In late August 1987, he was wounded in action but managed to bring his helicopter home.

Mi-24 based in the southern part of East Germany scrambled to 'intercept' an AH-1G which manoeuvred a few hundred yards from the wire mesh fence running along the border. Russian sources described the Cobra pilot as 'a real pro', who would follow the border at low level, repeatedly accelerate and then pitch up sharply, to bleed off speed. The Mi-24 had a tough time staying on the Cobra's tail, yet the Soviet crew did not give up. Again the AH-1 put on a burst of speed and then pitched up, stopping short within seconds. Determined to stay with the Cobra, the Soviet pilot hauled back on the stick but the big, heavy 'Hind' started to tumble. The pilot did the only thing possible and pushed the stick forward sharply, putting the helicopter into a dive to gain forward speed, but he was too low and had to pull back on the stick just as sharply to avoid hitting the ground. Seconds later the main rotor blades struck the tailboom and the helicopter crashed, killing the crew.

Mi-24VP (Izdelye 258)

Experience with the Mi-24P proved that cannon were the way to go, yet the fixed cannon of the 'Hind-F' and the need to aim it by pointing the helicopter was a liability. The 30-mm cannon was also too much firepower in some circumstances when a smaller and lighter 23-mm cannon would have done the job. A new version designated Mi-24VP (V, *pushechnii* = 'cannon-equipped Mi-24V'), Izdelye 258,

was developed in 1985. It differed from the 'Hind-E' in having the USPU-24 barbette and YakB-12,7 machine-gun replaced by a new NPPU-24 barbette with a GSh-23 cannon (NPPU, *nes'yomnaya podveezhnaya pushechnaya ustanovka* = non-detachable movable cannon installation). The Mi-24 finally received the armament which Mikhail L. Mil had wanted it to have all along. State acceptance trials began in 1985 and dragged on for four years. The Mi-24VP entered production in 1989 but, unfortunately, only 25 were completed before 'Hind' production was 'terminally terminated' same year.

Weapons development

New weapons options were developed for the various versions of the 'Hind' in the late 1970s. The first of these was the massive GUV gun pod (*gondola universahl'naya vertolyotnaya* = versatile [gun] pod for helicopters), aka 9A669. It could be configured with either a YakB-12,7 four-barrelled machine-gun flanked by two 7.62-mm (0.30-in) TKB-621 four-barrelled Gatling machine-guns or a 30-mm (1.18-in) AGS-17 Plamya (Flame) automatic grenade launcher. Next came the UPK-23-250 pod (*unifit-seerovannii pushechnii konteyner* = standardised gun pod) containing a GSh-23 gun with 250 rounds.

The UB-32-57 and UB-32A FFAR pods with 57-mm S-5 rockets were supplanted by B-8V20 pods with 20 80-mm (3.15-in) S-8 rockets apiece, B-13 pods with five 122-mm

(4.8-in) S-13 rockets apiece and single 250-mm (9.84-in) S-24 rockets. Other stores included illumination flare packs for night operations, KMGU sub-munitions pods (*konteyner dlya malogabaritnykh gruzov universahl'nii* = versatile small items container, typically loaded with anti-tank or anti-personnel mines) and various free-fall bombs weighing up to 500 kg (1,102 lb).

Air-to-air role

The Mil OKB experimented with giving the 'Hind' counter-air capability as well, to which end R-60 (AA-8 'Aphid'), R-73 (AA-11 'Archer') and 9M39 Igla-V ('Needle') air-to-air missiles were tested on the Mi-24. Even though the results were not particularly encouraging, a few Mi-24Vs were retrofitted in service with launchers for R-60 AAMs in the late 1980s. One of the units involved in testing the R-60 installation was the 1038th TsPLS (Tsentr pereuchivaniya lyotnovo sostahva = conversion training centre) in the Turkestan Defence District which undertook much test work to investigate the helicopter's capabilities.

The pilot aimed the R-60s by means of the ASP-17V gunsight, turning the helicopter until he got a lock-on from the missiles' IR seekers. During early tests the missiles were fired against flare bombs, with considerable success. However, in mock combat with helicopters fitted with IR-suppression exhaust mixers (when the pilot did everything short of actually firing a missile), target acquisition

range was no more than 600 m (1,968 ft), and less against piston-engined targets. The climate of Central Asia did not help, either, as ground temperature reached 60°C (140°F) and confused the missiles' seeker heads during NoE flying. As a result, the R-60 was not widely used on the Mi-24, but a few 'Hind' squadrons, including some stationed in East Germany, had their helicopters equipped with AAMs.

The Soviet Air Force's interest in the Mi-24 as an air defence weapon against slow-flying targets grew considerably following Matthias Rust's notorious landing in Moscow's Red Square, on 29 May 1987. Consequently, several Mi-24 squadrons were transferred to the Air Defence Force's fighter arm, IA PVO (istrebeetel'naya aviahtsiya protivovozdushnoy oborony). The 'fighter' 'Hinds' saw real action against intruders into Soviet airspace, notably in the Kaliningrad PVO District where Mi-24s often had to deal with wayward aircraft – and forced them down on Soviet airfields in several instances.

On the other hand, it has to be said that Mikhail L. Mil's 'flying IFV' concept, which was the core of the Mi-24's design philosophy, was seldom put into practice. The 'Hind' was only sporadically used as a troopship, mostly for inserting and extracting search and destroy groups. For example, during the Zapad-81 (West-81) exercise, two Mi-24 squadrons from Prouzhany AB, Belarus dropped off Spetsnaz groups tasked with seizing bridges and the opposing force's air base command centres. Each helicopter

Above: This low-flying Czech Mi-24D is seen in service with the 51st Helicopter Regiment, based at Prostejov in 1992. The strap-on ASO-2V chaff and flare dispensers under the rear tailboom can carry 32 expendables and are usually fitted in blocks of three.

Inset: This classic head-on view of a Hungarian Mi-24D shows the 'Hind' at its most predatory. The cluttered cockpit of the WSO contrasts with that of the pilot sitting behind him. Also of note are the downward-sloping exhausts, a feature of late-model 'Hind-Ds' and all subsequent versions.

Three colour schemes are used on Bulgaria's Mi-24s. The oldest is an equally-spaced light and dark green camouflage – the original ex-Soviet colours in which they were delivered. An overall dark green scheme, with vertical stripes of even darker green, was applied on a number of helicopters that underwent major overhauls at the Sofia-based TEREM Letetz repair facility in 1993-1994. A third 'lizard camouflage' (equally-spaced green and brown stripes) was applied to Mi-24s after overhaul in Hungary in 1994-1996. BVVS 'Hinds' wear no squadron markings, with exception of three of the six Mi-24Vs.

Mil Mi-24 'Hind'

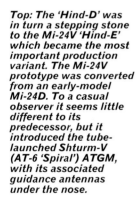

Top: The 'Hind-D' was in turn a stepping stone to the Mi-24V 'Hind-E' which became the most important production variant. The Mi-24V prototype was converted from an early-model Mi-24D. To a casual observer it seems little different to its predecessor, but it introduced the tube-launched Shturm-V (AT-6 'Spiral') ATGM, with its associated guidance antennas under the nose.

Above: Production Mi-24Vs had several small changes compared to the prototypes – differences which also set them apart from the similar-looking Mi-24D. The doors over the undernose optical sight (starboard) had a revised twin-arm hydraulic actuator while the (fixed) egg-shaped radio antenna for the missiles was rounder than the Mi-24D's, with a black dielectric nose.

carried six commandos which disembarked while the 'Hind' was moving at a couple of dozen feet and 50 km/h (31 mph). Despite its under-use as a troopship, the 'Hind' could well qualify for the title of the most battle-proven helicopter in the world: in less than 20 years, it has participated in some 30 wars and regional conflicts on three continents.

'Hind' combat debut

The Mi-24 received its baptism of fire in early 1978 when Somalia's leader, General Siad Barré, sent his troops into neighbouring Ethiopia, trying to capture provinces which Somalia regarded as its own. Flown by Cuban pilots, Ethiopian Mi-24As raided Somalian positions with virtual impunity, knocking out armoured vehicles and artillery.

Hostilities did not end when General Barré's troops were forced out of the country. Ethiopia was soon torn apart by a prolonged civil war in which the Addis Ababa government fought to quell separatism in the northern province of Eritrea. Once again, more than 40 'Hind-As' were thrown into battle against the Eritrean Liberation Front guerrillas. The helicopters were used in the CAS role, their main armament being S-5 FFARs. None is known to have been shot down, but several were destroyed on the ground by Eritrean separatists which overran Asmara air base on the night of 21 May 1984.

Soviet military advisors and technicians assisted the government forces in training 'Hind' crews and maintaining the helicopters. "Mi-35s were delivered from the USSR in 1988," Major S. A. Melnichenko, one of the advisors,

recalled. "The graduates of the local flying school flew them successfully. Besides flying the usual missions of the Mi-24, they had to seek and destroy separatist gunboats in the Red Sea. These fast craft were the scourge of shipping in the area, appearing out of nowhere, attacking ships moored in the harbours and disappearing just as quickly. After the helicopters had sunk eight of these boats, the enemy gave up using them. In February 1989 UPK-23-250 gun pods were used with great success against tanks. An armoured convoy moving along a canyon was attacked by two groups of Mi-35s which took turns strafing it, destroying eight tanks."

As the conflict escalated, the separatists managed to shoot down several 'Hind-As'. No 'Hind-Es' were lost to enemy action until early 1990, but one Mi-35 was damaged beyond repair in a wheels-up landing. When spares supplies from the Soviet Union dried up, most of the Ethiopian Air Force's helicopters became unserviceable. A few 'Hinds' were flown to the rebels by Ethiopian defectors and used against the government forces until 1991, when Eritrea became a sovereign state.

War in Afghanistan

The most famous conflict in which the Mi-24 participated was undoubtedly the Afghan war. The type was introduced into Afghanistan in April 1979 when the Afghan air force took delivery of its first Mi-24As and Mi-25s. The helicopters were immediately pressed into action against the Mujahideen guerrillas of Burhanuddin Rabbani and Gulbuddin Hekmatyar, or 'the irreconcilable opposition', as they were referred to in the Soviet press. The Afghan pilots had been well trained and put the 'Hind' to good use. Still, it was not long before the Mujahideen air defences, weak as they were at the time, claimed their first victim. The first Mi-24 was shot down near Khost on 30 May 1979, crashing into a mountain slope after being hit by ground fire. The Kabul government kept urging the Soviet leaders to supply 20 or 25 more 'Hinds', but it was not before the Soviet Union put troops into Afghanistan on 25 December 1979 that a new batch was delivered.

The Kremlin strategists assessing the situation in the Democratic Republic of Afghanistan did not seem to realise that the country was, in effect, already in the throes of a civil war. The sporadic character of the war, and the ambush and hit-and-run tactics favoured by the Mujahideen, demanded quick and accurate response to enemy action. Thus, air support was of prime importance –

all the more so because, in Afghanistan's mountainous terrain, he who had the high ground was in control of the situation. In a nutshell, it looked like this was going to be a 'helicopter war', and the Mi-24 was to prove its worth in it.

Afghan tactics

After the first encounters with the enemy and the first shoot-downs, the helicopters began working in pairs, at the very least, so that if one went down the other could provide cover for the downed crew. Usually, however, the Mi-24s operated in flights of four or in groups of eight; this made for maximum strike effectiveness in areas providing ample natural cover for the enemy. The Mujahideen were well armed and returned fire whenever possible, so having strength in numbers allowed the helicopter crews to utilise many tactics which a pair might have found it impossible to use. These included the 'wheel of death' (introduced by Ilyushin Il-2s during World War II) during which the helicopters circled the target, spraying it with fire; the *konveyer* ('assembly line', or rather 'disassembly line') technique in which the helicopters approached in echelon formation and the wingmen consecutively turned head on to the target; and the innocuous-sounding 'daisy', whereby the helicopters fanned out in all directions in a manner reminiscent of the bomb burst aerobatic manoeuvre to intermittently pound the target from all directions at minimum intervals. To avoid AA fire, pairs of helicopters would zigzag or fly in a scissor pattern, alternately climbing and descending to complicate aiming for Mujahideen gunners; the higher-flying pair would provide protection for the attacking one.

Mi-24 crews did everything to maximise the effect of their fire, sometimes to the detriment of flight safety, and there were cases when the flight leader who had just finished a firing pass found his wingman's rockets whizzing past him on either side before he had time to get out of the way! Flexibility in tactics and mission planning was all-important, as following a rigid routine immediately led to blows; even following the same avenue of approach twice could lead to an ambush. On the way to and from the target and on combat air patrol (CAP) missions, the helicopters in a pair kept a distance of 1200 to 1500 m (3,937 to 4,921 ft) to avoid being hit by the same burst of ground fire; this gave the crews time to react, either taking evasive action or taking out the enemy right away.

The 'Hind' was fast but its high speed had a price – rotor disc loading was 50 per cent greater than the Mi-8's, which significantly impaired controllability in Afghanistan's

extreme conditions ('hot-and-high', plus dusty). Worse still, the ingrained piloting techniques for normal conditions were often useless and could even cause accidents. The overly high rotor disc loading meant that sharp stick (cyclic) movements would cause the helicopter to sag; the pilot would then pull collective, trying to keep the helicopter airborne, but engines weakened by the 'hot-and-high' conditions could not accelerate quickly enough and the result would be an unceremonious landing.

At low speed or low altitude, where the frequent ground winds came into play, the 'Hind' would start acting up. Due to its inadequate directional control, the tail rotor would try to pull the helicopter into an uncommanded left turn and, at worst, could cause it to flip into a spin, with almost certainly disastrous results. The main rotor blades stalled during high-g manoeuvres at high speed and high Alpha, causing the Mi-24 to pitch up uncontrollably and fall through sharply. This phenomenon, known as *podkhvaht* ('pick-up'), often resulted in a hard landing on the wing endplates and FFAR pods. A 'pick-up' could be avoided by sticking to the book (in other words, taking it nice and slow), but this was hardly possible in combat.

Self-inflicted injuries

As a result of the 'pick-up' phenomenon or during recovery from a high-g dive, the main rotor blades could strike the tailboom. One such incident was recorded in August 1980 when two 'Hinds' flown by Squadron Leader Major Kozovoy and his deputy Major Alatortsev came back from a sortie with holes torn in their tailbooms caused by blade strikes. Both helicopters were repaired, but in its post-repair check-out flight Major Kozovoy's Mi-24 was hit by ground fire. A burst of a 12.7-mm DShK fire took one of the tail rotor blades right off, causing violent vibration; the hastily repaired tailboom broke and the helicopter crashed out of control, killing the crew.

Pulling out of a 20° dive at 250 km/h (155 mph), the Mi-24 could lose up to 200 m (656 ft). At low altitude and during all-out manoeuvring there was no room for error, and manoeuvre speed and co-ordination became all-important. There was a macabre joke among 'Hind' crews that flying in this fashion was 'just as easy as walking a tightrope'. The unit stationed in Kunduz learned it the hard way, losing six Mi-24Ds in the first year of the war, in accidents. Some of the helicopters collided with mountains due to fog or wind shear, and others were written off in unsuccessful landings on slopes or in cramped landing zones.

Development of the Mi-24V 'Hind-E' was driven largely by experience in Afghanistan, where the original TV3-117 engine of the Mi-24D was found to be wanting, especially when the helicopters were heavily loaded in 'hot-and-high' conditions. Though the 'Hind-E' also introduced an improved weapons and sensor fit, arguably the most important change was under its skin. Mil fitted the more powerful TV3-117V turboshaft, rated at 2,225 shp (1660 kW) compared to the 1,640 shp (1111 kW) of the TV3-117. 'Hind' engines are set at a slight angle of 4.5° and are interchangeable (left to right) once the exhaust has been rotated through 180°. This Czech Mi-24V wears the pale grey and dark grey/green camouflage scheme applied to all Czech 'Hind-Es'. The Mi-24Ds were delivered in a three-tone grey-green camouflage, but many were repainted with a green and brown scheme after overhaul in Hungary. Czech 'Hinds' have now started appearing in an all-new two-tone grey and dark green scheme.

Above: The cowlings of the Mi-24's TV-3 engine were purposefully designed to be used as a maintenance platform in the field. This aircraft is also carrying PTB-450 drop tanks. Like all the earlier Mi-24 versions, the Mi-24V was introduced with conventional engine air intakes. However, the 'Hind' would inevitably kick up a local dust storm when operating from dirt pads – this became a serious problem in Afghanistan. To prevent excessive engine wear and foreign object damage (FOD), vortex-type intake filters called PZU (piilezaschchitnoye ustroystvo = anti-dust device) were developed and introduced on production 'Hind-Es' in 1981. These proved extremely effective and were fitted as standard to later versions of the Mi-24 (and retrofitted to many 'Hind-Ds' and some 'Hind-As').

Right: These Mi-24Vs, not yet fitted with the PZU filters, operated from a forward airfield in winter during early service trials of the 'Hind-E'. The tactical codes applied to the forward fuselage (over the butterfly camouflage pattern) are noteworthy.

In April 1980 General Designer Marat N. Tischchenko visited several Mi-24 units in Afghanistan and the 'aerial hooligans', as the pilots were wryly referred to by the army top brass, demonstrated some of the officially banned manoeuvres to him, taking the helicopter to its limits. After watching a session of 'aerobatics' featuring ultra-steep climbs, spectacular spins and even the allegedly impossible (for a 'Hind') barrel roll performed by Major V. Kharitonov, the amazed OKB boss exclaimed, "I thought I knew what my helicopters could do, now I'm not so sure!"

The daredevil demonstration created a lasting impression, and the positive after-effect followed very soon when, in the summer of 1980, the Mil OKB began working on an upgrade package for the Mi-24. This included readjustment of the engines' automatic fuel controls to reduce power loss in 'hot-and-high' conditions (made *in situ* by the manufacturer's technical teams) and a contingency increase in

turbine temperature for the duration of the war, as the crews preferred to risk having a turbine casing burn through than to suffer from lack of power when they needed it most.

The engine air intakes were fitted with vortex-type dust filters which extracted 70 to 75 per cent of the dust and sand ingested by the engines, reducing compressor blade wear 2.5 to 3 times. The Mi-24 received the filters before the Mi-8 – even though the 'Hip' operated from unprepared landing zones (LZs) more often than the 'Hind' – because its TV3-117 turboshafts had higher idling rpm and mass flow than the Mi-8's TV2-117As and thus ingested sand more readily, making the engine wear problem more acute. (It has to be said that very few 'first-generation' Mi-8s have been retrofitted with these filters; conversely, they are standard on the 'second-generation' Mi-8MT/Mi-17 'Hip-F' and its versions, both civil and military.)

Mi-24Vs began arriving in Afghanistan in 1981, with TV3-117V engines giving 15 to 20 per cent more power in 'hot-and-high' conditions. Earlier Mi-24Ds were retrofitted with the new engines during overhauls.

Hitting the target

By the end of 1980 the helicopter element of the 40th army had been doubled to 200 aircraft. The combat helicopters made both planned sorties and extra sorties as requested by the ground forces if a pocket of resistance was encountered. Army aviation accounted for 33 per cent of all planned strike missions; by contrast, its share in real CAS missions was 75 per cent. By then there were three levels of ground force operations – army ops, unit ops and the so-called implementation (performed at division, brigade and battalion level, respectively). Each type invariably involved helicopter support, and the 'Hind' with its comprehensive weapons range was used as an armoured fist.

If a mix of bombs and rocket pods was carried, the pilot would let loose a salvo of FFARs at 1200 to 1500 m (3,937 to 4,921 ft) range and then hose down the area with machine-gun fire, allowing the WSO to aim and drop the bombs accurately. For such pinpoint strikes, which were made at high speed and low altitude, the bomb detonators were set with a delay of up to 32 seconds (as on attack aircraft) so that the aircraft was not hit by the bombs' fragments. This did not always work, as when, for example, in the summer of 1985 an Mi-24 operating from Ghazni in central Afghanistan came home with 18 fragments of its flight leader's bombs in its fuselage. Fully loaded, the 'Hind' could take up to 10 100-kg (220-lb) bombs on MBD2-67u multiple racks (MBD, *mnogozamkovii bomboderzhahtel'* = multiple bomb rack). In a simultaneous drop, accuracy was rather low, but this technique worked well against area targets such as Mujahideen camps.

Bombed-up Mi-24s often spearheaded assault groups, demolishing the thick adobe walls of Afghan houses which became death traps for Mujahideen gunners. Another favourite weapon for these missions was the UPK-23-250 gun pod. The GSh-23L cannon had a high muzzle velocity and proved far more effective against such structures than S-5 FFARs, for the shells pierced the walls to explode inside.

The Mi-24 could also carry large-calibre HE bombs, such as four 250-kg (551-lb) FAB-250s or two 500-kg (1,102-lb) FAB-500s (FAB, *foogahsnaya aviabomba* = high-explosive bomb). These bombs were used against ancient fortresses, which were abundant in Afghanistan and made convenient bases for the rebels, being strategically located on insurmountable cliffs, protecting settlements and road junctions, and had stone or adobe walls 3 m (10 ft) thick which were impervious to S-5s. In June 1980 eight Mi-24Ds toting big bombs played a vital role in the capture of Mt Sanghi-Douzdan, the famous Mountain of Thieves near Faozabad which Alexander the Great had failed to capture in his time. The mountain was riddled with caves

and passages and had sheltered local bandits from time immemorial, hence the name, and had become a major Mujahideen base. Truck-mounted BM-21 Grad ('Hail') multiple-launcher rocket systems pounded the mountain without respite, paving the way for the ground troops. The 'Hinds' joined in at night, flying sortie after sortie without a WSO, so that the helicopter could take more bombs.

Fuel/air explosives

August 1980 was probably the first time Mi-24Ds used fuel/air bombs against a Mujahideen ambush in the Faozabad canyon. Knowing that trials had shown lower-than-average reliability of these munitions, the pilots of two 'Hinds' covering the lead pair immediately fired a salvo of rockets into the resulting cloud of fuel mist for good measure. The bombs had been dropped at 300 m (984 ft), which was higher than usual, yet the blast wave caught up with the helicopters. As the pilots themselves put it, "The first thing we knew was our teeth snapping." Reliability problems with fuel/air bombs persisted throughout the war. Their efficiency was affected by many factors, including drop speed, altitude and 'hot-and-high' conditions; some sources claim that only 15 to 20 per cent of these bombs detonated properly. Hence, fuel/air bombs were used sporadically, and then usually in combination with HE or incendiary bombs. When they did work properly they were

a terrifying weapon, and not for nothing have been called 'the poor man's atomic bomb'. Buildings were flattened completely, and troops arriving on the scene would find charred bodies and a few deaf and blind survivors.

Mi-24 strike groups were sometimes accompanied by an Mi-8 fire director helicopter with a spotter on board. The latter was usually a local from the HAD (the Afghan secret service) who helped tell friend from foe in the vegetation below and identify the right house in a village, i.e., the one in which the enemy had hidden. Intelligence came from prisoners, friendly villagers, undercover agents in Mujahideen gangs or paid informers. The latter source was the least reliable as, all too often, an informer, having sold information on enemy positions, immediately went to the Mujahideen to warn of an impending air raid and get paid by them as well. Another pair of 'Hips' always tagged along as SAR helicopters. They also photographed the attack results and, in the case of heavily protected high-priority targets, undertook post-attack reconnaissance which helped assess possible enemy retaliatory action.

In March 1982 a squadron of 'Hinds' was tasked with eliminating a gathering of opposition leaders in Asadabad. A flight of Mi-24s was to keep the Mujahideen air defences busy while another secured the perimeter of the city block to stop anyone getting in or out. The Afghan spotter identified the building where the target was and the entire squadron

This Mi-24V of the 337th OVP (Independent Helicopter Regiment) was one of the 'Hind-Es', based at Mahlwinkel, in the former East Germany. It is seen here tucking up its gear at its German base for the last time, on 16 July 1994, when the unit finally returned to Russia. The 337th OVP had always been an important forward-deployed assault helicopter unit, latterly supporting the 8th Guards Infantry Army. The unit accepted its first Mi-24Ds in the mid-1980s before transitioning to the more capable Mi-24V. The 337th OVP also operated Mi-24Ps alongside Mi-8 'Hips'.

Another Mi-24V operator attached to the Group of Soviet Forces in Germany was the 439th OVP, based at Damm (known to NATO as Parchim). Like most other Russian 'Hind' units in East Germany, it operated a mix of Mi-24Vs and Mi-24Ps (with Mi-8 troopships), but its aircraft were unusual in carrying 'nose-art' – the badge of Soviet Army Aviation. This aircraft is also carrying B8V20A 20-round 80-mm rocket pods.

Above: The cannon-armed Mi-24P 'Hind-F' transformed the type into the ultimate helicopter gunship. Trials of the twin-barrelled Gryazev/Shipunov GSh-30K 30-mm cannon began as early as 1976. The 'Hind-F' was not widely exported but one customer was the former East Germany, which acquired 12 from 1986 onwards. These aircraft were fitted out to the highest specification and were eagerly flown and evaluated by the Luftwaffe (and other agencies) following German reunification.

came in, obliterating it. The spotter fled as soon as the heli-copters returned to base, and it transpired that the house he had indicated belonged to a local 'big shot' and a long-time enemy of his; he simply saw the opportunity to take his revenge. Another tragi-comical incident which happened in Kandahar was a classic case of crew miscommunication. The spotter pointed to a house below which was promptly attacked; it turned out that the poor devil, who spoke no Russian at all, had merely wanted to show them his own home!

Bombing and shooting accuracy was affected by wind turbulence from the mountains, which could cause the bombs and rockets to drift far off course. Mi-24V pilots had been taught by experience to rely more on their eyes and good judgement than on the ASP-17V automatic gunsight and VSB-24 ballistic shooting and bombing computer (VSB, *vychisleetel' strel'bii i bombometahniya*). Sniper Pilot (a grade reflecting expertise) Nikolay Malyshev made no secret of his way to success: "It's all about hitting the target, not about taking aim." WSO Ivan Manenok operating from Jalalabad became something of a local legend for his ability to lob bombs squarely on top of Mujahideen fortresses and machine-gun emplacements. During operations against villages he could place HE bombs at right angles precisely at the base of a wall. In an attempt to hide from Soviet raids the Mujahideen began setting up shelters and AAA positions behind rocky outcrops. The 'Hinds' would get them even there, using the lob-bombing technique.

Some Mi-24s were armed with S-24 heavy unguided rockets with 123-kg (271-lb) warheads which could be launched at a range of up to 2 km (1.24 miles) without taking the helicopter within range of the enemy's air defences. A 'Hind' unit commanded by Colonel Gorshkov made 50 successful launches. The S-24 could be used successfully only by experienced crews and so did not find wide use, the reason being that the heavy missile produced an extensive smoke trail which enveloped the helicopter, causing considerable risk of engine surge.

ATGMs were used successfully not only against vehicles but against bunkers and gun emplacements if their positions were known in advance. At 1.5 to 2 km (0.93 to 1.24 mile) range, a WSO with good aim could place a 35-kg (77-lb) rocket squarely in an embrasure or the mouth of a cave. The 9M114 Shturm-V ATGM was especially effective for this if equipped with a fuel/air warhead which blew the bunkers apart from within. When fired at Mujahideen vehicle convoys, the Shturm-V had a kill rate of 75 to 80 per cent; pilots even complained there were 'too few suitable targets' for these weapons.

Right, and below right: An early Mi-24D, with no intake filters, was converted into the Mi-24P prototype. 'Red 70', seen here, is an Mi-24P pre-production aircraft. Originally, the cannon had short barrels which terminated almost level with the end of the LLLTV/FLIR pod. This proved to be less than optimal, as the violent vibration generated by the cannon shook the avionics to pieces. A lengthy redesign and trials programme followed, and in the definitive version the barrels were nearly twice as long, extending beyond the nose and terminating in large funnel-shaped flame dampers that did not 'blind' the missile guidance sensors. This configuration was tested on the second prototype, a converted late-production Mi-24D or Mi-24V.

Right: These 'Hind-Es' are attached to the 248th OVE of the Belarussian air force, based at Minsk-Slepyanka. Belarus has retained the old-style Soviet red star marking and operates about 80 'Hinds', mostly Mi-24V/Ps.

As noted earlier, the 'flying IFV' concept did not prove feasible in combat. The crews were reluctant to fly a 'battlebus' full of 'passengers' firing out the windows, as the Mi-24 was decidedly overweight and sluggish with a full payload, so armour plating and troop seats in the cabin were often removed to save weight. For the same reason, the payload was often limited to two FFAR pods or bombs (enough for most missions) and the fuel tanks were rarely filled more than two-thirds. Only 16 per cent of the sorties were flown fully loaded, and then for short distances only.

Day and night hunter teams

'Hinds' were often used as 'hunters' to patrol areas of interest and destroy targets of opportunity. The missions, known officially as 'reconnaissance/strike operations' (i.e., armed reconnaissance), were usually flown by pairs or flights of Mi-24s. The softer-skinned and less heavily armed Mi-8TVs ('Hip-C/Es') and Mi-8MTV-2s ('Hip-Hs') were rarely used alone for these dangerous missions but could provide welcome support for the 'crocodiles'. The normal weapons fit comprised two FFAR pods, two anti-tank missiles and 500 to 700 machine-gun rounds.

The helicopters assumed echelon formation angled at 15 to 20° with intervals of 600 to 800 m (1,968 to 2,624 ft) and patrolled the area at 1500 to 1700 m (4,921 to 5,577 ft), which gave everyone good visibility and freedom of manoeuvre. Having located a convoy, they would fire warning shots across its path, forcing it to stop and keeping it in check until the inspection group arrived in several Mi-8s. However, increasingly often the convoys included 'trap-mobiles' with heavy machine-guns hidden under tarpaulins,

so soon the hunters began simply shooting suspicious convoys, leaving the inspection group little to do except collect the booty and burn what trucks were left (if any).

At night, when the enemy moved about more freely under cover of the darkness, the hunters patrolled roads and mountain paths in pairs, keeping a difference in altitude of 80 to 100 m (262 to 328 ft) for safety's sake. Having located vehicle headlights or camp fires and received confirmation that there were no friendlies in the area, the group attacked immediately; quick reaction was crucial to prevent the Mujahideen from vanishing into the night. Usually, all lights on the ground were promptly extinguished when the helicopters put in an appearance, but the 'Hinds' fired special S-5-O (*osvetitel'nii*) illumination FFARs to 'pin down' the target, then dropped flare bombs and dived below them to attack. This tactic was later refined, so that the helicopters attacked from above the 'chandeliers' (as the flare bombs were called in Air Force slang), staying invisible to the enemy.

Night hunter operations required extensive training, but were extremely effective. On one occasion in April 1986, a Soviet tactical reconnaissance group reported a Mujahideen convoy approaching Gharkalay village near Kandahar and a flight of 'Hinds' took off to intercept. A single firing pass sent the Mujahideen scattering, abandoning six trucks full of weapons. In December 1986 the Mi-24 tested 'blinding bombs' near Bagram. These munitions were modified flare bombs which produced a tremendous flash, putting enemy personnel within a radius of 30 to 50 m (98 to 164 ft) out of action for several hours but not causing permanent blindness.

From the spring of 1980, the lean, predatory silhouette of the Mi-24 became an increasingly familiar sight in Afghan skies, and before long the mottled green 'crocodile' was a true symbol of the war. The 'Hinds' flew 'lower, slower and over shorter distances than anyone else', as their crews put it (paraphrasing a Soviet slogan of the 1930s, 'fly higher, faster and farther than everyone else'), but were far more effective in the strike role than supersonic fighters and fighter-bombers which streaked over the target without having time to do any real damage – those aircraft earned the disdainful generic nickname of svistok (whistle).

The 'Hind-F' brought with it much needed firepower, though the slower firing rate of its heavy cannon meant they were a less effective area weapon at short range.

'Hind' Trainers

Mi-24U 'Hind-C' (Izdelye 244)
A trainer derivative of the Mi-24A designated Mi-24U (Uchebnii = training (attrib.)), or Izdelye 244, was built in small numbers. Outwardly it differed from the 'Hind-A' in lacking the nose-mounted A-12,7 machine-gun, the wingtip ATGM launch rails and associated guidance system fairing under the nose. The instructor sat in the former WSO's position in the extreme nose which featured additional navigation equipment and full dual controls. The trainer version was codenamed 'Hind-C'.

Mi-24DU/Mi-25U 'Hind-D' (Izdelye 249)
A trainer version of the Mi-24D appeared in 1980. Designated Mi-24DU (D-uchebnii) or Izdelye 249, it differed from the standard 'Hind-D' in having a smoothly faired nose (instead of the USPU-24 gun barbette) and dual controls. The first prototype (coded 'Yellow 48') lacked the wingtip launchers for the Falanga-PV missiles and associated guidance equipment under the nose, but these were retained on later prototypes and production aircraft. The export version of the Mi-24DU was designated Mi-25U.

Mi-24V trainer version
A trainer version similar to the Mi-24DU was supplied to the Indian Air Force. Outwardly it differed from the Mi-24DU in having Mi-24V-style bearers for 9M114 Shturm ATGMs on the wing endplates instead of the earlier launch rails for 9M17P Falanga-P missiles and the associated restyled command link antenna pod. No separate designation is known. It should be noted that there never was a production 'Mi-24VU' for the Soviet Army, so the Indian trainers were probably custom-built.

Above right: 'Yellow 48', the Mi-24DU prototype, was the only Mi-24DU to lack the undernose Raduga-F system.

Right: India's 'Hind-E'-based Mi-24V trainers are unique in the world, and were built to order. All other active 'Hind' trainers are based on the 'Hind-D' airframe.

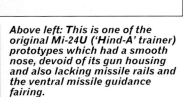

Above left: This is one of the original Mi-24U ('Hind-A' trainer) prototypes which had a smooth nose, devoid of its gun housing and also lacking missile rails and the ventral missile guidance fairing.

Above: The difference in expression between the instructor in the front seat of this Mi-24DU 'Hind-D' trainer, and the trainee in the back, is amusingly clear.

Opposite page, top: The GUV gun pods designed to boost Mi-24D/V firepower were not widely used. They were far too heavy, and crews agreed to fly with the 450-kg (992-lb) pods only when threatened by disciplinary action. As they rightly pointed out, the 4,350 rounds in each GUV were simply overkill – there were no targets in Afghanistan which could merit such a hail of fire. Soviet Army Aviation definitively lost interest in the GUV when the cannon-armed Mi-24P arrived. Identical in calibre to the pod's alternative 30-mm AGS-17 grenade launcher, the Mi-24P's GSh-30K cannon had twice the range and five times the weight of fire. Some 'Hind-Fs' were fitted with a laser rangefinder for increased accuracy. Recoil from the big cannon caused fatigue problems, and cracks and deformations appeared in the fuselage skin and frames after 1,500 to 2,000 rounds had been fired. This was alleviated by installing an external Duralumin reinforcement plate and two hefty L-section profiles, which extended the guaranteed life to 4,000 rounds.

One of the rotary-wing element's main roles in the war was vertical envelopment, i.e., insertion of troops in the vicinity of villages, roads and other points of importance held by the rebels. In these operations the Mi-24 acted as a steamroller, crushing enemy resistance with bombs and rockets to clear the way for incoming Mi-8s and Mi-6 'Hook-As'. One or two pairs of 'Hinds' escorted the transport helicopters (numbering as many as 60 at a time) all the way to the LZ, flying along the flanks and 200 to 400 m (656 to 1,312 ft) higher. The landing was preceded by artillery fire and strikes by attack aircraft, followed rapidly by one or two flights of Mi-24s. Before the confused enemy had time to collect his wits, the heliborne assault was coming in, covered by several pairs of helicopters which circled over the LZ at 1200 to 1800 m (3,937 to 5,905 ft), taking out any surviving enemy gunners. Another flight of Mi-24s stayed at the base on ready alert, replacing the ones which had expended their ammunition, if required.

Patrolling the roads
From the summer of 1980, the 'Hinds' were tasked with the important mission of escorting supply convoys, which accounted for 15 to 17 per cent of sorties. The 40th Army's daily needs amounted to hundreds of tons of fuel, ammunition, food, etc., and the convoys delivering them were perpetually ambushed by the rebels.

Several pairs of Mi-24s would take turns patrolling above the convoy, zigzagging at 150 to 170 km/h (81 to 92 kt). The crews checked the surroundings 2 to 3 km (1.24 to 1.86 miles) on each side of the road – this was the rebels' usual attack range – and 5 to 8 km (3 to 5 miles) ahead of the convoy. Having detected a Mujahideen ambush, the helicopters made a flank attack if possible, coming in along the road to avoid blue-on-blue incidents. *Ad hoc* helipads were built along the roads for refuelling and 'changing of the guard', as providing constant escort to convoys crawling along at 15 to 20 km/h (9 to 12 mph) would otherwise

have been impossible. The first stretch from Termez on the Soviet side of the border (Uzbekistan) to the infamous Salang pass was protected by 'Hinds' based in Kunduz, using helipads in Khairaton, Mazar-i-Sharif, Tashkurgan and Pul-i-Khumri. At the Salang pass, Mi-24s from Bagram took over, later passing on the convoys to crews from Jalalabad, Ghazni and other bases.

Still, losses were heavy; thousands of vehicles were lost each year and an army driver's profession was one of the most dangerous. In April 1983 a convoy of 180 trucks escorted by a tank battalion was ambushed in the Dori River valley not far from Kandahar. The place was crawling with Mujahideen, who opened fire from hideouts behind fences and in the jungle. When Mi-24s arrived on the scene, 20 fuel trucks and six tanks were ablaze on the road below. The helicopters fired 80-mm S-8 FFARs, marking the first operational use of this weapon; those on the ground mistook them for cannon fire of tremendous density and power. The rest of the convoy broke through, luckily for the Russians, for the fuel dump at Kandahar had only enough fuel for a couple more sorties.

The B-8V20 pods with 20 S-8 rockets apiece earned the highest praise in Afghanistan. The 3.6-kg (7.93-lb) warhead had considerable demolition effect and produced a large number of 3-g (0.1-oz) fragments with a kill radius of 10 to 12 m (33 to 39 ft). The new rockets began supplanting the S-5, yet the earlier model remained in use until the Soviet pullout from Afghanistan, despite pilots' complaints that the S-5s were only good for 'tickling the dookhi's [Mujahideen] heels' and fanned out 'like a tulip' when fired. To give credit where credit is due, the S-5 was still fairly effective in open spaces, it was simple and reliable, and the UB-32A pods were quickly and easily loaded, which was an undoubted asset during intensive operations with five or six sorties a day. Last but not least, huge stockpiles of S-5s had been built up at ammunition dumps and had to be expended to make room for new weapons.

As 'Hind' crews became more experienced and battle-hardened, tactics changed. Some 75 per cent of the sorties were flown in the early morning hours to escape the blistering mid-day heat. The first raid was made at dawn to get the Mujahideen in the open, when they were saying their morning prayers. Targets were distributed among crews in a strike group and the helicopters were armed accordingly; some crews would suppress the air defences and take out enemy personnel with FFARs and cluster bombs, while others destroyed buildings and other structures with HE bombs. Some 100-kg (220-lb) bombs were fitted with delayed-action fuses to act as mines, and explosions would continue for the next 24 hours, preventing survivors from getting out of the rubble. (However, there were cases when this method backfired; the Mujahideen would send some of their own men to disarm the bombs as punishment for transgressions and then use the bombs as land mines to mine roads ahead of Soviet convoys.) The last strike sortie of the day was flown late in the afternoon, again with a view to getting the Mujahideen in the open, since their religion required them to bury their dead before sunset.

Training for the war

Before being transferred to the Afghan Contingent, helicopter crews underwent special training at the mountain training range near Chirchik, Kazakhstan, and the desert range in the Kagana Desert near Bukhara, Uzbekistan, for 15 to 20 days to become accustomed to 'hot-and-high' conditions and operating in mountainous terrain. Upon arrival they were given a 'scenic tour' of the main areas of action in an Mi-8 by pilots who had completed their Afghan tour and were going home. Later, 12 to 15 per cent of the flying time was set aside for training, primarily combat manoeuvring and unconventional take-off and landing techniques.

The Flight Research Institute in Zhukhovskii near Moscow devised a radical take-off technique involving a precarious 10° to 12° tail-up run. Rolling along the tarmac on the nosewheels only, the helicopter accelerated quickly and became 'unstuck' after only 50 to 75 m (164 to 146 ft); another advantage was a 1000 to 1500-kg (2,204 to 3,306-lb) increase in MAUW. This technique, however, called for a lot of practice and a steady hand. On one occasion in November 1986, an Mi-24 pilot scrambling from Bagram began his take-off run directly from the flight line and over-rotated, the main rotor blades striking the tarmac. The helicopter became airborne and completed the mission, even though the blade tips were badly bent. The pilot, however, was too ashamed to come home with the damaged main rotor screaming like a banshee and so landed in a nearby field, waiting until the repair crew arrived.

Landing at unpaved LZs was fraught with danger, as the helicopter kicked up a dust storm and it was extremely easy to roll over after hitting an unseen pothole or stone. The solution was to land with a forward speed just high enough to keep the cockpit ahead of the dust cloud so that landing roll would be minimal. Roll was kept down to a few dozen feet by descending steeply with the engines at high rpm,

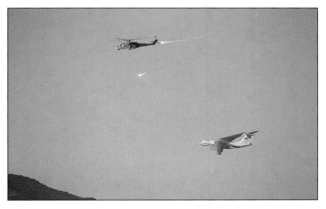

increasing collective pitch immediately before touch-down to avoid a hard landing, then immediately hauling back on the stick and standing on the brakes. This technique was hard on the tyres and brake discs, which were worn down to paper-thin condition in no time (this was known as 'Afghan wear'); in contrast, in normal conditions the brake discs lasted a year or more.

Afghan operations took an even heavier toll on the engines, which suffered from compressor blade erosion caused by sand ingestion and from combustion chamber and turbine casing failures (the higher turbine temperature was telling, after all). More than 50 per cent of the TV3-117 turboshafts had to be changed prematurely and, of them, 39 per cent were accounted for by compressor blade erosion and nearly 15 per cent by engine surge. Turbine blades failed extensively, causing loss of power, and, on one particular engine inspected in Bagram in the autumn of 1986, 17 of 51 turbine blades were missing!

Above: Vertical take-offs were all but impossible in the rarefied air where the helicopters had trouble keeping themselves up, never mind their payload. Thus, rolling take-offs were standard operational procedure, the helicopters becoming airborne after 100 to 150 m (328 to 492 ft).

Left: Mi-24s loaded with flares had to accompany all transport aircraft in and out of Kabul airport, to protect them against shoulder-launched SAMs. The 'Hinds' would routinely launch flares but, if they detected a Stinger launch, the helicopter pilots were ordered to meet the missile head-on, firing a salvo of flares and, if all else failed, present themselves as the target to save the transport. With typical macabre humour, the 'Hind' crews called themselves 'Matrosovs by order'. (Aleksandr Matrosov was a wartime hero who sacrificed himself by throwing his body across a German machine-gun emplacement to clear the way for a Soviet assault.)

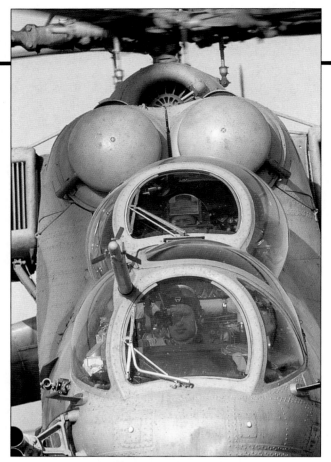

Other than the problems caused by sand-ingestion and extreme operational wear-and-tear, the 'Hind' generally had a good reliability record in Afghanistan. This reliability and – even more importantly – the very high workload which kept the men at the airfields from the crack of dawn until darkness, led to the 'Hinds' being operated on a 'technical condition' basis – with maintenance undertaken only as required, rather than as prescribed by the manuals. Time-expired engines were allowed to amass up to 50 hours of 'life after death' before replacement, and some other equipment items were simply used until they packed up. This well-worn Mi-24P and its equally well-worn crew are seen just prior to departure for another operational mission.

All basic Mi-24 pilot training included combat manoeuvring, and this paid off in the war. Many new flying techniques invented in Afghanistan took the helicopter outside its normal flight envelope but allowed the crew to destroy the target more effectively, or saved them from being shot down. Apart from the customary turns and yo-yos, many skilled pilots practised NoE flying to the target, with a last-moment 3g zoom climb to fire the weapons and a 50° climb after the firing pass, followed by a sharp turn with bank angles exceeding 90° for an immediate second attack.

Dust would get into fuel tanks and congeal into a black slime which clogged fuel filters, pumps, etc., preventing engine start or putting the engine on a 'diet' at the worst possible moment (loss of power caused by clogged filters was known locally as 'quiet surge'). APU turbine casings often burned through, and many APUs were long since time-expired. Rotor blade leading-edge protective strips were eaten away completely by the sand, and when they came apart the remnants began flapping wildly, causing vibration and a high-pitched screech. Tail rotor pylons had to be replaced periodically due to fatigue cracks in the main ribs caused by high *g* loads during violent manoeuvring.

To avoid wasting time and service life on ferry flights, the 40th Army rotated only the crews; the helicopters were stuck there for the duration, or at best until they were due for a major overhaul. Not all Mi-24s were so lucky, as the Soviet contingent lost eight to 12 per cent of its helicopter component annually. Utilisation averaged 360 to 380 hours per year, being much higher in areas with especially bitter fighting. A pair of brand-new 'Hinds' delivered to the unit at Bagram in August 1986 clocked 1,000 hours (the limit set for the first overhaul) within a year.

Ground crews displayed, to put it in the words of Rudyard Kipling, infinite resource and sagacity, making field modifications and carrying out repairs which one would hardly think were possible in field conditions. Clogged filters were cleaned with compressed air. Helicopter batteries which perpetually boiled on hot days were cooled by immersing them in ditches with running water. Tanks and BMP-2 IFVs were used as ground power carts to fire up the APU (or the engines of 'Hip-C/Es'). Downed and recovered helicopters were cannibalised for spares for operational ones; in the autumn of 1982, having run out of spare engines, the technicians at Kandahar managed to assemble a usable TV3-117 from parts of three trashed engines.

Overall workload in Afghanistan may have doubled compared to normal conditions, but the weapons arming workload was 24 (!) times greater. Every available man had to handle bombs, load FFAR pods with rockets, cut open the zinc boxes of machine-gun ammunition and work the 'meat grinder' device which filled ammunition belts with bullets. Ammunition briefly was stocked next to the helicopters but this practice was soon discontinued because it split human resources and was plainly dangerous – a single well-aimed Mujahideen mortar could blow the entire flight line sky-high. Therefore, ammunition was prepared in advance in specially-designated areas and carted to the helicopters as soon as they came back from a sortie. Some units established an 'assembly line' routine, whereby the helicopters taxied to the arming area. The Mi-24's built-in weapons hoists were not very user-friendly and mobile bomb lifts were plagued by leaky hydraulics, so the ground crews often hooked up the heavy bombs with belts or crowbars, then the armourer would run around the helicopter adding and arming the detonators.

Heavy losses

For a long time the most potent adversaries of the 'Hinds' were the DShK HMGs and AA guns, which accounted for 42 per cent and 25 per cent of all Mi-24 losses, respectively. The engines and hydraulics were among the most frequently damaged items, surpassed only by the electrics and control runs which were all over the helicopter. Still, twin-engined reliability and systems duplication often allowed the Mi-24 to make it home. The engines had automatic power reserve, the good engine going to full power if the other one was hit. Even with main gearbox oil pressure down to zero, the helicopter could stay aloft for another 15 to 20 minutes, which was usually enough to get the crew out of immediate danger.

On 12 June 1982 a pair of Mi-24Vs piloted by Volkov and Lantsev spotted two Toyota Land Cruisers approaching a Mujahideen base near Kandahar and gave chase. Both jeeps were destroyed, but in the heat of the chase the attackers found themselves over the enemy camp and were shot up badly. The wingman was fired upon by three DShKs and, with hydraulic lines and wiring shot out, damaged rotor blades and dead instruments, he managed to limp back to base. There, the wounded technician had to open the cowling while the rotors were still turning and shut down one of the engines manually, as it would not shut down because of a damaged control rod.

The helicopter crews made up the majority of the aircrew fatalities in the Afghan Contingent. It was worse in the summer when the men were wearied by the heat and hard work, and the 'hot-and-high' conditions impaired aircraft performance, making them vulnerable. Sometimes, three or four crews would be lost per month. The dry formula 'injuries incompatible with life' found its way into the lexicon of military medics. Such injuries were usually sustained in crash-landings or inflight fires. Some 30 per cent of the fatalities were caused by head and spinal injuries, 55 per cent by extensive burns and 9 per cent by internal injuries. A helicopter pilot's death is an ugly one.

The once-popular lightweight blue flying suits were quickly discarded because they were made of a mixed fabric and, in a fire, the synthetic fibres melted, adhering firmly to the skin. Instead, camouflaged cotton field uniforms were introduced in 1984 (the helicopter crews were the first in the VVS to get them) and increased the chances of survival in a forced landing – as did the Kalashnikov AKS-74 5.45-mm collapsible-stock assault rifles with which crews were supplied; the more shrewd men strapped the AKS to their thigh or flank so as not to lose it when they bailed out. The standard-issue 9-mm Makarov PM pistols were exchanged for the more reliable Tokarev TT handguns, Stechkin APS automatic pistols or captured 20-round Berettas. The survival kit was 'revised' so that most of the food was omitted, leaving only the water flasks and a few chocolate bars, to make room for extra 30-round Kalashnikov clips and four RGD-5 hand grenades.

As noted earlier, Mi-24 pilots kept urging the Mil OKB to provide some protection for the rear hemisphere but the NSVT-12.7 Utyos machine-gun installation tested in 1985 proved disappointing. The 'Hind' had to make do with a technician who sat in the cabin and doubled as the tail gunner. To give him a bigger sector of fire, the cabin doors were modified so that the upper segment could be opened separately, the lower segment providing support for the gunner. The usual defensive armament was a 7.62-mm Kalashnikov PK general-purpose machine-gun (or the PKT vehicle-mounted version) which had earned respect for its range and accuracy. Sometimes two were carried to avoid wasting time transferring the MG to the other side of the cabin (which, incidentally, was dangerous; there was a case

in Kabul when the technician accidentally pulled the trigger while lugging the MG and shot up his own helicopter). Some crews used the lighter and more user-friendly infantry version, the RPK. When the Soviet high command ordered in the spring of 1986 that the technicians should stay on the ground 'to reduce unwarranted casualties', the crews objected, agreeing to fly without an extra gunner only if they chose to (i.e., when cutting weight was more important than extra protection).

Stopping the SAMs

Another 'Afghan upgrade package' introduced in the early 1980s was aimed at reducing the threat posed by shoulder-launched SAMs – FIM-43A Redeye and FIM-92A Stinger, Shorts Blowpipe and, ironically, captured Strela (Arrow)/SA-7 'Grail'. Large triple-lobe air/exhaust mixers were fitted to the engine jetpipes to reduce the IR signature; being draggy and inconvenient to use, they did not become obligatory until 1983, when SAMs became a distinct threat. Originally, two pairs of ASO-2V chaff/flare dispensers were strapped beneath the tailboom, but in 1987 they were replaced by triple ASO-2Vs on the fuselage sides immediately aft of the wings, angled forward for wider coverage and sometimes faired to cut drag. Finally, an L-166V-1E (SOEP-V1A Lipa) active IRCM jammer was fitted aft of the main rotor head.

Some of the proposed 'Afghan upgrades' (more powerful control actuators and the addition of vibration dampers) got stuck in bureaucratic red tape and were never introduced. Others created new problems as they eliminated old ones. For example, 'Hinds' and 'Hip-Hs' were fitted with a

The SAM threat to the Mi-24, and all Soviet tactical aircraft in Afghanistan, rose rapidly as Western intelligence agencies shipped increasingly sophisticated shoulder-launched weapons to the Afghan resistance. (Many of these weapons are now believed to be loose on the international arms market, ready to be used against their original suppliers.) To deal with the SAMs, the Mi-24s were fitted with boxy EVU infra-red suppressors over the exhaust stubs. These saved many aircraft, though they never completely prevented losses. Even though many Mi-24s were claimed by ground fire, the 'crocodile' was treated with respect by its enemies, as illustrated by an incident which took place near Toloukan in May 1983. Having run out of ammunition, Major Anatoliy Volkov continued to make mock attacks on a group of Mujahideen, scaring them off with just the sight and sound of the roaring, sinister-looking helicopter diving straight at them, thereby saving the lives of a company of troopers getting out of the bush. (Afghanistan is not all mountains, and some parts of the country are similar to the jungles of Vietnam.) This tactic earned him the nickname of 'proud falcon' (an allusion to the 1930s and 1940s when Soviet fighter pilots were referred to as 'Stalin's falcons'). On the subject of nicknames, the Mujahideen called the Mi-24 shaitan-arba ('devil's chariot').

Right: Technicians check out a battle-weary Mi-24V prior to its departure on an escort mission from a forward airstrip.

Far right: This Mi-24V, 'Red 28', is seen on patrol over Kabul city in the late 1980s.

Above: Flown by Captain G. Pavlov, this Mi-24P was one of those shot down in the summer of 1985. The crash site recovery team is already hard at work, removing any items from the aircraft that might be of use to the Mujahideen – including a Kalashnikov PK machine-gun from the cabin.

water/methanol injection system designed to compensate for the power loss caused by other modifications (the intake filters and the exhaust IR suppressors both removed 5 to 6 per cent of the total power output). However, when the system was switched on, power would increase explosively, which was hard to handle (in one case an Mi-24 lost control and rolled over during take-off in Kabul when the system kicked in). The system also required distilled water, which was unavailable in Afghanistan, and ordinary tap water quickly clogged the injector nozzles with sediment.

By 1987 the 40th Army's recovery and repair service was so well organised that 90 per cent of the damaged helicopters could be returned to service, compared with 70 per cent at the start of the campaign. To be able to fix a lightly damaged helicopter on the spot and get out of enemy territory, the crews trained in repair techniques and the 'Hinds' carried repair kits containing the most vital tools and spares. In the event of serious damage, a recovery team would be summoned to make hasty repairs so that the helicopter could be flown back to base. Such a team was usually composed of experienced and battle-hardened mechanics who could not only repair a helicopter quickly but fight back a Mujahideen attack, which they often had to do. There were cases when, arriving on the scene a couple of hours after the shoot-down, the recovery team found out the hard way that the helicopter had been booby-trapped by the Mujahideen.

Non-flyable helicopters were extracted by 'Hip-Hs' after being stripped down to 2500 kg (5,511 lb), the Mi-8MT's maximum payload. In the winter of 1986 an Mi-24 brought down near Ghazni landed on a dry lake-bed – not dry enough, as it turned out – and became firmly stuck in the mud. When all else failed the repair crew replaced the damaged engine and tail rotor, removed all non-essential items, literally chopped the helicopter free in the early morning hours when the mud had frozen, and Squadron Leader Shmelyov managed to pull the 'Hind' out 'by the hair', as they put it, and bring it home.

To boost their firepower 'Hinds' started carrying gunners in the main cabin, who had a wide field of view not covered by the Mi-24's main armament. Side gunners were particularly important in protecting the aircraft once on the ground. This crewman, Captain N. Goortovoy (above left), has a PKT machine-gun with a copious stock of 7.62-mm ammunition and the luxury of a swivelling seat, taken from a shot-down Mi-8. As in any war, the unsung heroes of Soviet 'Hind' operations in Afghanistan were the armourers and other ground crew – such as this one loading flare cartridges into ASO-2V dispensers scabbed onto the fuselage sides (above right). Other armourers are seen here removing jammed 30-mm shells from a GSh-2-30K cannon (right) and loading 12-kg (26-lb) S-8KO rockets into a B-8V20 pod (far right).

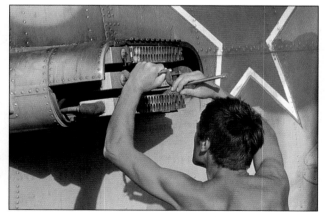

It finally became clear that the war was going nowhere and a political solution to the conflict would have to be found. An armistice was declared in early 1987 but proved of little use due to the general lack of good faith on both sides. The opposition continued to pressure the weak Kabul government, squeezing its troops out of the provinces. In mid-August 1987 a full-blown battle broke out for Bagram in which the local Soviet helicopter unit lost four aircraft and 10 men. In April 1988 one of the so-called contract gangs (operating under contract with the opposition) attacked government positions right outside Bagram air base. The entire Bagram wing had to be scrambled to fight back the bandits; for two days the aircraft spun an uninterrupted wheel of death, dropping bombs right next to the parking areas immediately after getting the wheels up. On another occasion the helicopter unit at Ghazni was fired upon by Afghan tanks which were supposed to protect it; it transpired that the tank crews had received a ration of sugar for every shot they fired, from the Mujahideen. Several Mi-24s were turned over to the Mujahideen by defectors. Two 'Hind-Ds' were flown to Pakistan in 1985 by defecting Afghan Air Force pilots who had been hired by the Pakistani intelligence service, and the ultimate fate of these helicopters is unknown.

Escape from Afghanistan

Of course, the Soviet command could not tolerate having the aircraft attacked and shot down over their own base, and preventive measures were taken. By 1987 the Soviet air bases were guarded by 25 army battalions, and as early as 1984 round-the-clock air cover and patrolling of the surrounding areas had been introduced. The helicopter crews spent virtually all their time on the flight line, sometimes relieving each other in the cockpits to maintain round-the-clock readiness.

Escorting Antonov An-12s and Ilyushin Il-76s carrying personnel out of the country became the highest priority. Each aircraft was escorted by a flight of 'Hinds'; one pair of helicopters searched the outskirts of the airfield while the other flew ahead or on the flanks, looking for a possible Mujahideen ambush. Sometimes a third pair followed close behind, firing IRCM flares until the steeply descending or climbing airlifter was out of range of a possible Stinger attack. Throughout the war, Kabul was still served by scheduled Aeroflot passenger jets which, of course, had no IRCM equipment (unlike the military transports), so the

local Mi-24s protecting them were fitted with double the usual number of ASO-2V flare packs.

Even liaison and SAR aircraft needed helicopter escort, as demonstrated by a tragic incident on 4 March 1987. Two Mi-8s took off to pick up the crew of a two-seat Su-17UM-3 who had ejected less than 2 miles (3.2 km) from Bagram. Unfortunately, the escorting Mi-24s were delayed, and when they arrived on the scene both pilots of the 'Fitter' had been killed and both 'Hips' shot down.

Disenchanted with the pointless war, the Soviet leadership realised it was time to pull out. In the concluding stages of the war the Soviets did not engage in major operations, keeping the Mujahideen in check by air strikes. Most sorties were planned ones against rebel camps and positions from which they shelled Soviet bases. For example, the helicopters regularly patrolled the areas around the villages of Gourdjay and Chakaray, which were good vantage points for shelling Kabul. These operations had limited success, as the Mujahideen made ever-increasing use of timer-actuated truck-mounted rocket launchers which disappeared immediately. As Colonel Aleksandr V. Rutskoy (a Su-25 pilot who later gained notoriety as one of the instigators of the failed 1993 coup) put it, "The air force flew just for the sake of flying and crushing stone."

Top: This rather bucolic scene, photographed during the Soviet disengagement from Afghanistan, shows a late-model Mi-24P (note RWR antennas on the nose) in standard camouflage, alongside two heavily-armed Mil Mi-8TV 'Hip-Hs' – both of which are fitted with the EVU IR-suppressors.

Above: One of the most important tasks for 'Hinds' in Afghanistan was to provide air cover for the resupply convoys that were the life blood of the Soviet garrisons in the field. This Afghan air force Mi-24V, carrying a full load of rockets, is escorting a convoy departing Kabul.

A village named Ada near Jalalabad, from where the air base was regularly shelled, was 'soup of the day' for the local helicopter pilots, who eventually levelled the luckless village. Many other villages near air bases met the same fate; caught in the perpetual crossfire between Afghan and Soviet forces, they were reduced to rubble and burnt-out fields.

Even the final months of the war were marked with losses. Two Mi-24s were shot down on 21 August and 30 September 1988, killing the crews. On the night of 2 February 1989, 50th OSAP CO Colonel A. Golovanov and his WSO S. Peshelhodko were killed in action while reconnoitring the pull-out route. Their helicopter was the last of 333 'Hinds' shot down in Afghanistan.

Iran-Iraq war

The Iran-Iraq war of 1980-1988 became another major chapter in the career of the 'Hind'. Iraqi Air Force Mi-24As and Mi-25s were used for a variety of tasks, including destruction of soft-skinned and armoured vehicles, personnel, artillery, emplacements and bridges, escorting heliborne assaults, providing CAS for armoured groups and commandos, minelaying, reconnaissance, artillery spotting and even chemical warfare.

In the course of the war there were 118 aircraft/helicopter engagements and 56 helicopter/helicopter engagements, including 10 between Iraqi 'Hinds' and Islamic Iranian Air Force AH-1J SeaCobras. The outcome of such engagements depended mainly on the situation and crew skill. If the SeaCobra pilots were lucky enough to spot the enemy first they tried to take him out with TOW anti-tank missiles at long range. If they missed, the AH-1J had no chances of outrunning the Mi-24 and would start turning sharply to prevent the 'Hind' crew taking accurate aim. In so doing, the Iranians would try to lure the pursuer within range of their air defences or would radio to Iranian fighters for help. If the Iraqis managed to catch the enemy off guard, they would climb to 1000 m (3,280 ft) and dive at the Cobra, trying to get it from behind.

The first air-to-air engagement involving a 'Hind' happened a few days before the Iran-Iraq war 'officially' began. On 7 September 1980 five Mi-24s crossed the border, attacking an Iranian border post; IRIAF fighters scrambled to intercept and shot down one of the attackers. The first helicopter duel in history took place in November 1980 near Dezful, Iran. Sneaking up unnoticed on a pair of Mi-24s, two SeaCobras attacked them with TOWs. One 'Hind' went down immediately, the other was damaged and crashed about 10 km (6 miles) away; the Iranians landed at the crash site and took a surviving Iraqi major prisoner. A second encounter between Mi-24s and AH-1Js happened on 24 April 1981 near Panjevin, and the scenario was repeated – the Iranians shot down both 'Hinds' with no losses themselves.

It was not until 14 September 1983 that the tables were turned, when an Mi-24 shot down a SeaCobra near Basra. On 5 February Iraq claimed the destruction of three more SeaCobras by Mi-24s. On 25 February 1984 a group of 'Hinds' attacked a group of AH-1Js, destroying three. Another SeaCobra fell victim to a 'Hind' on 13 February 1986, the Iranians also claiming one 'kill'. Three days later 'Khomeini's falcons' lost another AH-1J but took their revenge on 18 February, shooting down an Mi-24.

The last engagement between the two types was recorded on 22 May 1986 when Mi-24s attacked a pair of SeaCobras, destroying one of them. Thus, judging by the above data, the overall 'kill' ratio is 10:6 in favour of the 'Hind', although some Western experts claimed the opposite. Iraqi Mi-24s had encounters with other Iranian helicopters, as well: in May and June 1988 they shot down six AB 214s and one AB 212. By the end of the war Iraqi pilots flying Mi-8s, Mi-24As and Mi-25s and SA 342L Gazelles had destroyed 53 Iranian helicopters.

Iraqi 'Hinds' in the 1990s

One of the least known (and most shameful) pages in the operational history of the 'Hind' is the use of Mi-24s by Saddam Hussein to quell the Kurdish uprisings in northern Iraq. These operations, which deserve to be called genocide, included the use of chemical agents, though it is not clear whether the Mi-24 was the delivery vehicle. The type also participated in the Iraqi invasion of Kuwait in early August 1990, escorting Mi-8T and Mi-17 troopships, suppressing pockets of resistance and destroying a few Kuwaiti tanks. Fifteen Iraqi helicopters were lost to ground fire during the invasion, including a few 'Hinds'.

Conversely, Iraqi 'Hinds' were not used against the coalition during the Gulf War of 1991, and Saddam Hussein obviously wanted to save his combat helicopters for use

against 'the enemy within', i.e., the Kurds. Yet, losses were not altogether avoided. One Mi-25 was knocked out by an LGB dropped by a USAF F-15E, three more were destroyed on their hardstand by the vanguard of the US Army's 24th Infantry Division and a fifth was captured almost intact by the vanguard of the US Army's 28th Airborne Division at Basra.

After the coalition victory, 'No-Fly Zones' were established in northern and southern Iraq, but Iraqi air force aircraft regularly violated these zones, especially in the south where they were in action against Shiite rebels. 'Hinds' were used in these operations, which were finally terminated on 22 August 1992 when the USA threatened renewed strikes against Iraq. An Iraqi 'helicopter gunship' – almost certainly an Mi-25 – was destroyed along with several other military aircraft and an ammunition dump at Tikrit on the night of 26 May 1995. It is certain that the aircraft were sabotaged by oppositionary Iraqi National Congress forces.

Libyan 'Hinds'

Libyan Arab Republic Air Force (LARAF) Mi-25As and Mi-25s were actively used in the long and bloody civil war in Chad, supporting Goukouni Oueddi's pro-Libyan rebels who were fighting the regime of Hissen Habre backed by

France and the US. In October 1980 LARAF 'Hinds' participated in the battles for the Chadian capital of N'djamena along with other Libyan aircraft, helping Oueddi to seize the city and win a temporary victory.

However, hostilities resumed a year later. In 1983 Libyan Mi-24As and Mi-25s saw action near Oum Chalouba, Abéché and Faya (Largeau), and raided Habre's bases in Sudan when the Kalat enclave was occupied by the Libyans. When luck turned against Oueddi in late 1986/early 1987, the 'Hinds' were used during the defence of Bardao, Zouar and Falah. One helicopter was shot down near the latter town on 3 January 1987.

In March 1987 Habre's troops began an offensive, seizing the LARAF base in Ouadi-Doum in northern Chad. The assorted aircraft captured there included three Mi-25s in reasonable condition. Habre turned them over to France, which, having thoroughly tested the helicopters, gave one 'Hind' to Great Britain and another to the US.

More frustration came on 8 August when Chadian forces overran Auzu, an LARAF base in the territory disputed by Chad and Libya, destroying one Mi-24 on the ground. From 17 to 23 August the Libyans launched a counter-offensive, to which the Chadians retaliated by shooting down nine LARAF aircraft (including an Mi-24 on the first day of the offensive) with captured Strela-2 (SA-7 'Grail')

Above and below: The Mi-24 has played a part in the ongoing and bitter civil war in Sri Lanka, between the Sinhalese-dominated government and the rebel Liberation Tigers of Tamil Eelam (LTTE). The LTTE, established in 1976, is conducting an armed struggle to gain independence for a separate Tamil state in the northern and eastern portions of Sri Lanka – a struggle which has claimed in excess of 40,000 lives since outright, open warfare began in 1983. In 1995 the Sri Lankan Air Force introduced its first six Mi-24Vs – three of which soon fell to hostile fire. Sri Lanka's 'Hind' force has since been quietly boosted to 13 aircraft, seven of which are now believed to remain in service.

of mistaken identity when a pair of Syrian 'Hinds' attacked two Soviet Navy support vessels (a tug and diver boat) 70 km (44 miles) west of the port of Tar-toue, damaging them and injuring seven sailors. Damascus acknowledged its fault and presented an official apology.

Angolan 'Hinds'

In Angola the Mi-24V (Mi-35) was introduced in the mid-1980s. Originally flown by Cuban and East German crews, Angolan 'Hind-Ds' saw action against the UNITA guerrillas led by Doctor Jonas Savimbi and supported by the South African Defence Force (SADF). In addition to their usual missions, they always escorted major supply convoys which were a vulnerable and lucrative target. The Mi-25s were much used against UNITA near Mavinga and Cassinga, which were the scene of fierce fighting. Western reports that by late 1985 all Angolan Air Force 'Hinds' had been destroyed or rendered unserviceable gives some indication of the intensity of the fighting; e.g., an Mi-25 was shot down on 3 June 1985 and another on 23 June.

The opposing forces admitted the high survivability of the 'Hind', noting that weapons with a calibre of less than 23 mm were useless against it. Hence, both UNITA and the SADF made wide use of Soviet-built air defence systems captured from the Angolan Armed Forces – ZU-23-2 AA guns, ZSU-23-4 quadruple self-propelled AA guns, Strela-1 SAM batteries and Strela-2/-2M and 9K38 Igla-1 (SA-18) shoulder-launched SAMs. SADF units were also armed with Bofors AA guns and Cactus SAM batteries. Angolan helicopter pilots responded to this threat by inventing new tactics. Flying at treetop level was one; the dense jungle effectively muffled engine noise and rotor slap, and the enemy could not detect the helicopter until it was on them. Not to be outdone, UNITA soon began putting 'crocodile hunters' armed with shoulder-launched SAMs in the tree-tops to deprive the Angolans of this advantage.

A fresh batch of Mi-35s was delivered to the Angolan Air Force in 1986 as attrition replacements. Between October 1987 and early 1988 they were in action against the SADF near Cuito Cuanavale, inflicting heavy losses in both personnel and materiel. After the South African withdrawal from the conflict, UNITA had to deal with the omnipresent 'crocodiles' on its own. At least three Mi-35s were shot down on 27 September 1988, 22 August 1989 and 25 February 1990. Another 'Hind' was lost on 28 January 1990 when it crashed during a sand storm, killing two of the seven occupants and injuring the other five.

When Soviet, Cuban and East German military advisors left, the Angolan Air Force immediately faced huge problems maintaining equipment and skills. Today, only a handful of Angolan 'Hinds' remains operational because new equipment and spares supplies from Russia have been reduced to a trickle or dried up completely. These few are still in action against UNITA rebels.

Vietnamese 'Hinds'

The Vietnam People's Air Force (VPAF) took delivery of its first Mi-24s in the mid-1980s, using them in Vietnamese Army operations against the Khmer Rouge in neighbouring Kampuchea. A few were also operated by the Kampuchean (Cambodian) Air Force. The Vietnamese were known to use the same tactic the US Army had used

shoulder-launched SAMs and vehicle-mounted S-175 Koob (SA-3 'Ganef') SAMs. Finally, on 5 September, Chadian forces entered Libyan territory, raiding Maaten-as-Sarah air base and knocking out two 'Hinds', one of which was shot down while taking off, killing the crew.

The Western press often wrote that, owing to a shortage of local personnel, Libyan military aircraft were flown by Pakistani, North Korean, Syrian and Palestinian crews. Quite possibly, Soviet personnel were also involved.

Syrian 'Hinds'

Syrian Air Force 'Hinds' made their debut in June 1982, combating Israeli tanks in Lebanon during the fifth Arab-Israeli war. Even though, generally, the Syrian Air Force was no match for the Israelis during the June campaign, Syrians helicopter operations can be deemed successful. Together with SA 342L Gazelles, the Mi-24s made 93 sorties, scoring most of the 55 kills against Israeli tanks claimed by the Syrian Air Force; they were especially successful in an operation against an Israeli tank brigade near the mountain village of Aon Zgalta. There were no 'Hind' losses during the summer campaign.

After the war, Syrian Mi-24s saw more action in Lebanon – this time against paramilitary right-wing Christian extremist groups. Their missions included blockading the Lebanese coast in the areas controlled by the extremists. On 11 April 1989 a routine patrol mission ended in an incident

against them in the Vietnam War. When a spotter aircraft – a Cessna O-1 or an Antonov An-2 – patrolling over the jungle located a target, the crew fired FFARs or dropped hand grenades filled with white phosphorus (the An-2s were locally modified with UB-16-57 FFAR pods). The burning phosphorus produced a dense white smoke that could be seen for miles, guiding the attack helicopters.

Indian 'Hinds'

The Indian Air Force (IAF) had a chance to evaluate the Mi-24 a few years before acquiring the type, and press reports indicated that groups of IAF pilots were in action in Afghanistan, practising and studying strike helicopter operations. Shortly after buying the first batch of Mi-25s in late 1984, India used them against the Pakistan Army when fighting broke out over the disputed Siachin Glacier in 1987.

The most celebrated action of the Indian 'crocodiles' was the Indian Peacekeeping Force operation in Sri Lanka in 1987-1989, an attempt to put an end to the prolonged civil war in that country (see *World Air Power Journal*, Volume 4). The Mi-25's first operation in that mission was the defence of Jaffna against the rebel Liberation Tigers of Tamil Eelam (LTTE) in October 1987. The 'Hinds' hunted and destroyed LTTE groups, escorted Mi-8T and Mi-17 transport and troopship helicopters of the IAF's 109th, 119th and 129th Squadrons during Operations Trishul and Viraat, cut the rebels' communications, and were used against LTTE boats carrying weapons and supplies across the Palk Strait. Other major actions were a battle with the Tigers in March 1989 which went on for several days (in which Mi-25s operating from Trincomalee and Vavuniya supported five Peacekeeping Force battalions) and Operation Checkmate held in the autumn of 1989 to prevent the LTTE from disrupting the municipal elections.

Throughout the peacekeeping mission, IAF Mi-25s and Mi-35s used only FFARs and machine-guns against LTTE targets. The ATGM launchers were removed, since there were no targets that merited a guided missile. There were no losses on the Indians' part, as the rebels' small arms fire was useless against the 'Hind'.

Sri Lankan 'Hinds'

In November 1995 the Sri Lankan Air Force acquired its own Mi-24Vs, using them with considerable success in a major air/land/sea assault called Operation Riverisa (Sunshine) and later in Riverisa II and Riverisa III. One 'Hind-E' (CH 614) was lost on 19 March 1997 when it exploded and crashed into the Bay of Bengal off Mullait-tivu, killing the pilot. Since Mullaittivu is in the north of the island held by the LTTE, the helicopter was almost certainly shot down by the rebels who had obtained some shoulder-launched SAMs during the brief ceasefire of 1995.

Another was shot down near the same spot by a Stinger missile on 10 November 1997 while escorting SLAF Mi-17 troopship helicopters. The helicopter managed to deflect

the first Stinger with its IRCM equipment but was immediately hit by a second missile and crashed into the Kokilai lagoon. Two crew were killed and another two were rescued by Navy divers. The explosion also damaged one of the Mi-17s, which force-landed with no injuries to the occupants. Previously, on 12 September a third Mi-24V had been hit by AA fire near Puliyankulam during Operation Jaya Sikurui; this left the SLAF with just three serviceable 'Hinds'.

Nicaraguan 'Hinds'

A batch of Mi-25Ds was delivered to Nicaragua in 1983-1984 to help the Sandinista government of Daniel Ortega fight the Contras.

The 'Hind' was used both in the attack and counter-air roles, its high performance enabling it to intercept all types of aircraft used by the Contras. These were mostly light aircraft equipped for the COIN role, but sometimes the Mi-25s encountered more potent adversaries. For example, on 13 September 1985 as Fuerza Aérea Sandinista Mi-25s attacked enemy positions near Jalapa not far from the Honduran border, several F-86 Sabres and A-37 Dragonflies came to the rescue from across the border. One helicopter was damaged and force-landed, though it is not known whether the Contras or the Honduran Air Force was credited with this kill.

The biggest threat came from the Stinger and Redeye shoulder-launched SAMs used by the Contras, to which two 'Hind-Ds' were lost on 5 March and 19 June 1987. Another Mi-25 was lost in December 1988 when its pilot, Edwin Estrada Leiva, defected to Honduras – possibly lured by an ad in the *Soldier of Fortune* magazine offering US$10,000 to anyone who accomplished this 'feat'.

When the Contras won and the civil war ended in 1990, poverty-stricken Nicaragua could not afford to keep the Mi-25s and soon sold them to Peru. The latter nation was already a 'Hind' operator, having acquired 12 Mi-25s from

Opposite page and above: India acquired its first 'Hinds' in 1984, all Mi-25V 'Hind-Es' (along with the IAF's unique Mi-25V trainers). India's 'Hinds' have fought in border skirmishes against Pakistan, but received their true baptism of fire in 1987 during India's ultimately unsuccessful military actions in support of the Sri Lankan government, against the LTTE. The 'Hinds' flew sustained CAS missions, often armed with four 250-kg (551-lb) OFAB-250 bombs (opposite page), as the 'Hind' is an accurate dive-bomber. The Mi-25s also escorted Mi-8 troopships on airborne assault missions. The last Indian forces left Sri Lanka in 1990. As a result of their combat experience, India's Mi-25s were refitted with improved side-mounted ASO-2V chaff/flare dispensers. Also added were L-006 RAWS antennas (above).

Upgraded Mi-24M

On 4 March 1999 the prototype Mi-24M upgraded for the Russian army made its 25-minute official maiden flight (two brief and unofficial hops were made in February). The Mi-24M has a new main rotor system with composite blades and a redesigned tail rotor. The changes made to the 'Hind' increase its service ceiling from 2200 m (7,200 ft) to 3100 m (10,200 ft) in standard conditions, and from 1750 m (5,700 ft) to 2150 m (7,000 ft) in ISO +10° C. Climb rate has increased from 576 m/min to 744 m/min (1,890 ft/min to 2,440 ft/min). The new non-retractable gear inhibits cruising speed by 6 kt (11 km/h) to 167 kt (309 km/h, 192 mph).

The Mi-24M prototype has been converted from an Mi-24VP, the youngest variant in Russian service. Changes to note include the new tail rotor, fixed main gear and the much-modified stub wings.

Above: The rear (pilot's) cockpit of this Czech 'Hind-E' has been fitted with a new navigation display panel, but otherwise is completely standard.

Left: Two 9A669 GUV weapons pods are fitted with AGS-17 30-mm grenade launcher and TKB-621 7.62-mm machine-guns.

Weapons and systems of the Mi-24 'Hind'

Mi-24VP: The last 'Hind'

The 9M17P Falanga missile (below left) was the first guided weapon to be fielded on the Mi-24. After launch it relies on radio guidance from the associated Raduga-F SACLOS (semi-automatic command line of sight) system undernose (below right).

The Mi-24VP was the last production 'Hind' variant, and never gained a NATO codename. Based on the 'Hind-E' airframe it added a new NPPU-24 nose turret with a twin GSh-23 cannon. The Mi-24VP entered service in 1989, but only 25 were ever built.

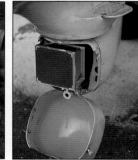

Above: The Mi-24P 'Hind-F' is armed with a Gryazev/Shipunov GSh-30K 30-mm cannon, the heaviest gun ever carried by an Mi-24.

Above: This Mi-24D 'Hind-D' is carrying a standard load of 9M17P Falanga (AT-2 'Swatter') missiles and UB-32A-24 rocket pods.

Above: The Mi-24V 'Hind-E' had revised endplate pylons allowing it to carry the tube-launched 9M114 Shturm (AT-6 'Spiral') anti-tank missile.

Mi-24 Testbeds

Fenestron

In 1975 an uncoded 'Hind-B' – one of the original prototypes or possibly one of the 10 pre-production aircraft – was fitted experimentally with a large-diameter eight-bladed fenestron replacing the standard tail rotor and pylon. The stub wings were removed, probably to save weight.

Rear protection

During the Afghan war Mi-24 pilots kept urging the Mil OKB to give the 'Hind' some protection for its rear. While the Mi-8, another Afghan war workhorse, had a hatch in the port half of its clamshell cargo doors where a Kalashnikov RPK machine-gun or equivalent could be mounted to cover the rear hemisphere, the Mi-24 had no such measures and was often shot up after making an attack. About 48 per cent of all damage from ground fire on the Mi-24 was in the rear hemisphere, compared to some 27 per cent on the Mi-8.

In 1985 an Mi-24V coded 'Red 43' was fitted experimentally with a 12.7-mm NSVT-12,7 Utyos (Cliff) machine-gun in a bulged enclosure replacing the aft avionics bay. The gunner's station was accessed from within via a crawlway passing through the rear fuel tank between the mainwheel wells. Trials promptly showed that the rear gunner's station was not a success. It caused a major shift in the helicopter's centre of gravity position and was always full of engine exhaust gases, making things almost unbearable for the gunner. The crunch came when the modified helicopter was demonstrated to VVS top brass and one of the portly generals got stuck in the narrow crawlway when he wanted to check the gunner's station, and the idea was abandoned. Instead, rear view mirrors were installed on operational 'Hinds' so that pilots could see they were being fired upon and take evasive action.

Mi-28 'Havoc'

A number of Mi-24s served as systems and avionics testbeds for the Mi-28 'Havoc'. One of them, possibly an uncoded early-production Mi-24A with starboard-side tail rotor, was used to test the new main rotor. The helicopter in question featured a large lattice-like

boom with air data sensors on the fuselage nose (the machine-gun had to be removed, of course). There was also a similarly equipped Mi-24A without stub wings and missile director antenna, which quite possibly was the same aircraft at a later stage. Another 'Hind' served as a testbed for the Mi-28's squashed-X tail rotor.

Filters

A Mi-24D coded 'Red 74' was used to test an early model of the vortex-type intake filters which became standard on late 'Hinds'. Unlike the production model resembling partly deflated footballs, these looked like large buckets. The helicopter still sits derelict at the flight test facility in Lyubertsy.

PrPNK-28

Two Mi-24Vs coded 'Red 19' and 'Red 73' were converted into testbeds for the PrPNK-28 targeting/flight instrumentation/navigation system. The entire nose section of a 'Havoc' with the revolving laser rangefinder/LLLTV turret and thimble radome for the missile guidance system was grafted onto the nose of the 'Hind' in lieu of the usual excrescences, giving the helicopter a bizarre appearance.

'Red 73' is now withdrawn from use at the helicopter flight test facility in Lyubertsy (just outside the Moscow city limits) used by both Mil and Kamov bureaux.

Green 'Hind'

An Mi-24V (identity unknown) was converted by the Polyot (Flight) Scientific and Production Association into an environmental survey aircraft for detecting oil spills in bodies of water, monitoring air pollution, etc. The USPU-24 gun barbette was replaced by a flat fairing containing sensors, making the helicopter appear to be rudely sticking out its tongue; the LLLTV/FLIR pod and missile launchers were deleted, but the missile guidance antenna 'egg' was retained. Test instrumentation was carried in large slab-sided pods on the outer wing pylons, the inner ones being occupied by fuel tanks. The test engineer (operator) had the cabin all to himself. The demilitarised 'Hind' was one of the exhibits of the annual industry fair in Nizhny Novgorod in September 1991.

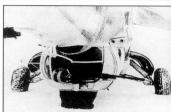

Above: Development of the Mi-24 fenestron was discontinued because the new system was found to be ill-suited for helicopters in the weight class of the 'Hind'.

Right and below: The gunner could not be accommodated entirely and his legs stuck outside, scantily protected by rubberised fabric 'trousers'.

Above: This is the Mi-24D testbed used to develop new engine intake filters for the 'Hind'.

Right: This early-production 'Hind-A', outfitted with an air data test rig, may later have become an Mi-28 dynamic testbed.

Mi-24PS

A special troopship version designated Mi-24PS (in this case, *patrool'no-spasahtel'nii* = patrol/rescue (attrib.)) has been developed for the Russian Ministry of the Interior. Its missions are transportation and deployment of militia (police) search groups, support of police operations and SAR.

The Mi-24PS exists in two versions. The first prototype is a converted Mi-24P and retains the fixed 30-mm GSh-30K cannon. The LLLTV/FLIR fairing on the starboard side of the nose and the ATGM guidance antenna 'egg' on the port side are replaced by downward-pointing quadruple loudspeakers and an FPP-7 searchlight, respectively. The nose fairing is cut away to hold a gyrostabilised optical system in a neat ball turret and a weather radar. The cabin accommodates an assault group of six policemen. Special brackets and handrails are mounted on the fuselage sides to ease disembarkation (up to four troopers can simultaneously rappel down lines dropped from the helicopter), and an LPG-4 hoist installed on the port side

aft of the cabin door can lift up to 120 kg (264 lb) during SAR operations, etc. The Mi-24PS is equipped with satellite communications gear and a communications system as used by the Russian Army special forces (the famous Spetsnaz); the presence of additional communications equipment is revealed by two extra whip aerials on the tailboom.

The second prototype which was unveiled at the MAKS-95 air show is a converted Mi-24V; the c/n has been quoted as [353]2420338200 but this cannot be correct, as the quarter of manufacture appears to be zero (!) and the 'famous last five' digits are much too high. Unlike the first prototype, this helicopter is unarmed; the wing endplates and inboard pylons have been removed, leaving only the outboard pylons for drop tanks. There is no radar and the USPU-24 gun barbette is replaced by a thermal imager 'ball'. The rest of the equipment is identical to the first prototype. The helicopter is white overall with blue side flashes, Russian flag, Mil logos and Russian Militsiya titles but no civil registration, tactical code or visible c/n. A Mil representative said the Mi-24PS is similar in performance to the Mi-24V.

This is the second prototype of the decidedly unconventional Mi-24PS, which did not sport the 30-mm cannon of its predecessor.

The Mi-24PS carries a FLIR and loudhailer system (above), operated from the front cockpit (right).

'Hind-G1'

Mi-24R (Mi-24RKhR) 'Hind-G1' (Izdelye 2462)
Mil developed a dedicated NBC reconnaissance 'Hind' to replace the Mi-8VD of the mid-1970s. Service designation was Mi-24R (*[vertolyot-] razvedchik* = reconnaissance [helicopter]) or Mi-24RKhR (*dlya rahdiatseeonno-khimeecheskoy razvedki* = for NBC reconnaissance). The latter designation has been misrepresented as 'Mi-24RKR' or even 'Mi-24RCh' in Western publications. NBC designation was Izdelye 2462, suggesting that it was based on the Mi-24D (Izdelye 246).

The Mi-24R would measure radiation and chemical/biological contamination levels and transmit this data to C³I centres by datalink. It had an air-sampling unit which breathed through a large protruding ventral intake offset to port aft of the nose gear, exhausting through a slit in the fuselage side above it (usually covered by wire mesh). The ATGM launchers on the wing endplates were replaced by unique remote-controlled claw-shaped devices for

The 'Hind-G1' was built because it was assumed that future wars would be fought in an NBC-contaminated environment. The Mi-24R's inboard pylons were usually occupied by drop tanks and the outboard pylons by additional mission equipment in small square-section pods, leaving the helicopter with only the nose-mounted machine-gun (or rockets, if required).

taking soil samples (called 'excavators' in OKB parlance), so the Raduga-F was deleted, as was the strike camera on the port wingtip.

The cabin, which accommodated mission equipment control consoles and two equipment operators, featured an enhanced life support and NBC protection system, yet the crew wore full NBC suits on operational missions. The two small windows in the upper segment of the port cabin door were replaced by a single elongated blister window to give one of the operators a degree of downward view. Finally, a triangular plate of unknown purpose (possibly a counterweight to balance the equipment in the nose) was mounted on the tailskid of production Mi-24Rs.

The uncoded prototype was converted in late 1978 from an early-production Mi-24V built in late 1977 (c/n 3532424708820). Production Mi-24Rs had

c/ns commencing with 353462. Curiously, the prototype lacked intake filters and had IRCM flare packs scabbed on outboard of the 'excavators'; in production these were carried as usual, under the tailboom or on the aft fuselage sides. Some 152 Mi-24Rs were built between 1983 and 1989.

Mi-24RA 'Hind-G1' (Izdelye 2462)
In 1989 some Mi-24Rs were equipped with an upgraded intelligence processing and communications suite and the crew was reduced to three (pilot, WSO and one equipment operator). 'Hind-G1s' thus modified were redesignated Mi-24RA. It is possible that these aircraft lacked the wingtip 'excavators', the port one being replaced by a small equipment pod, and had the standard strike camera. One such aircraft coded 'Yellow 46' was stationed in Germany.

'Hind-G2'

Mi-24K 'Hind-G2' (Izdelye 201)
In 1979 Mil rolled out the prototype of the Mi-24K (*korrekteerovschchik*) photo reconnaissance/artillery spotter version, aka Izdelye 201. Based on the Mi-24V, it was intended to replace the Mi-8TARK (Mi-8T *artillereeyskiy razvedchik-korrekteerovschchik* = artillery recce/spotter). Its mission was battlefield observation and tactical reconnaissance, spotting for artillery and missile units, and aerial photography.

The Raduga-F LLLTV/FLIR was replaced by an Iris wide-angle optical sensor system (possibly with other modes than optical) in a contoured fairing with a characteristically curved upward-hinging protective cover over the sensor window; it featured a system of movable mirrors to increase the field of view. The cabin housed an AFA-100 oblique camera (*aerofotoapparaht* = aircraft camera) and a Ruta reconnaissance and spotting suite comprising an optical target identification system, a computer and a 'data processor' [*sic*, possibly meaning a data presentation system]. This necessitated major structural changes: the port-side cabin door was eliminated, leaving only the two rearmost windows, and a large rectangular camera window with optically-flat glass was added low on the fuselage side where the front end of the lower door half would have been. The starboard door was retained for access to the equipment.

The camera and optical sensors were operated by the WSO from the front cockpit. The Mi-24K had no provision for ATGMs (with no launch rails or guidance system fitted), but the machine-gun and rocket pods were retained.

The Mi-24K entered production in 1983, and 163 had been completed by 1989. Neither the Mi-24R nor the Mi-24K was exported, but both were stationed outside the Soviet Union (in former East Germany).

This Mi-24K 'Yellow 23' was based at Parchim with the 439th OVP. The reconfigured windows on the starboard side provided a field of view for the large onboard optics.

the Soviet Union in the early 1980s. Peruvian Mi-25s were used against the local drug cartels, the infamous Sendero Luminoso (Shining Path) Maoist terror organisation, and the equally radical Tupac Amaru Liberation Movement.

Sierra Leone 'Hinds'

In Sierra Leone the ill-trained government forces were steadily losing ground to the Revolutionary United Front (RUF), in effect a bunch of thugs led by Corporal Alfred Foday Sankoh with Libyan affiliations, anti-Western ideas and a determination to seize power. The tiny Sierra Leone Air Force, consisting of a single Mi-17-1V (Mi-

8MTV-2) gunship and a single Mi-24V (both flown by Belarussian contract crews and presumably acquired in Belarus), was used against the RUF on armed reconnaissance missions and, while greatly intimidating the rebels, had difficulty finding and attacking them in the dense jungle. Things got better only when the ruling military junta, the National Provisional Ruling Council (NPRC), hired Executive Outcomes (EO), a 'proactive security organisation' based in Pretoria, to conduct operations against the RUF and provide tactical planning and personnel training (see *World Air Power Journal*, Volume 28).

The 'Hind' was used mostly as a troopship and an escort aircraft, providing top cover for the 'Hip-H' gunship and EO's own Mi-17s,

US Army 'Hinds'

The US Army has at least two operational Mi-24s, with others held for spares support and testing. The flying 'Hinds' include this 'Hind-D' (above and right, new and old paint scheme) and an Mi-24P (below).

The Mi-24 'Hinds' of the US Army's Operational Test and Evaluation Command Threat Support Activity

Biggs Army Air Field is situated in southwest Texas near the border city of El Paso and is part of the Fort Bliss complex. At one time Biggs AAF was host to B-36s of Strategic Air Command. Now home to a variety of US Army rotary- and fixed-wing aircraft, the base is relatively quiet except for occasional exercises such as Roving Sands. The Biggs AAF flight line is bordered by hangars built in the 1940s and 1950s. One hangar, situated in the middle of the flight line, is surrounded by chain link fencing, itself covered with material that makes looking inside nearly impossible. The surrounding area is monitored by television cameras, and electric gates control entry and exit from the hangar. Additionally, access to the ramp from the hangar is controlled by electrically operated gates. The reason for this degree of security is the presence of the US Army's Operational Test and Evaluation Command Threat Support Activity (OTSA). This unique Army unit flies a variety of Russian aircraft including Mil Mi-2s, Mi-8s, Mi-17s, Mi-24s and Antonov An-2s.

In addition to supporting the joint Roving Sands exercises, OTSA aircraft contribute to USAF Red Flag and Green Flag exercises, held at Nellis ASFB, Nevada, and to the US Army's battalion-level training exercises held at the National Training Center, Fort Irwin, California. During an exercise such as Green Flag or Red Flag, Red force OTSA aircraft fly primarily in the interdiction role. Operating from the surface to a maximum of 200 ft (61 m), their role is to assault Blue (friendly) forces which enter their area of operations. This would include C-130s attempting to insert troops or materials. The OPTEC 'Hinds' would also interdict any BLUFOR helicopter operations such as SAR or long-range patrols. As a component of OPFOR – the US Army's 'Opposition Force' – OTSA maintains a presence at Fort Polk, Louisiana, home of the Joint Readiness Training Center. OTSA also provides threat simulation for the Apache and Comanche development programmes. Additionally, any Department of Defense agency can call on OTSA to test improvements to new US air defence systems and programmes anywhere in the world.

A select few US Army pilots and civilian technicians were first introduced to a captured Mi-24 'Hind' in the mid-1980s. The exact date is still classified and the sources and methods of acquisition of the remainder of the OTSA fleet of Russian-designed aircraft are also officially classified (see Mi-24 operators section for further details of the current aircraft). The OTSA fleet is kept airworthy by a staff of experienced maintainers drawn from the civilian/commercial rotary-wing field, as well as from the military.

OTSA operates three Mi-24/Mi-25 'Hinds' of different sub-types, all of which have been slightly modified (through the addition of the MILES laser training system) for their new-found training role. Two aircraft are believed to be former East German aircraft, acquired following German reunification in 1990: an Mi-24D named *Wild Thing* (with Tasmanian Devil nose-art) and an Mi-24P, *Patience*. The third aircraft, *Warlord* (?), is an Mi-25D captured from Iraqi forces in the aftermath of Operation Desert Storm (this aircraft was exhibited in full Iraqi camouflage and markings but its current status is unknown). It is likely that OPTEC had access to other aircraft in previous years, thanks largely to the French, who captured Libyan 'Hinds' in Chad during the mid-1980s. It is possible that one of the 'Hinds' which defected to Pakistan from Afghanistan in the early 1980s also found its way to the USA.

David F. Brown

---

which inserted and extracted search-and-destroy and mortar teams and carried supplies. CAS missions were also flown occasionally. The aircraft operated by EO were based at Freetown-Lungi airport, but purpose-built helipads were also established near Koidu.

The Mi-24's armament usually consisted of UB-32A FFAR pods and sometimes GUV gun pods in both machine-gun and grenade-launcher configurations. The nose-mounted YakB-12,7 machine-gun was described as 'deadly accurate' and the AGS-17 grenade launcher was found to be very effective against area targets. The Belarussians were Afghan veterans and used that experience to advantage, including the use of S-5S 'meat grinder' flechette rockets against RUF personnel. Drop tanks were rarely carried because they only left two wing stations free for weapons; the problem of limited range was solved by using the Mi-17s to carry fuel drums to helipads. The main problem with Mi-24 operations was that neither the Belarussians nor the South Africans spoke each other's language. Hence, a Sierra Leone officer who spoke Russian had to be carried as an interpreter, which complicated operations and increased the risk of 'friendly fire' casualties during CAS missions.

EO accomplished more in a week (not counting planning, training and preparation time) than the Republic of Sierra Leone Military Force had in four years of bush warfare. Soon EO and RSLMF personnel had recaptured the diamond-rich Kono district, and the first of the 30,000-odd inhabitants forced out of the area by the rebels' raids began to return. Eventually, the RUF was forced to call a ceasefire (though mainly in order to regroup and re-arm, as intelligence reports plainly indicated) and begin negotiations with the government.

UN 'Hinds' in Croatia

In the spring of 1996 the specially-formed 8th Combat Helicopter Squadron of the Ukrainian Army Aviation commanded by Colonel A. I. Lev was seconded to the United Nations Transitional Administration in Eastern Slavonia (UNTAES). UNTAES had been established in June 1996 to oversee the transition of this fertile and oil-rich enclave occupied by separatist Serbs since 1991 back to Croatian rule (the local Serb minority had raised a rebellion when Croatia declared independence from federal Yugoslavia).

On 10 April 1997 the squadron's six Mi-24P 'Hind-F' gunships and four Mi-24K 'Hind-G2' reconnaissance helicopters arrived at Klisa airport, located between Osijek and Vukovar. Only a few days earlier Klisa had been the scene of fierce fighting between Serbs and Croats. The helicopters were painted in the UN peacekeeping forces' white colour scheme with 'United Nation' titles. This was the first time that the Mi-24 – or the Ukraine – had participated in UN operations (see *World Air Power Journal*, Volume 30).

"We landed on an airstrip with Serb guns a mere 1.5 km [0.93 miles] away," Ukrainian Army Aviation Commander Colonel A. D. Korniyets recalled. "Now that peacekeeping operations are in progress, our pilots are patrolling the demilitarised zone, conducting reconnaissance and escorting Mi-8MT transport helicopters operated by a second Ukrainian squadron. Sorties are flown with full armament, including ATGMs; luckily, we haven't been forced to fire yet. In the first two months, 8th Sqn helicopters have logged 288 hours in 237 sorties and earned praise from the UNPF commander, the Belgian Major General Jozef Schoups. It should be noted that the UN pays the Ukraine US$2,900 for every hour of Mi-24 operations and the contract amount for the [first] six months in Eastern Slavonia is US$8 million."

The one-year UNTAES mandate was later extended for a second year and Ukrainian 'Hind' operations in Eastern Slavonia continued. The two Ukrainian squadrons were later combined into a single unit (17th Sqn) under Colonel Vladimir Pastukhov. It quickly turned out that the language barrier hampered operations, so translators were drafted in from the Ukrainian armed forces and tactical interpreters were carried for communication with NATO forces. By May 1997 UNTAES' 'Hip-Hs' and 'Hinds' had flown a total of 2,500 hours and carried some 7,000 passengers.

Croatian Mi-24Vs acquired in 1993-94 were used in the civil war in the former Yugoslavia, operating against the army of 'the current Yugoslavia' (Serbia and Montenegro). The 'Hinds' were acquired because neither the MiG-21bis nor the Mi-8TB could provide adequate battlefield support for the Croatian Army (and the slower 'Hips' were sometimes shot down on CAS missions). Armed with FAB-250 and -500 HE bombs, ZB-500GD napalm bombs (*zazhi-*

ime 'Hinds'

i-24's high power-to-weight ratio and spacious
gave it ample development potential. A multi-role
version designated Mi-24M (morskoy = naval) or
e 247 was developed in 1970. However, Mikhail
shelved the project so as not to undermine the
n of the Kamov OKB, which was the Soviet
traditional supplier of maritime helicopters. Mil
back to the idea of navalising the Mi-24 in 1973,
demand of the Soviet government which
ly wanted a mine countermeasures (MCM)
ter. To this end, an Mi-24A was extensively
ed as the prototype of an MCM version
nated Mi-24BMT (buksirovschchik minnovo trahla
e-clearing sled tug). The Mi-24BMT lacked stub
, armament and armour plating. The landing gear
xed. The aft fuselage incorporated a winch and
ge for the mine-clearing sled, and an extra fuel
vas installed to increase endurance. The Mi-
T remained in prototype form, this time because
i-8BT developed in 1974 for clearing mines in the
Canal was found to be more efficient in the MCM
s was the later Mi-14BT 'Haze-B'.

Mil Mi-24P 'Hind-F'
Soviet Army Aviation, Afghanistan

The 'Hind-F' was the penultimate production version of the Mi-24, but boasted the last word in heavy helicopter armament. The addition of the twin Gryazev/Shipunov GSh-30K 30-mm cannon gave it immense firepower which proved invaluable in Afghanistan. This aircraft is carrying a light load of just two 9M114 Shturm (AT-6 'Spiral') tubes and two B8V20 80-mm rocket launchers. The weight of the cannon affected the overall warload of the Mi-24P, and 'Hinds' in Afghanistan always tended to operate with less then the optimum combat load due to the 'hot-and-high' conditions.

e of the Afghan
Lipa) active IRCM
head. The IRCM
istracted by the
e would start
ong way from the
nroughout the
uld manoeuvre into
ts jammer for
ly during an attack
ous spots where
just to be on the
noeuvre was
an incoming
rp turn and fire a

Indestructible 'Crocodiles'
In Afghanistan, hopelessly damaged aircraft were destroyed on the spot to prevent them from falling into enemy hands. This was no small task, as the Mi-24 could not be set alight by incendiary bullets and would not explode even when hit by FFARs, which merely pierced the structure, going clean through. A specially developed manual required the crew to "put all remaining S-5 FFARs in the troop cabin and cockpit(s), place the bombs beneath the fuselage, rupture fuel and hydraulic lines in the lower fuselage, lay tarpaulins soaked in jet fuel to make a fuse at least 20 m long so as to allow the crew to take cover."

Employing rockets
Rockets were one of the principal weapons of the Afghan war. However, until recently, the 130-mm S-13 FFARs and 250-mm S-24 heavy unguided rockets (both common weapons of the Su-25) were not widely used by the Mi-24 because its targeting system was ill-suited for these weapons and accuracy was poor; this was not helped by the type's higher vibration level compared to the 'Frogfoot'. Additionally, there was considerable risk of engine surge after ingesting rocket exhaust gases. However, during the Chechen war Russian Air Force Mi-24 pilots developed a technique of firing S-24s after pitching up the helicopter into a climb, and made more than 200 successful launches in this fashion.

Protecting the crew
Analysis of Afghan combat losses led to the obvious conclusion that crew protection was the first priority, for unless the crew was incapacitated, it could usually bring home a crippled helicopter. However, a head-on approach to the problem by fitting bullet-proof side windows inside the cockpits dismally failed, as the 35-kg (77-lb) glass panels impaired visibility and made the cockpits so cramped that the crew literally had no room to turn their heads. The specially-developed protective suit proposed in 1980 was a failure too, looking and weighing like a medieval knight's suit of armour. Bullet-proof vests were rarely used (and then mostly in winter, more for the sake of warmth than protection). The ZSh-3B helmets were criticised for their weight, the 3-kg (6.6-lb) helmet severely straining neck muscles during high-g turns, but things improved when the lightweight ZSh-5B titanium helmet became available.

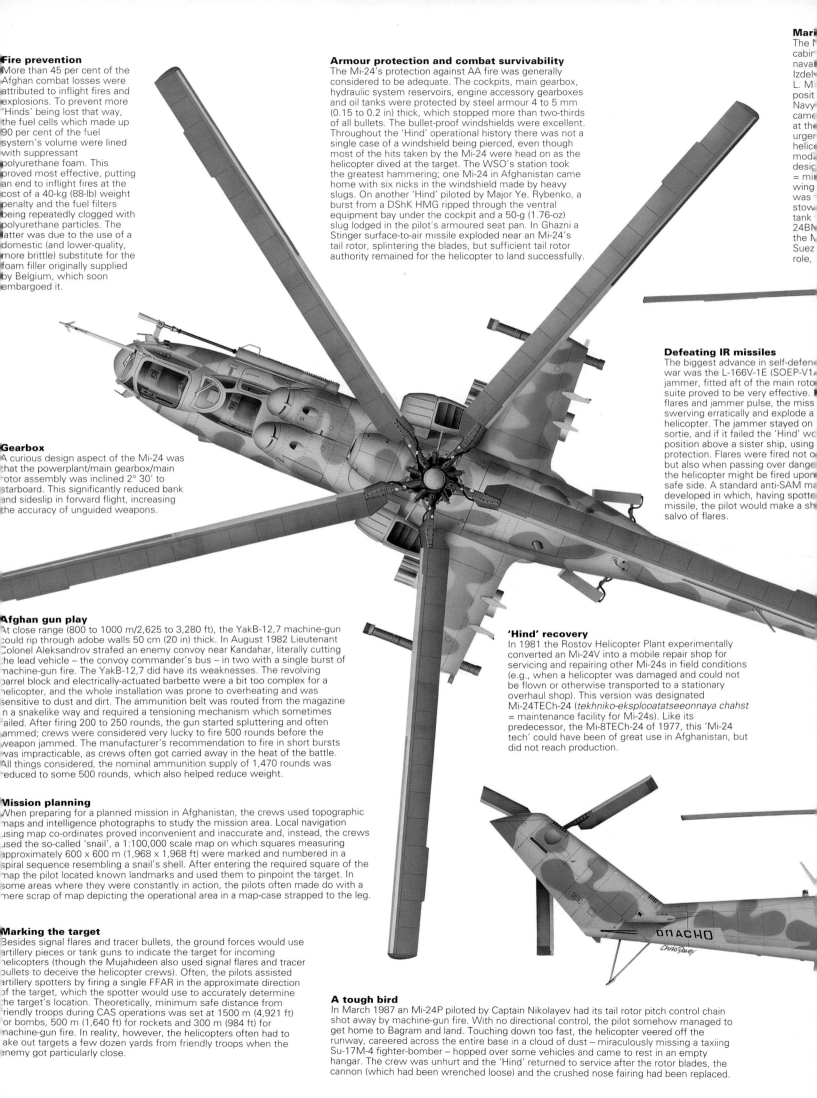

Fire prevention

More than 45 per cent of the Afghan combat losses were attributed to inflight fires and explosions. To prevent more 'Hinds' being lost that way, the fuel cells which made up 90 per cent of the fuel system's volume were lined with suppressant polyurethane foam. This proved most effective, putting an end to inflight fires at the cost of a 40-kg (88-lb) weight penalty and the fuel filters being repeatedly clogged with polyurethane particles. The latter was due to the use of a domestic (and lower-quality, more brittle) substitute for the foam filler originally supplied by Belgium, which soon embargoed it.

Gearbox

A curious design aspect of the Mi-24 was that the powerplant/main gearbox/main rotor assembly was inclined 2° 30' to starboard. This significantly reduced bank and sideslip in forward flight, increasing the accuracy of unguided weapons.

Afghan gun play

At close range (800 to 1000 m/2,625 to 3,280 ft), the YakB-12,7 machine-gun could rip through adobe walls 50 cm (20 in) thick. In August 1982 Lieutenant Colonel Aleksandrov strafed an enemy convoy near Kandahar, literally cutting the lead vehicle – the convoy commander's bus – in two with a single burst of machine-gun fire. The YakB-12,7 did have its weaknesses. The revolving barrel block and electrically-actuated barbette were a bit too complex for a helicopter, and the whole installation was prone to overheating and was sensitive to dust and dirt. The ammunition belt was routed from the magazine in a snakelike way and required a tensioning mechanism which sometimes failed. After firing 200 to 250 rounds, the gun started spluttering and often jammed; crews were considered very lucky to fire 500 rounds before the weapon jammed. The manufacturer's recommendation to fire in short bursts was impracticable, as crews often got carried away in the heat of the battle. All things considered, the nominal ammunition supply of 1,470 rounds was reduced to some 500 rounds, which also helped reduce weight.

Mission planning

When preparing for a planned mission in Afghanistan, the crews used topographic maps and intelligence photographs to study the mission area. Local navigation using map co-ordinates proved inconvenient and inaccurate and, instead, the crews used the so-called 'snail', a 1:100,000 scale map on which squares measuring approximately 600 x 600 m (1,968 x 1,968 ft) were marked and numbered in a spiral sequence resembling a snail's shell. After entering the required square of the map the pilot located known landmarks and used them to pinpoint the target. In some areas where they were constantly in action, the pilots often made do with a mere scrap of map depicting the operational area in a map-case strapped to the leg.

Marking the target

Besides signal flares and tracer bullets, the ground forces would use artillery pieces or tank guns to indicate the target for incoming helicopters (though the Mujahideen also used signal flares and tracer bullets to deceive the helicopter crews). Often, the pilots assisted artillery spotters by firing a single FFAR in the approximate direction of the target, which the spotter would use to accurately determine the target's location. Theoretically, minimum safe distance from friendly troops during CAS operations was set at 1500 m (4,921 ft) for bombs, 500 m (1,640 ft) for rockets and 300 m (984 ft) for machine-gun fire. In reality, however, the helicopters often had to take out targets a few dozen yards from friendly troops when the enemy got particularly close.

Armour protection and combat survivability

The Mi-24's protection against AA fire was generally considered to be adequate. The cockpits, main gearbox, hydraulic system reservoirs, engine accessory gearboxes and oil tanks were protected by steel armour 4 to 5 mm (0.15 to 0.2 in) thick, which stopped more than two-thirds of all bullets. The bullet-proof windshields were excellent. Throughout the 'Hind' operational history there was not a single case of a windshield being pierced, even though most of the hits taken by the Mi-24 were head on as the helicopter dived at the target. The WSO's station took the greatest hammering; one Mi-24 in Afghanistan came home with six nicks in the windshield made by heavy slugs. On another 'Hind' piloted by Major Ye. Rybenko, a burst from a DShK HMG ripped through the ventral equipment bay under the cockpit and a 50-g (1.76-oz) slug lodged in the pilot's armoured seat pan. In Ghazni a Stinger surface-to-air missile exploded near an Mi-24's tail rotor, splintering the blades, but sufficient tail rotor authority remained for the helicopter to land successfully.

Defeating IR missiles

The biggest advance in self-defen war was the L-166V-1E (SOEP-V1, jammer, fitted aft of the main roto suite proved to be very effective. flares and jammer pulse, the miss swerving erratically and explode a helicopter. The jammer stayed on sortie, and if it failed the 'Hind' wo position above a sister ship, using protection. Flares were fired not o but also when passing over dange the helicopter might be fired upon safe side. A standard anti-SAM ma developed in which, having spotte missile, the pilot would make a sh salvo of flares.

'Hind' recovery

In 1981 the Rostov Helicopter Plant experimentally converted an Mi-24V into a mobile repair shop for servicing and repairing other Mi-24s in field conditions (e.g., when a helicopter was damaged and could not be flown or otherwise transported to a stationary overhaul shop). This version was designated Mi-24TECh-24 (tekhniko-eksplooatatseeonnaya chahst = maintenance facility for Mi-24s). Like its predecessor, the Mi-8TECh-24 of 1977, this 'Mi-24 tech' could have been of great use in Afghanistan, but did not reach production.

A tough bird

In March 1987 an Mi-24P piloted by Captain Nikolayev had its tail rotor pitch control chain shot away by machine-gun fire. With no directional control, the pilot somehow managed to get home to Bagram and land. Touching down too fast, the helicopter veered off the runway, careered across the entire base in a cloud of dust – miraculously missing a taxiing Su-17M-4 fighter-bomber – hopped over some vehicles and came to rest in an empty hangar. The crew was unhurt and the 'Hind' returned to service after the rotor blades, the cannon (which had been wrenched loose) and the crushed nose fairing had been replaced.

patrolled over the front lines, escorted vehicle convoys and transport helicopters and suppressed artillery. Of course, both the Armenians and the Azeris fired at the helicopters with whatever weapons they had, from shotguns to 'anti-hail' guns (World War II-vintage AA guns firing special rounds filled with rainmaking compounds).

Mi-24s were among the heavy equipment used in a notorious riot control action in Baku. About the same time, a 'Hind' was seriously damaged by 'anti-hail' artillery near Gyandzha, making a forced landing. In July-August 1991 the press reported that Soviet Army Aviation helicopters were in action on the Azeris' side in Nagornii Karabakh. These operations were not altogether without incident, as when on 20 July 1991 three 'Hinds' were damaged by ground fire while attacking Armenian positions near Bouzʰouk village in the Shaoumian region of the enclave and one crew member was wounded.

The conflict escalated still further after the break-up of the Soviet Union. The Azeris 'nationalised' a squadron of Mi-24s based at Sangachaly AB, as did the Armenians with the helicopters based near Yerevan.

Unfortunately, Russian Army units of the Transcaucasian Defence District also became involved in the hostilities. On 3 February 1992 Russian Army 'Hinds' escorting an Mi-26 'Halo' heavy transport helicopter carrying Armenian refugees were forced to drive off an unmarked Mi-8 which attempted an attack on the transport. However, the Mi-26 was downed by a shoulder-launched SAM and six people died in the ensuing crash. From 23 February to 7 March, the Mi-24s provided cover for Russian Air Force Mi-6s and Mi-26s airlifting 366th Mechanised Infantry Regiment personnel and equipment out of Stepanakert, Azerbaijan; one of the 'Hinds' was damaged and forced down by the Azeris. On 12 May several Russian 'Hinds' participated in the evacuation of the bodies of those killed in the 3 February shoot-down.

Azeri Mi-24s – piloted by ex-Soviet Air Force mercenary pilots hired by the Azeris – were first noted in Nagornii Karabakh on 19 February 1992 when they attacked Armenian positions near Karagaly village. The helicopters saw much action against Armenian tanks and fortifications. The Armenians claimed two Azeri 'Hinds' shot down in March 1992, another on 18 September that year and one more on 1 September 1993; not all of the crews lived.

In April 1992 the Armenians hijacked two Mi-24s operated by an independent squadron of the Russian Army's 7th GvVP (Gvardeyskiy vertolyotnii polk, Guards helicopter regiment) but returned them a few days later. The earliest confirmed reports of Armenian 'Hinds' date to August 1992. The Armenians used the type mostly for tactical reconnaissance and the 'Hinds' participated in most major operations against the Azeris, such as the Kelbojar operation. Losses included one Mi-24 shot down in September 1992 and another on 12 November. According to Western sources, by early 1993 Armenia and Azerbaijan had 11 and eight 'Hinds' on strength, respectively.

Civil war in Georgia

Even before the break-up of the Soviet Union, a prolonged civil war began in Georgia where South Osetia strove for independence. The South Osetian city of Tskhinvali was home to a Russian Army helicopter regiment flying Mi-8s and Mi-24s, which had orders to stay out of the conflict but frequently disobeyed them. On 12 February 1991 the 'Hinds' forced down a Georgian Civil Aviation Directorate Mi-8T which had violated the 'No-Fly Zone' over South Osetia and which, in addition to 'innocent civilians', was carrying weapons and ammunition. In June 1992, by when the Soviet Union was no more, the Mi-24s flew a sortie against Georgian APCs which habitually attacked the airfield with machine-gun fire. One of the APCs was put out of action; the enraged crew threatened to go in and murder the pilots but had no time to carry out

gahtel'nii bahk ghidroreagheerouyouschchevo deystviya = literally 'water-reacting incendiary tank'), B8V-20 FFAR pods, 9M114 Shturm ATGMs and even Mk 44 auto-tracking torpedoes, the 'Hinds' operated from numerous agricultural fields in the war zone.

CIS conflict – Azerbaijan and Armenia

The Mi-24 has also seen quite a lot of action in its home country. Shortly before the break-up of the Soviet Union, a spate of bloody ethnic conflicts erupted in the southern republics. The first was the Nagornii Karabakh enclave, the subject of a long-standing territorial dispute between Armenia and Azerbaijan. As the Soviet Army was put into action to disengage the belligerents, Army Aviation 'Hinds'

Angola's 'Hinds' (properly export Mi-35s) were a mixture of Mi-24Ds and Mi-24Vs. This rocket-armed aircraft (left) is a late-model Mi-24D with PZU engine intake filters, L-006 RHAWS fit, L-166V-11E Ispanka IR-jammer and ASO-2V chaff/flare dispensers. This Mi-24V (below) is also armed with B8V20 rocket pods.

the threat, as the unit was disbanded in the same month and the helicopters were turned over to the Georgian army.

Less than two months later the new owners put the helicopters to good use when a new civil war broke out, this time in Abkhasia in the northwest of the republic. In addition to supporting Georgian troops which seized the Abkhasi capital of Sukhumi, the Mi-24s were used against Abkhasi armoured vehicles and boats, and filled the COIN role. On the night of 27 December 1992 they foiled an attempt to insert an Abkhasi sabotage group, damaging a gunboat. The first Georgian 'Hind' was shot down on 5 October 1992, and another was lost on 4 July 1993. There are reasons to believe that both helicopters fell victim to Strela-3 shoulder-launched SAMs.

It should be noted that, whether wilfully or by mistake, Georgian Mi-24 pilots frequently attacked Russian facilities in the area, ranging from a military seismic research laboratory to health and holiday resorts. At an early stage of the conflict, on 27 August 1992, a Georgian Mi-24 attacked the Russian Kometa-44 passenger hydrofoil in the Black Sea, killing one passenger and injuring 11 more. The Abkhasi war was followed by a new conflict in which the Georgian 'Hinds' were in action against armed groups loyal to the deposed President Zviad Gamsakhourdia.

Abkhasia, Tajikistan and Osetia

The Russian Army was dragged into the Abkhasi war as well. Russian Mi-24s flew primarily escort missions for transport helicopters and were fired upon by both Georgians and Abkhazis. Occasionally, however, they had to fire in anger when called upon to unblock Russian vehicle convoys. In October 1992 it was a case of 'crocodile eat crocodile', when an unmarked (probably Abkhasi) Mi-24 unsuccessfully attacked an Mi-8 carrying future Georgian President Eduard A. Shevardnadze to the conflict zone and was driven off by the escorting 'Hinds'.

In the same year, Tajikistan joined the list of places in the former Soviet Union where the 'Hind' was at war. Russian, Uzbek and Tajik Mi-24s were in action all over the republic against the armed Islamic opposition striving to topple the Dushanbe government. Starting in August 1992, they were tasked with destroying tanks which the Islamists had stolen from the Russian Army's 181st Armour Regiment/201st Mechanised Infantry Division in Kurgan-Tyube. In December the tri-national 'Hind' force participated in the defeat of the opposition forces near Kofirnihon, losing one helicopter to ground fire on 18 December. The next spring it helped to squeeze out of the Gharm region. Later, the main action moved south to the Afghan border; the Islamists' bases and training camps were located on Afghan territory, and sometimes the 'Hinds' would cross the border to get at them.

In the autumn of 1992 there was trouble again in Osetia, this time in North Osetia, which is part of the Russian Federation. A breach occurred between the Osetians and the Ingushes, and in November Russian federal troops (including helicopter units) were pulled into the conflict zone. The Mi-24s were tasked mainly with reconnaissance but sometimes flew strike sorties as well, as when on 4

November an 'unidentified' (as official reports phrased it, meaning suspicious) convoy consisting of two APCs and four trucks was destroyed.

A pair of Mi-24Vs overflew the Russian Federal Government building (known as the White House) during the failed hard-line Communist coup of October 1993.

Chechnya

In September 1994 the Mi-24 made its debut in Chechnya. Four well-used examples were flown by contract pilots hired by the Provisional Council of the Chechen Republic (PCCR) which opposed the government of General Dzhokhar Dudayev and his separatist tendencies. More 'Hinds' were acquired later and used with considerable success against government forces. On 30 September, 10 and 25 October and 25 November 1994, they raided airfields controlled by Dudayev, destroying or damaging several aircraft and helicopters.

On 23 November 1994 a joint strike group composed of Russian Air Force Su-25s and Chechen opposition 'Hinds' attacked a Chechen government armour regiment at its home base in Shali, destroying 21 tanks and 14 APCs, and killing 201 men. Three days later seven Mi-24s supported an unsuccessful armoured assault on the Chechen capital of Groznii in which Dudayev's forces claimed one helicopter shot down. In early December the Russian Federal Border Guards reported that PCCR Mi-24s had shot down an unidentified transport aircraft heading for Azerbaijan.

Meanwhile, as a result of Dudayev's separatism and the activities of illegal armed units, Chechnya was rapidly turning into a rogue state. Deciding it had had enough, Moscow issued an ultimatum demanding compliance with federal laws, which Groznii ignored. On 11 December 1994 the Russian federal armed forces began an all-arms offensive in Chechnya. It soon turned into a full-scale war which went on for 18 months until a ceasefire was signed in Khasavyurt on 30 August 1996. Even now, the situation in and around the republic is far from peaceful.

Angola is a former Portuguese colony, which won its independence in 1975 after a 15-year guerrilla war. The various nationalist movements that had fought for independence then split into opposing factions. The Soviet-backed MPLA formed the new government. From then on, the US-backed FNLA and the South African-backed UNITA waged a new guerrilla war against their former colleagues. In return, the MPLA government backed SWAPO guerrilla operations in Southwest Africa (later Namibia), aimed against South Africa. South Africa was involved in what became known as the Bush War against Angola, from 1976 to 1987. This conflict escalated into major mechanised infantry battles with tank engagements, air strikes and air-to-air combat. Several Angolan Mi-25s fell to the guns of South African fighters and more were shot down by gun fire. Today, the survivors fly with the reorganised Força Aérea Nacional de Angola, which was renamed in 1992 from the Força Aérea Popular de Angola/Defesa Anti-Aérea.

Right: Seen on 11 December 1994, this Mi-24V climbs away over the shattered remains of Groznii-Severnyy airport. The most widely publicised operations involving Russian Army 'Hinds' in Chechnya were the repeated attacks on Bamut village and the deactivated ICBM launch pad nearby, which the Chechens had turned into a fortress, and the (largely unsuccessful) liberation of hostages in Kizlyar.

Above: In the latter stages of the Chechen war, 'Hinds' were mainly used in the COIN, armed reconnaissance and convoy escort roles. FFARs and 9M114 Shturm ATGMs were the Mi-24's main weapons. The rockets were used strictly against area targets only, while the guided missiles were generally used against pre-set targets, such as ammunition dumps and Chechen tanks and IFVs.

Top: This typical scene across a Russian camp outside Groznii comes replete with bad weather and primitive facilities.

Two squadrons of Mi-24s were in action in Chechnya. Current Russian army aviation utilisation norms state that 65 to 70 per cent of the flight time in a combat situation should be allocated to actual combat operations, 15 per cent to transport operations and 5 to 10 per cent to 'special missions'. However, in the opening stage of the war (December 1994/January 1995) actual combat operations – mostly CAS and convoy escort – accounted for just 17 per cent of the flight time; this decreased still further from 6 January due to the seizure of Groznii by the ground forces. While the 'Hinds' were not used for troop support during street fighting in Groznii (presumably to avoid blue-on-blue incidents), they joined other helicopters in carrying troops, ammunition, wounded personnel and refugees. Mi-24s saw much action against the Chechen separatists in the south of the republic, each crew making five or six sorties (averaging 40 to 45 minutes) per day.

Generally, helicopter operations in the Chechen war were rather limited, due partly to the helicopters' inadequate navigation capabilities. Operations resembled World War II

in that CAS sorties were mostly flown in the daytime and in good visibility. The 'Hinds' flew only when visibility exceeded 1.5 km (0.93 miles) and the pilots were able to see the target clearly. Another factor limiting Mi-24 operations was that most 'Hinds' seconded to the federal forces in Chechnya had already served 15 years or more and, unbelievably, were not fitted with IRCM equipment for protection against the rebels' heat-seeking missiles. Finally, ammunition was in short supply and sorties were flown with the rocket pods and gun ammunition boxes half-full at best. Small wonder the pilots called themselves 'kamikazes'!

Planning and execution

Intelligence gathered by spotters on the forward edge of the battle area (FEBA) was processed by a special Russian Army unit at Khankala AB (once held by the rebels). The data were sorted in order of importance and sent to the higher HQ in Mozdok where the ultimate decisions as to the use of army and tactical aviation were made. Some of the spotters admitted that "the war in Chechnya was a rather strange one" and illogical decisions were often made. For example, having received information on concentrations of enemy forces or the whereabouts of Chechen tactical bases which absolutely needed to be taken out with an air strike, the HQ in Mozdok would often cancel sorties. Infuriatingly, the Chechens somehow would learn about it, and in such instances the Russians' forward positions would receive an especially vicious hammering.

The spotters believed that in all 'friendly fire' incidents involving helicopters the pilots were at fault. There are three main reasons for this. Firstly, the pilots had lost the touch of operating in a combat environment and were often not ready psychologically to fly in the forward area. If the pilots were sure that the Chechens had SAMs in the area they were supposed to attack, they would often fire the rockets hastily and exit without determining where the rockets went. Secondly, ordnance was sometimes defective. There were cases of uncommanded FFAR launches, and cases when the rocket motors failed immediately after launch. Finally, the commanders on the ground were reluctant to mark the FEBA, fearing that the Chechens might use the markers for their own purposes. However, the latter fact – and arguably the second one, too – renders the spotters' 'guilty on all counts' statement somewhat tenuous.

By early March 1995, Russian Army Aviation had lost two Mi-24s in the war. On 27 September 1994 an Mi-24 operating from Mozdok was hit by heavy machine-gun fire and made a forced landing, one of the crew being fatally wounded. On 30 April 1995 an Mi-24 was damaged by machine-gun fire near the township of Gilyany but made it back to base. A third 'Hind' was shot down on 24 May over Chechen-Aoul village and the three crewmen were killed. On 4 June another Mi-24 was downed near the township of Nozhay-Yourt 70 km (43 miles) southeast of Groznii and both pilots were killed. Thus, four 'Hinds' were lost in the first six months of the war.

Belarus retained the Mi-24s stationed on its territory after the break-up of the Soviet Union. While not being involved in ethnic conflicts, Belarussian 'Hinds' gained a place in infamy on 12 September 1995 when an Mi-24 crew shot down a wayward hot-air balloon which had been participating in an international air rally, near the town of Byaroza in the Brest region. The two American balloonists were killed. The official story was that the 'Hind' crew misidentified the brightly coloured balloon as an unmanned reconnaissance balloon – but nevertheless fired warning shots at it before shooting it down. To add insult to injury, the crew were later decorated for their 'brave' actions.

Upgraded Mi-24VM/Mi-35M

Various versions of the Mi-24 continue to make up the backbone of Army Aviation of Russia, other CIS states, and many other countries. This has led MVZ, led by Tischchenko's successor, General Director and General Designer Gheorgiy Aleksandrovich Sinelschchikov, to launch an upgrade programme by incorporating weapons and systems of the Mi-28 'Havoc'.

The helicopter which will emerge after Stage 1 of the programme is known as the Mi-35M1 and is basically an upgrade of 'Hind-D/Es' to Mi-24VP standard. Additionally, the TV3-117V engines will be replaced by TV3-117VMAs uprated to 2,500 eshp (1865 kW), and an extra oil cooler for the main gearbox will be installed. The standard KAU-110 control system actuators will be replaced by more powerful KAU-115 units.

The Mi-35M1 will be equipped with APU-8/4U launchers as fitted to the Mi-28 with eight 9M114 missiles apiece (APU, *aviatseeonnaya puskovaya ustanovka* = aircraft-mounted missile launcher). This will allow the outer portions of the wings outboard of the pylons to be lopped off, reducing airframe weight. The wings will incorporate new BD3-UV weapons pylons with built-in hoists.

For night operations the crew will use ONV-2 night vision goggles (*ochkee nochnovo veeden'ya*), and additional navigation equipment, such as GPS, will be available as an option. The S-13 strike camera will be replaced by an improved SSh-45 which registers the target's position in the WSO's or pilot's sight.

'Hinds' have cast their shadows over countless local skirmishes and regional flash points in the former Soviet Union. This Mi-24V is seen over a Russian mortar post on the Tajikistan-Afghanistan border, during December 1996. Islamic insurgents, backed by militants based in Afghanistan, had been waging a guerrilla campaign against the forces of Tajik President Emomali Rakhmonov. After the opposition forces took seven UN observers hostage in late December, peace negotiations were organised between the two sides in Moscow. However, while these talks were ongoing, fighting broke out across the border between Russian and guerrilla forces.

This unmarked and well-worn Mi-24P, armed with two B8V20 FFAR pods and just two 9M114 Shturm-V missiles, was photographed over the Stavropol region en route to Chechnya. The Chechen war saw the most intense Russian Mi-24 operations since Afghanistan, but the 'Hinds' did not perform with the same results.

The Mi-35M will have fibreglass main rotor blades, an improved swashplate and a low-noise 'squashed-X' four-bladed tail rotor borrowed from the Mi-28, all of which will produce a significant weight saving. Deletion of the landing gear retraction mechanisms will save another 85 to 90 kg (187 to 198 lb), although the fixed gear will incur a drag penalty. The Mi-35M1 will have an 8350-kg (18,408-lb) empty weight – 270 kg (595 lb) less than the 'Hind-E' – and an 11100-kg (24,470-lb) MTOW. Top speed will be 300 to 320 km/h (162 to 173 kt), cruising speed 270 to 280 km/h (146 to 151 kt), hovering ceiling (IGE) 2100 m (6,889 ft), service ceiling 4600 m (15,091 ft) and range with 5 per cent fuel reserves 420 km (227 nm).

Stage 2 will result in the Mi-35M2, which was exhibited at Paris and Moscow in 1995. Its weapons range will be complemented by the 9M39 Igla-V AAM. The 9M39 has passive IR homing, a fragmentation warhead and weighs 14 kg (31 lb) together with its tubular launcher. Minimum safe launch range is 800 m (2,624 ft), maximum range is

5200 m (17,060 ft). The missile is effective against targets flying between 20 and 3500 m (65 to 11,483 ft).

The air-cooled GSh-23L cannon will be replaced by the liquid-cooled version, GSh-23V (*vodyanoye okhlazhdeniye* = water cooling), which can fire in longer bursts and at shorter intervals without overheating. New communications equipment and a new ATGM guidance system are also planned. The Mi-35M2 will have a top speed of 312 km/h (168 kt), a climb rate of 12.4 m/sec (2,480 ft/min), a hovering ceiling (IGE) of 2500 m (8,303 ft) and a service ceiling of 5750 m (18,864 ft).

The upgrade programme will culminate in the Mi-35M3 (or Mi-24VM, in Russian Army Aviation service). The helicopter will feature the PNK-24 avionics suite broadly similar to the PrPNK-28 (*preetsel'no-peelotazhno-navigat-seeonnii kompleks* = targeting/flight instrumentation/navigation system) of the 'Havoc'. The Tor-24 (Toroid) weapons control system replacing the Raduga-F is also largely borrowed from the Mi-28.

Changes will be made to the ESM suite. The L-166V-1E active IRCM generator will be deleted, since it is useless against the latest heat-seeking missiles – it actually helps them zero in on the target. Instead, the Mi-35M3 will be fitted with a Mak-UFM (Poppy) IR-band missile warning system tested earlier on the Su-24M 'Fencer-D' tactical bomber and Su-25TK (Su-39) tank-buster version of the 'Frogfoot', as well as the Pastel RHAWS. These will control the UV-26 chaff/flare dispensers (UV, *ustroystvo vybrosa [pomekh]* = literally 'interference ejector') so that IRCM flares are launched only when required to decoy an incoming missile. Empty operating weight will be 8200 kg (18,077 lb), top speed 300 km/h (162 kt), hovering ceiling (IGE) 2400 m (7,874 ft), service ceiling 4800 m (15,748 ft) and range with 5 per cent fuel reserves 420 km (227 nm).

An important new addition is the NOCAS (Night Operation Capability Avionics System), which will allow the

'Hind' to operate around the clock for the first time. This is built around a CHLIO FLIR housed in a compact ball turret on the port side of the nose. The front cockpit is equipped with a TMM-1410 LCD display for FLIR imagery and ONV-2 night vision goggles. The pilot's cockpit has been refitted with SMD 45H and TMM 1410 LCD screens and a VH 100 HUD.

The static park at MAKS-97 (19-24 August 1997) included an Mi-35M in a rather different configuration. This appeared to be a converted Mi-24V retaining the standard main and tail rotors, retractable gear and USPU-24 gun barbette. Like the example demonstrated in 1995, this helicopter had clipped stub wings and a targeting/observation system; this, however, was manufactured by the Ural Opto-mechanical Plant (UOMZ, Urahlskiy optiko-mekhaneech-eskiy zavod) and was housed in a larger ball turret on the starboard side of the nose (placing it on the port side would have complicated entry for the WSO). There was no IRCM generator or chaff/flare dispensers but the prominent 'horns' of the SPO-15 RHAWS were in place.

Little funds, little future?

Currently, the CIS republics (and some other Mi-24 operators) are having great trouble keeping their 'croco-diles' alive – and their experience must be typical of most operators worldwide. In Ukraine, for example, only 25 per cent of the 'Hind' force remained airworthy by 1996 due to funding difficulties and the type is due for final retire-

ment in 2010; a replacement aircraft has not yet been selected. Russia, in theory at least, was in a better position to address the Mi-24's operational problems and the issue of an eventual replacement, but economic decline – coupled with the crash of 1998 – mean that some of these problems will have to wait a little longer still.

Russian Army Aviation Commander Colonel General V. Ye. Pavlov has stated that "nearly 100 per cent of our combat helicopters are obsolete. True, they are good and reliable aircraft that have proved their worth in Afghanistan, but they're outdated. This is especially true for the armament and avionics; we cannot fight in these helicopters at night. Now, it is equally true we have the [Kamov] Ka-50, but only 12 have been delivered so far, which is why there was no point in using them operationally in Chechnya. We need money to buy more, but that's a real problem too."

More to the point, the Mil OKB is up against the Kamov Ka-50/-52, and competition from its own Mi-28A and the night-capable Mi-28N. However, the Mi-28 still has to enter production and its prospects are clouded by a lack of state funding. Until Russia and the other CIS states can afford to radically renew their combat helicopter fleets, the next-best option may be the Mi-24VM/Mi-35M upgrade programme now offered by the Mil OKB and Rostvertol. The first upgraded Mi-24M earmarked for the Russian army flew from Panki on 8 February 1999, but the future beyond this is an unknown.

Yefim Gordon and **Dmitriy Komissarov**

Above: Hostilities in Afghanistan continued after the Soviet withdrawal and Afghan 'Hinds' were used in several major operations against the rebels, including the defence of Khost and Jalalabad. The latter operation marked the first large-scale use of (captured) armoured vehicles by the opposition forces, and the Mi-24 had a chance to prove its worth as a tank-buster. After the opposition seized Kabul in May 1992 the various warlords scrambling for power (Hekmatyar, Rabbani, Ahmad Shah Masoud and General Abdul Rashid Dostum) tore the Afghan AF apart and started using the Mi-24s against each other, but most helicopters were grounded by the lack of spares. In its current phase, the seemingly perpetual war (now led by the Taliban militia against other Afghan groups) is fought in the air with mainly fixed-wing aircraft. These Taliban Mi-24Vs were seen in action during August 1997, fighting opposition forces 25 km north of Kabul.

Above left: The remarkable sight of a UN-painted Mi-24 – this is one of the Ukrainian Mi-24K 'Hind-G2s' deployed to Croatia for peacekeeping duties – illustrates just how much the world has changed since Mikhail Leontyevich Mil drew up his first 'flying IFV' concept in 1966.

Mi-24 'Hind' Operators

Russia

Of all today's CIS republics, Russia has the largest 'Hind' force. Known examples are listed in the table below, and some old aircraft which were no longer flying at the time of the break-up of the Soviet Union are also included for the sake of completeness. Since Russia continues to use the Soviet system of tactical codes, making positive identification impossible, the aircraft are listed in construction number order. The split presentation of late-model Mi-24 c/ns (showing factory/version/quarter of manufacture/year of manufacture/last five) is used for the sake of convenience. The aircraft are sorted by version and listed in production order for the respective version, as each version appears to have its own c/n sequence.

The Russian Army Aviation's 4th Combat and Conversion Training Centre in Torzhok has its own display team, 'Berkooty' (Golden Eagles), flying mainly the Mi-24P and the rare Mi-24VP. Most of the team's 'Hinds' retain the standard two-tone 'green crocodile' camouflage – that is, except for the Russian flag fin flash and the cockpit section which is finished in the Russian flag colours of white, blue and red. So are the intake filters, which makes them look like bloodshot eyes, and, together with the white top of the forward fuselage, this gives the helicopter an eerie 'death's head' appearance in a head-on view.

A single Mi-24V, however, is painted flat black overall with gaudy red, yellow, blue and white trim, 'red eye' intake filters, a TsBP Vertikal-T (Vertical-T Combat Training Centre) titles, the 'T' probably standing for Torzhok. The aircraft is unusual in having the LLLTV/FLIR and ATGM guidance antenna pods removed; it is this aircraft that was referred to as 'Mi-24T' in *Krylya Rodiny*.

The 'Berkooty' helicopters carry B8V-20 FFAR pods converted into smoke generators, and some are equipped with built-in smoke generators to simulate a damaged engine during helicopter/helicopter dogfight demonstrations. The 4th Combat and Conversion Training Centre's regular workhorses included Mi-24D '102 White' and Mi-24DU 'White 101'.

Notes: UIVP = uchebno-ispytahtel'nyy vertolyotnyy polk – training and test helicopter regiment; UVP = uchebnyy vertolyotnyy polk – training helicopter regiment; GvOVP = Gvardeyskiy otdel'nyy vertolyotnyy polk – Guards independent helicopter regiment; OVPBU = otdel'nyy vertolyotnyy polk boyevovo upravleniya – independent combat control helicopter regiment.

This Mi-24R 'Hind-G1' (above), previously based at Sperenburg with the 113th OVE, wears a curiously mottled and worn camouflage, unlike this freshly painted Mi-24P of the 172nd OVP, formerly based at Parchim (right).

C/n	Tactical code	Version	Remarks
0200204	none	Mi-24 'Hind-B'	
			A-10 record aircraft, Mil OKB
2201201	'50 White'	Mi-24A (late)	Ex '90 Yellow'. Preserved Russian Air Force Museum (Monino); development aircraft (converted early A)? Now repainted as '50 Red'
2201407	'20 Red'	Mi-24A (early)	Preserved Riga-Spilve in poor condition
3201707	none	Mi-24A (late)	
3201902	'33 Red'	Mi-24A (late)	Preserved Moscow-Khodynka
3202109	none	Mi-24A (late)	Preserved Armed Forces Museum, Moscow
353.245.1.5.13548		not known Mi-24A (late)	
04274	'115 Yellow'	Mi-24D	Preserved Great Patriotic War Museum (Poklonnaya Gora), Moscow
353.246.2.5.05029	'06 Red'	Mi-24D	
353.246.2.6.09212	'69 Red'	Mi-24D	
353.246.1.7.15324	'02 Red'	Mi-24D	
353.246.1.7.15415	'03 Red'	Mi-24D	
03035	'60 White'	Mi-24V	Preserved Moscow-Khodynka
04102	'39 White'	Mi-24V	Mil OKB test aircraft, WFU Lyubertsy facility
10074?	'73 Red'	Mi-24V	C/n read off poor-quality photograph
353.242.3.7.07135	'16 White'	Mi-24V	55th OVP
353.242.3.7.07152	'32 White'	Mi-24V	55th OVP
353.242.3.7.07254	'22 White'	Mi-24V	55th OVP
353.242.3.7.07260	'09 White'	Mi-24V	55th OVP
353.242.3.7.07278	'36 White'	Mi-24V	55th OVP
353.242.3.7.07279	'06 White'	Mi-24V	55th OVP
353.242.3.7.07297	'15 White'	Mi-24V	55th OVP
353.242.3.7.07330	'05 White'	Mi-24V	55th OVP
353.242.3.7.07353	'40 White'	Mi-24V	55th OVP
353.242.3.7.07425	'02 Red'	Mi-24V	*Eight kill markings on nose*
353.242.3.7.07481	'48 White'	Mi-24V	55th OVP
353.242.3.7.07522	'35 White'	Mi-24V	55th OVP
353.242.3.7.07589	'38 White	Mi-24V	55th OVP
353.242.3.7.07610	'10 White'	Mi-24V	55th OVP
353.242.3.7.07700	'04 White'	Mi-24V	55th OVP
353.242.3.7.07707	'14 White'	Mi-24V	55th OVP
353.242.3.7.07733	'33 White'	Mi-24V	55th OVP
353.242.3.7.07750	'12 White'	Mi-24V	55th OVP
353.242.4.7.07757	'11 White'	Mi-24V	55th OVP
353.242.4.7.07804	'07 White'	Mi-24V	55th OVP
353.242.4.7.07810	'50 White'	Mi-24V	55th OVP
353.242.4.7.07821	'46 White'	Mi-24V	55th OVP
353.242.4.7.08013	'41 White'	Mi-24V	55th OVP
353.242.4.7.08088	'49 White'	Mi-24V	55th OVP
353.242.4.7.08149	'47 White'	Mi-24V	55th OVP
353.242.4.7.08174	'08 White'	Mi-24V	55th OVP
353.242.4.7.08201	'31 White'	Mi-24V	55th OVP
353.242.4.7.08257	'34 White'	Mi-24V	55th OVP
353.242.4.7.08411	'21 White'	Mi-24V	55th OVP
353.242.4.7.08499?	'19 White'	Mi-24V	55th OVP
	Misquote or mispaint (c/n should read 353.242.4.7.08499!)		
353.242.4.7.08511	'02 White'	Mi-24V	55th OVP
353.242.4.7.08533	'17 White'	Mi-24V	55th OVP
353.242.1.8.09288	'08 Red'	Mi-24V	
353.242.1.8.09296	'19 Red'	Mi-24V	
353.242.1.8.09298	'03 Yellow'	Mi-24V	
353.242.2.8.09299	'53 Yellow'	Mi-24V	
353.242.2.8.09315	'15 Red'	Mi-24V	
353.242.2.8.09333	'23 Yellow'	Mi-24V	
353.242.2.8.10009	'16 Red'	Mi-24V	
353.242.2.1.10028?	'54 Yellow'	Mi-24V	
	C/n doubtful (year out of sequence)		
353.242.2.8.10030	'41 Red'	Mi-24V	
353.242.2.8.10040	'14 Red'	Mi-24V	
353.242.2.8.10053	'16 Yellow'	Mi-24V	
353.242.2.8.10081	'21 Red'	Mi-24V	
353.242.2.8.10083	'28 Red'	Mi-24V	
353.242.2.8.10088	'57 Yellow'	Mi-24V	
353.242.2.8.10099	not known	Mi-24V	*written-off May 1994, no details known*
353.242.3.8.10137	'18 Red'	Mi-24V	
353.242.3.8.10141	'31 Red'	Mi-24V	
353.242.3.8.10142	'07 Red'	Mi-24V	
353.242.3.8.10148	'20 Red'	Mi-24V	
353.242.3.8.10168	'42 Red'	Mi-24V	
	Possible misquote for 353.242.3.8.10188 (same code)		
353.242.3.8.10181	'05 Yellow'	Mi-24V	
353.242.3.8.10188	'42 Red'	Mi-24V	
	Possible misquote for 353.242.3.8.10168 (same code)		
353.242.3.8.10218	'24 Red'	Mi-24V	
353.242.3.8.10271	'14 Yellow'	Mi-24V	
353.242.3.8.10301	'25 Blue'	Mi-24V	
353.242.3.8.10329	'27 Blue'	Mi-24V	
353.242.3.8.10415	'07 Red'	Mi-24V	
353.242.4.8.10450	'31 White'	Mi-24V	
353.242.4.8.10555	'29 Blue'	Mi-24V	
353.242.4.8.10853	none	Mi-24V	*Probably Mil OKB, development aircraft*
353.242.3.9.12808	'09 Yellow'	Mi-24V	
353.242.3.9.12851	'34 Yellow'	Mi-24V	
353.242.3.9.12961	'17 Yellow'	Mi-24V	
353.242.3.9.13077	'26 Red'	Mi-24V	
353.242.3.9.13113	'31 White'	Mi-24V	

344th TsBPiPLS, Totskoye
361st UIVP — Totskoye
696th UIVP — Totskoye
2881st RVB — Totskoye
113th OSAP — Kalouga

11th OA, HQ Kaliningrad
288th OVP — Neevenskoye

Operations Group Transdniestria, HQ Tiraspol
36th OVP — Tiraspol

Operations Group Transcaucasia, HQ Tbilisi
311th OVP — Vaziani

■ **Northern Defence District**
26th Army Corps, HQ Petrozavodsk
485th OVP — Alakurtti
Two more units may exist

30th Army Corps, HQ Vyborg
172nd OVP — Kaseemovo
332nd OVP — Preebylovo
One more unit may exist

■ **Moscow Defence District**
239th GvOVP — Yefremov

1st Army, HQ Smolensk
6th OVP
336th OBVP — Kalouga
440th OBVP — Vyazima

20th Army Corps, HQ Voronezh
41st OVP — Klakovo
178th OBVP — Kursk
440th OVPBU — Klakovo

22nd Army, HQ Nizhny Novgorod
225th OBVP — Protasovo

439th OVPBU — Kostroma
One more unit may exist

■ **Volga Defence District**
2nd Army, HQ Chernorechíye
36th OVP — Serdobsk
437th OBVP — Ozinki
+ one more unit

Syzraní Higher Military Flying School
131st UVP — Sokol
484th UVP — Syzraní
626th UVP — Pougachov

Ufa Higher Military Flying School
330th UVP — Ufa
851st UVP — Bezeníchouk

■ **North Caucasus Defence District**
58th Army, HQ Vladikavkaz
487th OBVP — Boudyonnovsk
+ one more unit
+ another unit may exist

67th Army Corps, HQ Krasnodar
55th OBVP — Korenyovsk
325th OBVP — Yegorlykskaya
326th OVP — Bataysk

Transbaikalian Defence District
55th Army, HQ Borzya:
Three units (bases unknown)

57th Army Corps, HQ Ulan-Ude
Three units (bases unknown)

■ **Far Eastern Defence District**
5th Army, HQ Ussuriysk
Three units (bases unknown)

25th Army Corps, HQ Petropavlovsk-Kamchatskiy:
Three units (bases unknown)

35th Army, HQ Belogorsk
Three units (bases unknown)

68th Army Corps, HQ Youzhno-Sakhalinsk
Three units (bases unknown)

■ **Siberian Defence District**
28th Army Corps, HQ Kemerovo
???th OVP — Omsk
Two units (bases unknown)

This table reflects known Mi-24 units, and their locations, as of late 1998.

Russia's 'Berkooty' Mi-24 display team has operated a curious mix of aircraft including this radically decorated and modified Mi-24V (above). The team's current colours are seen on this standard Mi-24V (right).

C/n	Code	Type	Unit
353.242.3.9.13230	'73 Red'	Mi-24V	
353.242.2.1.13881?	'05 Yellow'	Mi-24V	
C/n doubtful (quarter and year out of sequence)			
353.242.1.0.14635	'07 Yellow'	Mi-24V	
353.242.2.0.15011	'44 White'	Mi-24V	55th OVP
353.242.2.0.15017	'43 White'	Mi-24V	55th OVP
353.242.2.0.15056	'20 White'	Mi-24V	55th OVP
353.242.2.0.15070	'42 White'	Mi-24V	55th OVP
353.242.2.0.15074	'45 White'	Mi-24V	55th OVP
353.242.3.0.15397	'03 Red'	Mi-24V	55th OVP
353.242.3.0.15411	'39 White'	Mi-24V	55th OVP
353.242.4.0.15897	'44 Yellow'	Mi-24V	
Ex-'54 Blue'. Preserved Russian Air Force Museum (Monino); now repainted as '44 White'			
353.242.2.1.16789	'27 Yellow'	Mi-24V	
353.242.1.1.16859	'30 Yellow'	Mi-24V	
353.242.2.1.16874	'16 Yellow'	Mi-24V	
353.242.2.1.16882	'30 Red'	Mi-24V	
353.242.2.1.16931	'26 Yellow'	Mi-24V	
353.242.2.1.16967	'34 Yellow'	Mi-24V	
353.242.3.1.16981	'02 Yellow'	Mi-24V	
353.242.3.1.17112	'10 Yellow'	Mi-24V	
353.242.3.1.17155	'02 Blue'	Mi-24V	
353.242.3.1.17194	'04 Yellow'	Mi-24V	
353.242.3.1.17242	'08 Yellow'	Mi-24V	
353.242.3.1.17251	'06 Yellow'	Mi-24V	
353.242.3.1.17288	'06 Blue'	Mi-24V	
353.242.3.1.17293	'12 Yellow'	Mi-24V	
353.242.2.1.18608	'02 Yellow'	Mi-24V	
Possible misquote (quarter doubtful)			
353.242.3.2.18694	'01 Yellow'	Mi-24V	
353.242.3.2.18711	'09 Yellow'	Mi-24V	
353.242.3.2.18755	'17 Yellow'	Mi-24V	
353.242.3.2.18777	'19 Yellow'	Mi-24V	
353.242.3.2.18883	'21 Yellow'	Mi-24V	
353.242.1.3.19017	'40 Red'	Mi-24V	
353.242.1.3.19021	'06 Red'	Mi-24V	
353.242.1.3.19025	'39 Red'	Mi-24V	
353.242.1.3.19037	'25 Red'	Mi-24V	
353.242.1.3.19055	'11 Yellow'	Mi-24V	
353.242.1.3.19101	'65 Yellow'	Mi-24V	
353.242.1.3.19109	'40 Yellow (?)'	Mi-24V	
353.242.1.3.19304	'28 Red'	Mi-24V	
353.242.2.3.19393	'05 Red'	Mi-24V	
353.242.2.3.19408	'39 Yellow'	Mi-24V	
353.242.2.3.19427	'30 Red'	Mi-24V	
353.242.2.3.19437	'27 Red'	Mi-24V	
353.242.2.3.19548	'15 Yellow'	Mi-24V	
353.243.1.1.16157	'18 Red'	Mi-24P	
Displayed at Kubinka AB 29 May 1993			
353.243.4.2.16402	'33 Red (?)'	Mi-24P	
353.243.3.2.16851	'29 Yellow'	Mi-24P	
Quoted as Mi-24V c/n 353.242.3.2.16851 but quarter and year do not fit Mi-24V sequence			
353.243.3.3.17115	'01 Red'	Mi-24P	
353.243.3.3.17120	'34 Red'	Mi-24P	
353.243.4.3.18468	'02 Red'	Mi-24P	
Quoted as Mi-24V c/n 353.242.4.3.18468 but quarter and year do not fit Mi-24V sequence			
353.243.4.3.18475	'03 Red'	Mi-24P	
Quoted as Mi-24V c/n 353.242.4.3.18475 (error, as above)			
353.243.4.3.18482	'33 Red'	Mi-24P	
353.243.4.3.19511	'35 Red'	Mi-24P	
353.243.4.3.19542	'10 Red'	Mi-24P	
353.243.4.3.19546	'32 Red'	Mi-24P	
353.243.4.3.19564	'12 Red'	Mi-24P	
353.243.3.4.20469	'31 Red'	Mi-24P	
353.243.3.4.20487	'38 Red'	Mi-24P	
353.243.4.4.20874	'29 Yellow'	Mi-24P	
353.243.2.5.21472	'01 White'	Mi-24P	
353.243.2.5.21487	'51 White'	Mi-24P	
353.243.1.6.22374	'37 White'	Mi-24P	
Preserved Russian Air Force Museum (Monino), damaged			
353.243.1.7.23028	not known	Mi-24P	
353.243.1.7.23858	none	Mi-24P/Mi-35	
Mil OKB, Mi-35 prototype			
353.243.1.8.25138	'11 Red'	Mi-24P	
Displayed at Kubinka AB 11-4-92			
353.243.2.8.25894	'100 Red'	Mi-24P	
Displayed at Moscow-Khodynka 24-8-89			
353.243.1.9.26642	'08 Red'	Mi-24P	
Displayed at Kubinka AB 14-5-94			
353.258.4.9.10329	none	Mi-35M	
Mil OKB, prototype (converted Mi-24VM)			
353.242.4.7.08820	none	Mi-24R	
Mil OKB, prototype (converted early Mi-24V)			
353.462.4.5.11288	'41 Red'	Mi-24R	
353.462.4.6.11648	'21 Yellow'	Mi-24R	
353.462.4.6.11671	'19 Yellow'	Mi-24R	
353.462.4.6.11686	'58 Yellow'	Mi-24R	
353.462.4.6.11703	'18 Yellow'	Mi-24R	
353.462.4.6.11737	'41 Red'	Mi-24R	
353.462.4.6.11746	'20 Yellow'	Mi-24R	
353.462.4.6.11809	'45 Yellow'	Mi-24R	
353.462.2.7.12063	'10 Red'	Mi-24R	
353.462.2.7.12078	'11 Red'	Mi-24R	
353.462.4.8.12854	'41 Blue'	Mi-24R	
353.462.4.8.12875	'40 Blue'	Mi-24R	
353.462.4.9.13296	not known	Mi-24R	
353.462.4.9.13327	'44 Yellow'	Mi-24R	
353.201.4.5.11049	'43 Red'	Mi-24K	
353.201.4.6.11286	'24 Yellow'	Mi-24K	
353.201.4.6.11301	'22 Yellow'	Mi-24K	
353.201.4.6.11318	'23 Yellow'	Mi-24K	
353.201.3.7.11503	'47 Yellow'	Mi-24K	
353.201.3.7.11549	'19 Red'	Mi-24K	
353.201.4.7.11804	'63 Red'	Mi-24K	
353.201.4.7.11842	'12 Red'	Mi-24K	
353.201.4.7.11869	'19 Red' (?)	Mi-24K	
353.201.4.7.11906	'14 Red'	Mi-24K	
353.201.3.8.12696	'72 Yellow'	Mi-24K	
353.201.3.8.12719	'43 Red'	Mi-24K	
353.201.3.8.12743	'25 Yellow'	Mi-24K	

CIS States

Armenia

According to one acknowledged reference source, Armenia retained 100 Mi-24Ds and Mi-24Vs (the exact number of each model is unknown). However, this figure seems exorbitant, considering that (as noted in the main text) Armenia was reported to have had just 11 'Hinds' on strength in early 1993, plus two lost in the Karabakh war. The helicopters were based near Yerevan.

Azerbaijan

The same source quoted the 'Hind' population in Azerbaijan as 40 Mi-24Ds, which sounds more or less credible.

However, since only eight were reported to be in service in early 1993, plus four lost in Nagornyy Karabakh, the disposition of the remainder is uncertain. Azeri 'Hinds' were based at Sangachaly AB.

Belarus

As of October 1995 the Army Aviation of the Republic of Belarus had 76 assorted 'Hinds' on strength. Unlike the military aircraft of most CIS republics, they retained the Soviet-style red stars (also used by the Russian Air Force, Army Aviation and Naval Aviation) and tactical codes. The 50th OSAP/248th OVE at Minsk-Stepyanka (Lipki) AB operated six Mi-24Ps, including '07 Red'. The 276th OVP at Polotsk/North-West AB included 38 Mi-24Vs and Ps (the ratio is unknown) and two Mi-24Rs. Finally, the 181st OVP at Prouzhany AB operated a mix of 30 Mi-24Vs and Ps.

Georgia

It is believed that Georgia once operated approximately 40 Mi-24Ds and Mi-24Vs, inherited from the former Russian Army unit based in Tskhinvali. Two Georgian 'Hinds' were lost during the civil war in Abkhazia.

Kirghizia

The Kyrgyz Air Force (Kyrgyzstan) almost certainly has a complement of Mi-24s, since the unit at Lougovaya AB near Bishkek (formerly Frunze) undertook training for foreign operators of the type. Unfortunately, no details of current operations are available.

Moldova

The Air Force of the Republic of Moldova (FARM – Fortele Aeriene de Republica Moldova) retained 30 Mi-24s of an unspecified model, most probably 'Hind-Ds' and/or 'Hind-Es'. Unfortunately, no further information is available.

Tajikistan

Tajikistan is known to be an operator of the Mi-24. Unfortunately, no details of Tajik 'Hinds' are available.

Uzbekistan

Like Tajikistan, this Central Asian republic is understood to operate the 'Hind' but no firm details are known.

Ukraine

Ukraine inherited a large fleet of Mi-24s. Some sources claim that 360-plus assorted 'Hinds' were on strength in 1995; the Ukrainian Ministry of Defence stated that 297 were in service in May 1996. Only 26 were operated by the Ukrainian Air Force (UAF), the Air Defence Force and the National Guard, and of these, the helicopters operated by the Independent National Guard Squadron at Belaya Tserkov near Kiev were by far the most active.

The remaining 'Hinds', including 217 Mi-24Vs, Ps and VPs plus some 30 Mi-24Ks and a similar number of Mi-24Rs, belonged to Ukrainian Army Aviation. The Odessa Defence District boasted 42 Mi-24s at Raukhovka AB (287th OVP) and two Mi-24Rs at Odessa-Central AB with the 217th OSAE (otdel'naya smeshannaya aviaeskadril'ya – independent mixed air squadron). The 8th Tank Army's 441st OVP at Korosten operated 10 'regular' 'Hinds', six Mi-24Ks and four Mi-24Rs. The 111th OBVE (otdel'naya boyevaya vertolyotnaya eskadril'ya – independent combat helicopter squadron) at Brody-North AB (Carpathian Defence District) operated two Mi-24Rs. The 13th Combined Army included 48 'Hinds' with the 119th OVP at Brody, six Mi-24Ks and four Mi-24Rs with the 442nd OVP at Zhovtnevoye, plus three more Ks and two more Rs with the 119th OVP at Doubno. The 38th Combined Army had 44 'regular' 'Hinds', six Mi-24Ks and six Mi-24Rs with the 335th OVP at Kalinov, plus 35 'Hinds', six Mi-24Ks and six Mi-24Rs with the 488th OVP at Vapnyarka.

Government financing for the Ukrainian Armed Forces has all but disappeared. While the UAF's transport units can earn cash by transporting commercial cargo, Army Aviation has no such recourse. The situation improved somewhat in 1996-1997 when Ukraine was contracted by the UN to fly peacekeeping missions in Eastern Slavonia. In addition to generating cash, this contract allowed some much-needed pilot proficiency training.

"If it were up to me I'd use all that money to keep up the aircraft," Ukrainian Army Aviation Commander Colonel A. D. Korniyets said in an interview to the Ukrainian magazine *Aviatsiya i Vremya* (Aviation and Time). "Now only 25 per cent of our Mi-24s are airworthy because of the spending cuts. The helicopters' main rotor blades, tail rotors and VR-24 main gearboxes are due for replacement or overhaul, and there's no money for that. We're trying to find a way out together with the Mil company, which is considering extending the components' service life, given the low intensity of operations."

The Mi-24's planned service life will enable Ukraine to keep the greater part of its fleet flying until 2006, but the type is due for retirement no later than 2010.

Export 'Hinds'

According to official sources, the Soviet Union exported the Mi-24 to 21 nations (though this figure does appear to be understated). The number of foreign operators has now increased to nearly 30 as some aircraft have been sold on to other nations and some surplus 'Hinds' have been exported after the demise of the Soviet Union.

The remains of this one-time Afghan air force 'Hind-A' can be found in Taliban-held Kabul, alongside an equally unserviceable Il-28 and an Il-14T.

Afghanistan

Starting in April 1979, the Afghan Republican Air Force (Afghan Hanai Qurah) received 36 'Hinds'. Nineteen aircraft have been identified to date, including a late Mi-24A serialled 333, a late Mi-24U with intake filters serialled 344 (preserved at the Afghan AF Museum in Kabul), 15 Mi-24Ds or Mi-25s (315 through 319, 325, 330 through 332, 334 through 340) and a single Mi-24V or Mi-35 serialled 67. The latter aircraft was surrendered to the Mujahideen by a defector in 1988.

While Afghan Air Force Mi-24As retained the standard Soviet camouflage, the Mi-25s

had a 'Middle East' colour scheme patterned on that of Soviet 'Hinds' with large areas of yellow and olive drab, though Mi-24U '344' had small closely-spaced blotches of green on yellow which gave the aircraft a mottled appearance. Over the years the aircraft wore a variety of changing markings, including a red disc with yellow ornament and, in the latter stages of the Afghan war, a red star on a white roundel with green/red/black surround. As of mid-1993 the surviving Mi-24s, Mi-25s and Mi-35s were operated by the 332nd Combat Helicopter Regiment in Jurm, the

375th Combat Helicopter Regiment in Mazar-i-Sharif and the 377th Combat Helicopter Regiment at Kabul International airport. Some 'Hinds' have also fallen into the hands of the factions involved in Afghanistan's ongoing civil war between Taliban and rival northern opposition forces.

Taliban assets include all fixed-wing combat aircraft remaining in Afghanistan, though their Mi-24/Mi-35 disposition is unknown. A small number of Mi-35s (and Mi-8/Mi-17s) are still in service with the forces of Ahmadshah Massoud, the former defence minister, and chief opponent of the Taliban.

Algeria

The Algerian Air Force (FAA – Force Aérienne Algérienne) operated 38 Mi-24As and Ds. Unfortunately, no details of the fleet or 'Hind' operations in Algeria are known.

Angola

The Angolan air force (FANA – Força Aérea Nacional de Angola) took delivery of more than 30 Mi-25s and Mi-35s. Several aircraft were shot down by the South African Air Force during the 'bush wars' of the 1980s. Some 28 were reported to be on strength in early 1995.

Most of Angola's helicopters, including these Mi-24Vs (and Mi-8s), are now believed to be unserviceable, following the withdrawal of the Russian and Cuban advisors who used to fly and maintain them.

FAA 'Hinds'

Serial	Version	Remarks
H302	Mi-24D	Shot down in 1985
H314	Mi-24D	Shot down 7/85
H318	Mi-24D	
H320	Mi-24D	
H323	Mi-24D	Shot down 9/85
H365	Mi-24V	WFU, cannibalised
H367	Mi-24V	
H370	Mi-24V	
H373	Mi-24V	
H401	Mi-24V	Existence unconfirmed

Angolan 'Hinds' wore a tan and chocolate brown camouflage with pale grey undersurfaces and warning inscriptions in Portuguese. The H serial prefix stands for helicopter. The Mi-24Vs delivered in 1986 had a late-model ESM suite featuring RHAWS 'horns' aft of the rear cockpit, an L-166V-11E IRCM jammer and faired triple ASO-2V chaff/flare dispensers on the rear fuselage sides but, interestingly, were not equipped with air/exhaust mixers.

Bulgaria

The Mi-24s entered service with the BVVS (Bulgarski Voennovazdushni Sili, the Bulgarian Air Force) in June 1979. The first four Mi-24Ds arrived at the Plovdiv airfield piloted by Russian crews. The airfield was the home of the 44 VAP (Vertoleten Aviopolk – Helicopter Regiment). The 'Hinds' initially formed a new EOP (Eskadrila za Ogneva Podrajka – Fire Support Squadron) with the 44th VAP moving to Krumovo, a former reserve airfield, by the end of 1980. However, the 'Hinds', which were steadily increasing in number, went to Stara Zagora, another reserve airfield where the relevant ground infrastructure was rapidly built. On 13 August 1982 the youngest combat regiment of the VVS was formed – the 13th VPBV (Vertoleten Polk Boini Vertoleti – Helicopter Regiment of Combat Helicopters), a fully dedicated combat unit. The 13th VPBV consisted of two squadrons, the 1/13th and 2/13th EOPs. Each of the EOPs has five four-aircraft zvena (flights), for a total of 20 aircraft plus two more attached to the EOP's Comandvane (command flight), consisting of the EOP's

Commander, his Deputy, the Chief of Staff, the Navigator and the Weapons Training & Tactics Officer, all of whom are pilots. The 13th VPBV itself consisted of Headquarters, two full-strength EOPs and Maintenance Section.

In September 1994, the 13th VPBV, which was considered to be one of the best BVVS combat units, was renamed as the 23rd VABV (Vertoletna Aviobasa Boini Vertoleti – Helicopter Base of Combat Helicopters). This came as part of the post-Cold War reorganisation within the Bulgarian air arm. The 23rd VABV is controlled by the Plovdiv-based 10th CTA (Corpus Takticheska Aviatzia – Tactical Aviation Corps), which incorporates all the BVVS's strike, recce and helicopter assets. The newly created 23rd VBBV incorporates the existing helicopter regiment plus the logistics and the communication battalions based at Stara Zagora, which is forming the system and providing the flying and combat training activity of the two EOPs.

The main role of the Bulgarian 'Hinds' is to provide close air support (CAS) to the ground forces as well carry out anti-tank operations and air defence over the battlefield against a broad range of slow-speed/low-flying aircraft. In peacetime two 'Hinds' are kept on constant quick reaction alert (QRA).

The QRA-pair is tasked with intercept and identification of low-flying, low-speed aircraft should they cross the Bulgarian borders without the permission of the country's air traffic control authority.

Delivery of new 'Hinds' to the two EOPs of the 12th VPBV continued until 1986, comprising 38 Mi-24D 'Hind-Ds' plus six Mi-24V 'Hind-Es'.

When the 'Hinds' entered service in Bulgaria, Soviet instructors came with them to train the Bulgarian crews. Local instructors came later. Initially, a number of young fighter and fighter-bomber pilots converted to form the nucleus of the 'Hind' crews. Since 1986 special helicopter groups have been established at the Higher Air Force School in Dolna Metropolya. After completing this training, the young pilots fly four to five years as weapons operators in the front cockpit before they are promoted to full pilots, able to fly from the rear (the pilot's, or so-called commander's) cockpit.

The current strength of 44 'Hinds' was to be supplemented with 12 more second-hand ex-Russian ones promised as part of a

The numbering system of the BVVS 'Hinds' is simple and is based on the date of the helicopter's arrival. The first four Mi-24Ds, entering service in June 1979, were numbered 101, 102, 103 and 104. The last Mi-24D is 138. The first of the six Mi-24Vs is numbered 139; the last is 144. This style of numbering is a common feature across the BVVS helicopter fleet.

military aid package that included 100 T-72 MBTs and 100 BMP-1 IFVs. The transfer was to comply with the Conventional Forces in Europe (CFE) Treaty, which limits the number of BVVS combat helicopters to 67. However, the 'new' 'Hinds' were rejected following a close inspection by a Bulgarian technical team which revealed their extremely poor technical condition and low remaining service life.

To the end of December 1998, only one Mi-24D has been lost ('130'). The helicopter hit the ground while practising landing at the Bodrovo range in central Bulgaria on 30 January 1996, due to high winds. The three crew members managed to escape uninjured before the helicopter exploded.

This Bulgarian Mi-24D wears the dark green scheme, with blue undersides, applied to some helicopters overhauled at the Hungarian Mi-24 facility.

Cambodia

Several Mi-24s of an unknown version were transferred to the Kampuchean Air Force from Vietnam in the mid-1980s at the height of the civil war in Kampuchea. Only three remained in service with the Royal Cambodian Air Force in early 1995 (Kampuchea was again renamed Cambodia in late 1988).

Congo

There were reports of Force Aérienne Congolaise Mi-24s being engaged in combat in this Central African country in 1997. The Russian Foreign Ministry discounted them, stating that "no Mi-8s or Mi-24s have been delivered to the Republic of Congo lately." If these aircraft exist, it is equally possible that they are being flown by a mercenary operation, perhaps with Mi-24s acquired from a CIS nation.

Croatia

Starting in 1993, the Croatian Air Force (HZS – Hrvatske Zracne Snage, formerly HRZ i PZO – Hrvatsko Ratno Zrakoplovstvo i Protizracna Obrana) acquired 15 second-hand Mi-24Vs operated by the 29 Eskadrila Borbenih Helikoptera (combat helicopter squadron). Though nominally based at Pleso AB near Zagreb, they were often seen operating from Velica Gorica. The thoroughly battered 'Hinds' came from Russian or Ukrainian surplus stocks (photos of some Croatian Mi-24s plainly show crudely overpainted Russian star insignia and c/ns on the wing endplates). Unfortunately, only one aircraft (H-305) has been positively identified to date, since most Croatian 'Hinds' had no serials.

Initially, the helicopters wore spurious air ambulance markings to get around the trade embargo imposed on the ex-Yugoslavian states, and flew unarmed, but Western observers speculated they could be armed within hours. As HZS Commander General Imra Agotic stated, the armed aircraft "were purchased only to evacuate wounded soldiers and civilians out of so-called 'hot spots'. Several Mil-8s have been destroyed on such occasions. Their [the 'Hinds'] armament will only be used to defend themselves and the victims on the ground before going in." Two of the armed examples had RHAWS 'horns' in the forward position, while one of the (initially) unarmed aircraft was retrofitted with Garmin GPS and associated blade aerial atop the WSO's cockpit.

Croatian 'Hinds' are possibly unique in having a maritime attack role as well. Two HZS Mi-24Vs participated in an air show at Zemunik AB near Zadar in 1994; the one in

Croatia's Mi-24Vs are based at 91 Zrakoplovna Baza Pleso (air base 91, Pleso). They were initially attached to 1 EBH (battle helicopter squadron) and saw much combat in the recapture of Western Slavonia and Krajina, during 1995.

the static park was surrounded by an impressive array of ordnance, including two Mk 44 torpedoes. Five more Mi-24s may have been acquired later (some sources reported that Croatia had 20 by early 1995).

Czech Republic (Czechoslovakia)

As part of the modernisation of the Ceskoslovenske Vojenske Létectvo, or VL (Czech air force) at the end of the 1970s, Czechoslovakia ordered 'Hinds' in 1978. The pilots chosen to fly the new helicopters were retrained on Mi-8s, at Prostejov. Ten pilots and five flying engineers were then sent on a type conversion course at Lugovaya, near Frunze, in the former USSR. There they spent three months, from May to August, in 1978.

The first four Mi-24Ds for Czechoslovakia (4009 through 4012) landed at Prostejov's 51.vrtulnikovy pluk (51.vrp) airfield on 24 August 1978. The first flight by VL pilots took place, with Soviet instructors, on 22 November 1978. The next 'Hinds' arrived on 14 July 1980, serialled 0100 through 0103.

The first live firings of the 9M17P Falanga (AT-2 'Swatter') took place between 2 and 4 October 1979, on the range near Malacky in Slovakia. On 9 May 1980 the Mi-24D made its public debut when a flight led by Major Zdenek Dvornik participated in the VE-Day parade in Prague.

As the doctrine of attack helicopter operations was developed by the Warsaw Pact in the mid-1980s, Plzen-Bory airfield was developed as an Mi-24 base, due to its position close to the NATO border.

A new squadron, 4.letka, was established in Prostejov. This unit was allocated some of the existing Mi-24Ds and moved to Plzen in September 1982 with 12 helicopters.

An additional four Mi-24Ds were transferred to Plzen in August 1983 when 4.letka was reorganised into 11.vrtulnikova letka (11th helicopter sqn). Following this, the 11.vrtulnikovy pluk (11th Helicopter Regiment) stood up at Plzen on 15 April 1985. At the same time, Czechoslovakia ordered more 'Hinds' in the shape of the advanced Mi-24V, to equip the new regiment, allowing all Mi-24Ds to return to Prostejov.

To ease training of new pilots the Plzen regiment took on two new Mi-24DU trainers (6040 and 6050), on 8 October 1985. Ten brand-new Mi-24V 'Hind Es' arrived at Plzen on 21 December 1985 (serialled 0701

Mi-24D		0148	M340148	Mi-24V		0834	730834
4010	M34010		(Destroyed on crash 17.5.83)	0701	730701	0835	730835
4011	M34011	0151	150151	0702	730702	0836	730836
4012	M34012	0214	340214	0703	730703	0837	730837
	(Written-off after crash 12.9.85)	0216	340216	0705	730705	0838	730838
0102	M340102	0217	340217	0706	730706	0839	730839
0103	M340103	0218	340218		(Written-off after crash 31.8.88)	0928	730928
0140	M340140	0219	340219	0709	730709		(Destroyed on crash 17.11.98)
0141	M340141	0220	340220	0710	730710	0929	730929
	(Written-off after crash 11.11.87)	0221	340221	0788	730788		(Destroyed on crash 18.11.92)
0142	M340142			0789	730789		
0143	M340143	Mi-24DU		0790	730790	*This table includes aircraft in*	
	(Written-off after crash 25.10.85)	6050	7306050	0812	730812	*current Czech air force service,*	
0146	M340146			0815	730815	*and those written off earlier in*	
0147	M340147			0816	730816	*Czechoslovakian service.*	

through 0710). One Mi-24DU (6050) was transferred to Prostejov in mid-1986. More Mi-24Vs (0786 through 0790) arrived in June 1987, after which five Mi-24Ds were returned to Prostejov (4009, 4010, 0100, 0101 and 0102). Five Mi-24Vs (0812 to 0816) arrived at Plzen in December 1987, followed by another eight in 1988.

By the end of 1988, all the Mi-24Ds (except 4011 which was on overhaul) had returned to Prostejov. The last three Mi-24Vs arrived at Plzen in March 1989 (0927 through 0929). In all, Czechoslovakia bought 31 Mi-24s. Some of the Mi-24Vs (e.g. 0812) had strap-on chaff/flare dispensers under the tailboom and forward-mounted RHAWS 'horns', while later ones

(e.g., 0833, 0836 and 0927) had triple chaff/flare dispensers on the aft fuselage sides and the RHAWS 'horns' in the aft position.

By March 1989 (allowing for losses) the Czech air force had 24 Mi-24Ds and one Mi-24DU serving with two squadrons of 51.vrp, at Prostejov and 30 Mi-24Vs plus one Mi-24DU serving with two squadrons of 11.vrp, in Plzen-Bory. The 11.vrp was relocated in August/September 1991 from Plzen-Bory airfield to Plzen-Line Air Base.

On 1 January 1993 Czechoslovakia made the peaceful transition into two independent Czech and Slovak Republics. As with all of the aircraft in the Czechoslovakian Air Force inventory (except the MiG-29 force), the fleet of Mi-24s was divided between the Czech and Slovak AFs on a two-to-one basis. As a result, eight Mi-24Ds from Prostejov and 10 Mi-24Vs (plus one Mi-24DU) from Plzen-Line were sent to their new home of Presov in East Slovakia, where 4.vrtulnikovy pluk was established.

As originally delivered, the aircraft sported standard Soviet-style two-tone green/grey camouflage (not tan/stone) with pale blue/grey undersides and high-visibility

This Mi-24V of 331 Squadron was one of the first Czech 'Hinds' to appear in the new three-tone grey/green scheme adopted in late 1998.

black serials, outlined in white. Between December 1981 and January 1987, aircraft 4009, 4010, 4011, 4012, 0100, 0101, 0140 and 0141 were sent to the USSR for maintenance. They were repainted in a similar camouflage but with 'deeper' colours. From 1986 onwards all Mi-24Ds (except the crashed 0100, 0101 and 0140) were overhauled at Tokol, near Budapest in Hungary. The first overhaul was finished in September 1986 (0102), with the last in February 1991 (0221). Helicopters overhauled at Tokol were repainted in a dark green/dark earth camouflage, with blue undersides. The Mi-24Ds of 1.letka, 51.vrp all wore sharkmouths with a squadron badge (a tiger) on the starboard front fuselage and a regimental badge on the port side. One Mi-24D (4011) was decorated at Prostejov for the 20th anniversary of the regiment in mid-April 1994.

The end of 1994 saw a major reorganisation of the Czech Mi-24 units. Both regiments were disbanded and all 'Hinds' moved to the newly-established 33.Helicopter base at Prerov, which became operational on 1 January 1995.

All of the 36 Mi-24D, V and DUs (of which only 25 are in use – 12 Ds, 12Vs and one DU) are operated by 1.technicka letka (1st maintenance sqn) and were initially flown by pilots from 331.letka bitevnich vrtulniku (attack helicopter sqn). The pilots are now divided into two (331 and 332) squadrons.

Cuba

The Cuban Air Force (FAR – Fuerza Aérea Revolucionaria) operated 20 Mi-24Ds reportedly delivered in 1984. Unfortunately, no details are known because of the Cuban obsession with security.

Over the years, Czech 'Hinds' have flown in several display teams. In the early 1990s 51.vrp had a two-ship Mi-24D team, flying sharkmouthed 'Hinds'. At the same time, 11.vrp had a four-ship (later five) Mi-24V team. Both teams were disbanded in 1994 to form the current 'HINDS' team.

Ethiopia

The Ethiopian Air Force (EAF) operated more than 40 Mi-24Ds delivered in 1978 (probably ex-Soviet Army Aviation aircraft, as second-hand Soviet equipment made up much of the EAF's inventory). They were joined in 1988 by a batch of new Mi-35s. No serials are known; according to Russian sources, only 18 Ethiopian 'Hinds' remained operational in early 1995. On 3 December 1998 it was announced that Ethiopia would acquire "several Mi-24 attack helicopters" as part of a $150 million arms deal with Russia, that also includes four Sukhoi Su-27s and an unknown number of Mil Mi-8s. All the helicopters are believed to have been delivered between 10 and 23 December 1998.

France

Three Libyan 'Hinds' (including Mi-25 '302') captured by Chadian forces in Ouadi-Doum in March 1987 were turned over to France and evaluated by the French Air Force (Armée de l'Air). Most probably the test work was performed by the Centre d'Expérimentations Aériennes Militaires at BA 118 in Mont-de-Marsan. One helicopter later went to Great Britain and another to the USA; the fate of the third is unknown.

Germany (East and West)

The Mi-24 entered service with the East German Air Force (LSK/LV – Luftstreitkräfte und Luftverteidigung der Deutschen Demokratischen Republik – Air Force and Air Defence Force of the German Democratic Republic) in June 1978 when HG 5 (Hubschraubergeschwader – helicopter wing) at Basepohl AB near Stavenhagen in the Neubrandenburg district, Mecklenburg/Vorpommern, received its first four Mi-24Ds. Four more were delivered in the next year and another 18 in 1981. The unit later became HG 57 and then KHG 5 (Kampfhubschraubergeschwader – combat helicopter wing) 'Adolf von Lützow'.

On 1 December 1986 KHG 5 took delivery of its first Mi-24P. (It should be noted that the Germans always referred to their 'Hinds' as Mi-24D and Mi-24P, rather than Mi-25 and Mi-35P.) The Mi-24Ps came with a late-model ESM suite (with the RHAWS 'horns' in the aft position), GUV gun pods, KMGU sub-munitions containers and even air/exhaust mixers which were rarely seen on export 'Hinds' and were equally rarely, if ever, fitted in service. The unit also operated the armed Mi-8TB 'Hip-E'.

A second unit, KHG 3 'Ferdinand von Schill' at Cottbus, Brandenburg, flew the Mi-24D from 19 June 1982. No 'Hind-Fs' were operated by this unit, which received additional Mi-8TBs instead. Curiously, East German Mi-24Ds wore 'green crocodile' camouflage while the Mi-24Ps had the sand/brown variety.

Proficiency training took place at Basepohl where a PTV-241 simulator was commissioned on 15 July 1986; the simulator was modified locally to enhance its training modes. Somewhat surprisingly, a single Mi-24V (rather than a Mi-24DU) was ordered in 1990 for training purposes but was never delivered. Since local instructors could not handle the training workload, East Germany continued to send trainee groups to the Soviet Union. The final group, however, was pulled out in the middle of the semester because the East German government strongly disagreed with Mikhail Gorbachev's reformist policies.

The LSK/LV had many of its helicopters, including the Mi-24, overhauled at the Dresden Aircraft Repair Plant, where from 1984 and 1985, respectively, B- and C-checks were performed. This was no small task, as commonality between the Mi-2 previously overhauled at Dresden and the Mi-24 was low. The first 'Hind' arrived on 4 July 1984 and the final one was redelivered on 17 September 1991.

The Mi-24s were regularly detached to borderside helipads to provide protection for air defence radars located along the border between East and West Germany. In summer they were sent to Altensalzwedel and Gross Moltzahn, and in the winter to just the latter location.

When Germany reunited on 3 October 1990, the LSK/LV and the West German Air Force (Luftwaffe der Bundesrepublik Deutschland) merged into a single air arm, the Luftwaffe. Most East German military aircraft were, at least temporarily, taken on strength by the united armed forces (Bundeswehr) and received four-digit Luftwaffe serials. The old and new identities of the German 'Hinds' are indicated in the table below.

There are also photos of LSK/LV Mi-24Ds serialled 90, 340 and 526. However, these serials are obviously bogus, as the East German Air Force had a habit of changing the serials on military aircraft intended for public view (for security reasons); in reality, they were probably '390', '540' and '525'. In much the same way, Mi-24D '521', which was retired after an accident and used as a ground instructional airframe, became '5211'. Curiously, this aircraft has had the starboard 2P32M dual launch rails for 9M17P Falanga ATGMs replaced by a rack for 9M114 Shturm missiles – quite simply because the latter weapon was used by Mi-24Ps operated by the LSK/LV and ground crews had to be trained in handling it.

Two Mi-24Ps (96+40 and 96+47) and an Mi-24D (96+39) were transferred to WTD 61 (Wehrtechnische Dienststelle 61 für Luftfahrzeuge – military technical support unit, or rather Aircraft Test Centre No. 61) at Manching AB near Ingolstadt, Bayern, which also evaluated other Soviet military aircraft. The Mi-24Vs were properly reserialled 98+33 and 98+34 (the first two digits of Luftwaffe serials denote the type, with a few exceptions such as 98 which is reserved for test aircraft regardless of type). Two more were sold to the USA for evaluation. Most Mi-24s were placed in open storage after being operated briefly by HFS 70 (Heeresfliegerstaffel – Army aviation squadron) at Cottbus and HFS 80 at Basepohl and eventually sold to Hungary and Poland. Mi-24P 96+45 received a special retirement paint job with a huge blue/yellow/red flash running the full length of the fuselage and identically coloured wings.

Below: This KHG 3 Mi-24D is seen still wearing its old-style East German markings during one of its last flights in 1991.

Below left: A single German Mi-24P was decorated in this special scheme to commemorate the type's final withdrawal from service.

Below: WTD 61 test flew several LSK/LV types, including this Mi-24D. Note the blue unit badge and missions marks on the nose.

Serial	C/n	Version	Delivered	LSK/LV unit	Luftwaffe serial	Notes
357	340330	Mi-24P	12-89	KHG 5	96+40	To WTD 61 as 98+33
358	340331	Mi-24P	12-89	KHG 5	96+41	
361	340332	Mi-24P	12-89	KHG 5	96+42	
387	340333	Mi-24P	12-89	KHG 5	96+43	Preserved in Germany
390	110156	Mi-24D	5-81	KHG 3	96+01	Sold to Polish AF as 156
396	110157	Mi-24D	5-81	KHG 3	96+02	
403	B4001	Mi-24D	6-78	KHG 5	96+20	
406	B4002	Mi-24D	6-78	KHG 5	96+21	Preserved Imperial War Museum, Duxford, delivered 13-3-96
407	B4003	Mi-24D	6-78	KHG 5		W/O 26-8-80
408	110158	Mi-24D	5-81	KHG 5	96+22	Preserved International Helicopter Museum, Weston-super-Mare
412	B4004	Mi-24D	6-78	KHG 5	96+23	Sold, Polish AF – spares
414	B4069	Mi-24D	7-79	KHG 3	96+03	Sold, Polish AF – spares
415 (1)	B4070	Mi-24D	7-79	KHG 5		W/O 26-10-84
415 (2)	340334	Mi-24P	12-89	KHG 5	96+44	Sold, Hungarian AF 10-95
417	B4071	Mi-24D	8-79	KHG 5	96+24	
418	B4072	Mi-24D	8-79	KHG 5	96+25	
421	110159	Mi-24D	5-81	KHG 5	96+26	
422	340335	Mi-24P	12-89	KHG 5	96+45	
424	110160	Mi-24D	6-81	KHG 5	96+04	
433	110161	Mi-24D	6-81	KHG 3	96+05	
434	110162	Mi-24D	6-81	KHG 5	96+27	
439	340336	Mi-24P	12-89	KHG 5	96+46	
442	340337	Mi-24P	12-89	KHG 5	96+47	To WTD 61 as 98+34
444	340338	Mi-24P	12-89	KHG 5	96+48	
446	110163	Mi-24D	6-81	KHG 3	96+06	Sold to Polish AF as 163
447	110164	Mi-24D	6-81	KHG 5	96+28	
464	340339	Mi-24P	12-89	KHG 5	96+49	
480	340340	Mi-24P	12-89	KHG 5	96+50	Preserved in Germany
485	340272	Mi-24D	5-83	KHG 3	96+29	
487	110165	Mi-24D	7-81	KHG 3	96+07	
494	110166	Mi-24D	7-81	KHG 5	96+30	To US Army 12-4-91 as 88-0616
495	110167	Mi-24D	5-81	KHG 5	96+31	Sold to Polish AF as 167
496	110168	Mi-24D	3-81	KHG 5	96+32	
498	110170	Mi-24D	7-81	KHG 3	96+08	Sold to Polish AF as 170
512	340341	Mi-24P	12-89	KHG 5	96+51	To US Army 12-4-91 as 92-2270
520	110169	Mi-24D	8-81	KHG 3	96+09	Sold to Polish AF as 169
521	110171	Mi-24D	8-81	KHG 3		DBR 3-6-82, ground instructional airframe at Military Technical School Bad Deben as '5211'
522	110172	Mi-24D	8-81	KHG 3	96+10	
523	110173	Mi-24D	8-81	KHG 3	96+11	
524	340269	Mi-24D	5-83	KHG 3	96+12	Sold to Polish AF as 269
525	340270	Mi-24D	5-83	KHG 3	96+13	Sold to Polish AF as 270. C/n also quoted as 340227
528	340273	Mi-24D	4-83	KHG 5	96+33	
529	340271	Mi-24D	3-83	KHG 5	96+34	Sold to Polish AF as 271
530	340274	Mi-24D	4-83	KHG 5	96+35	
532	340275	Mi-24D	4-83	KHG 5	96+36	
533	340276	Mi-24D	4-83	KHG 5	96+37	Sold to Polish AF as 276
534	730209	Mi-24D	6-82	KHG 5	96+14	Sold to Polish AF as 209
536	730210	Mi-24D	6-82	KHG 5	96+15	Sold to Polish AF as 210
538	730208	Mi-24D	6-82	KHG 5	96+16	Sold to Polish AF as 208
539	730211	Mi-24D	6-82	KHG 5	96+17	Sold to Polish AF as 211
540	730212	Mi-24D	6-82	KHG 3	96+18	Preserved Cottbus 1990
543	730213	Mi-24D	6-82	KHG 3	96+19	Sold to Polish AF as 213
544	340277	Mi-24D	4-83	KHG 5	96+38	Sold to Polish AF as 277
547	340278	Mi-24D	4-83	KHG 5	96+39	

Hungary

A total of 40 'Hinds' – 30 Mi-24Ds and 10 Mi-24Vs – was delivered to the Hungarian air force (Magyar Légierö) by the Soviet Union. The first Mi-24Ds arrived in 1978, serialled 005-008, 104-112, 114-119 and 574-583. The only Hungarian Mi-24 loss to date has been an Mi-24D (113).

The 'Hind-Ds' were later supplemented by the Mi-24V (serials 711-721). Hungarian 'Hind-Es' have RHAWS 'horns' mounted between front and rear cockpits. Today all 'Hinds' are operated by the 87th 'Bakony' Combat Helicopter Regiment, based at Szentkirályszabadja. The Regiment has two component squadrons; the 1st 'Kerecsen' (falcon) Attack Helicopter Squadron, equipped with Mi-24Ds and the 2nd

Above: Hungary's 10 Mi-24Vs are all operated by the air force's 2nd Combat Helicopter Squadron.

'Phoenix' Attack Helicopter Squadron, equipped with six Mi-24D/Vs. Maintenance for Hungary's 'Hinds' – and most other Eastern European operators – was and is provided by the Danubian Aircraft Company facility, at Tököl.

It had been planned to establish a third squadron using six Mi-24Ds and 14 Mi-24Ps acquired from Germany in 1995. However, the integration of the early-model Mi-24Ds and the all-new Mi-24Ps with Hungary's existing 'Hinds' proved to be prohibitively expensive, as the 'gift' aircraft all needed reassembly and overhaul. Given Hungary's aspirations to join NATO, the 'Hinds' have become a burden and permission to sell them is unlikely to be granted.

Iraq

The Iraqi Air Force (al Quwwat al-Jawwiya al-Iraqiya) operated the Mi-25 from the late 1970s. There is no reliable information

This is one of several 'Hinds' captured by US forces in Iraq. While some of these aircraft are now museum pieces, at least one is flying with the US Army's OTSA evaluations unit.

regarding the number actually delivered. Russian sources state that 30 remained in service by early 1995, discounting at least seven aircraft lost during the Iran-Iraq war and five more destroyed or captured by the US Army during the Gulf War. Only three aircraft – serialled 2110, 2119 and 4492 – have been positively identified.

Nicaragua

The first three Mi-25s were delivered to the Nicaraguan Air Force (Fuerza Aérea Sandinista) in 1983, followed by nine more

in the spring of 1984 (some sources, though, claim that 18 were delivered in all). Known examples were serialled 329, 338,

Papua New Guinea

In mid-February 1997 the Papua New Guinean government acquired several Mi-24s from an undisclosed East European source via the UK-based defence consultant Sandline International for use in the suppression of a secessionist revolt in Bougainville. The helicopters arrived at Port Moresby in an 'unidentified large freighter of Russian origin' – almost certainly an Antonov An-124. However, an attempt to deliver two more 'Hinds' plus two Mi-17s, six UB-32A FFAR pods and 1,000 S-5 rockets purchased through the same source was foiled on 27 March. The An-124 carrying them to Port Moresby via Bangkok was forced down on the Royal Australian Air Force base at Tindal, Northern Territory, by

RAAF F/A-18s and the cargo was impounded by the authorities. The whereabouts of these Mi-24s is unknown.

The diversion had been arranged by PNG's acting prime minister who refused to allow the aircraft to land in PNG. The helicopters and armament had been bought before prime minister Sir Julius Chan was forced to step down after a confrontation with PNG's military leader, Brigadier General Jerry Singaroff, who demanded a judicial inquiry into alleged corruption in the deal with Sandline. The equipment was part of a US$36 million military aid package which also included the services of South African mercenaries, including pilots supplied by Executive Outcomes.

India

The Indian Air Force (IAF) bought its first 12 Mi-25s in late 1984. Known locally as the Akbar, the type was introduced to service by the 125th Helicopter Unit. They were later supplemented by an additional batch of 20 Mi-35s flown by the 104th and 116th Helicopter Units (the latter is based at Pathankot), including the unique Mi-25V trainer version similar to the Mi-24DU. India's Mi-25s had aft-mounted RHAWS 'horns' and faired triple chaff/flare dispensers. According to Russian sources, 32 'Hinds' were in service with the IAF by early 1995.

Above: India's 'Hind-Es' are late-model aircraft with Ispanka jammers, RHAWS and side-mounted flares.

Indian 'Hinds' wear a yellow/olive drab camouflage with light blue undersurfaces similar to that worn by Afghan Mi-25s.

In October 1998 the IAF signed a US$25 million contract with Tamam, one of the avionics divisions of Israel Aircraft Industries (IAI), for an upgrade of 25 Mi-24s. Before selecting Tamam to do the job the IAF had also looked at the French Sextant Avionique. The upgrade package will include a 30-kg (65-lb) Helicopter Mission Optimised Stabilised Payload (HMOSP) comprising LLLTV and FLIR, plus a helmet-mounted sight and a digital moving-map display.

Libya

According to Russian sources, the Libyan Arab Republic Air Force (LARAF) had 65 Mi-24s on strength in early 1995, some of which were based at Has-Lanouf, Bombah and Misurata (the latter two bases hosted flying schools with Polish instructors). However, their serviceability is doubtful because spares supplies have been cut off due to UN sanctions, which were imposed when Libyan terrorists blew up Pan American Airlines Clipper 103.

Mongolia

The Mongolian People's Army Air Force operated 12 ex-Soviet Army Mi-24Vs based at Nalaoh (originally 10, but two more were acquired in 1992). The helicopters, which appear to be coded consecutively from '01 Yellow' to '12 Yellow', retain warning inscriptions in Russian and have the national *zoyombo* markings painted over the existing red stars. By the summer of 1993 the unit had disbanded and the helicopters had been mothballed.

Mozambique

Fifteen Mi-24s of an unspecified version (probably 'Hind-Ds') were delivered to the Mozambique Air Force (FPA – Força Popular Aérea de Mozambique). Of these, only four aircraft serialled 102, 104, 105 and 106 were operational in early 1995.

339, 340, 341, 355 and 361; the latter aircraft later became a gate guard at Augusto César Sandino Airport, Managua. After the end of the war the Nicaraguan Air Force (renamed Fuerza Aérea Ejército de Nicaragua) sold all seven surviving Mi-25s to

Peru in 1992. (Some sources reported that two were still in service in early 1995 and that the Peruvian 'Crocodile' population numbered 15 at the same time. If this is true, it appears that only five were sold.)

Left: Nicaragua's 'Hinds' were secretive beasts and little seen, despite their very active service careers. The EVU IR-suppressors were essential equipment on all FAS combat helicopters (Mi-25s and Mi-17s).

North Korea

Fifty Mi-24s of an unspecified version were reported to be in service with the Air Force of the Korean People's Democratic Republic in early 1995. Nothing more is known.

Peru

The Peruvian Air Force (FAP – Fuerza Aérea del Peru) bought 12 late-production Mi-25s with intake filters from the Soviet Union in

the early 1980s. Seven Mi-25s were acquired from Nicaragua in 1992, and Russian sources stated that 15 were in service with the FAP in early 1995. The 'Hinds' were operated by Grupo Aéreo 3 at Jorge Chavez AB near Lima. At least one sported a huge shark-mouth. Only one aircraft (FAP 637) has been identified so far.

Peru operates a mix of Mi-25s delivered directly from the manufacturer and aircraft acquired from Nicaragua. Little is known about their operations, and the exact number and variants in service is not clear. This 'Hind-D' is one of the few FAP 'Hinds' to have been seen in public.

Poland

From 15 April to 3 July 1978, 10 carefully selected Polish Air Force (PWL – Polskie Wojsko Lotnicze) pilots went to the Soviet Union for training. The 37th PST (transport helicopter squadron) at Leønica Wielka took delivery of the first four Mi-24Ds on 20 September that year.

On 1 January 1979 an Attack Helicopter Flight was activated within 37 PST, and Mi-24 operations officially began on 11 January. On 22 April the 'Hinds' relocated to Awidwin. The flight made its mark in the autumn of 1979, participating in the Jubileusz-79 exercise, which also marked the public debut of the Polish 'Hinds'.

In 1981 the unit was reorganised and included into 49 PSB at Pruszcz-Gdanski, to where the helicopters relocated on 16 December, and 8 Eskadra (squadron) was established. A second 'Hind' unit was created in the spring of 1986 when 16 Mi-24Vs were delivered to 3 Eskadra, 56 PSB at Inowroclaw-Latkow. In the winter of 1987, Western observers got their first good look at the Polish Mi-24s when they attended a Polish military exercise (Opal-87) for the first time.

In 1984 the 'Hind-Ds' were retrofitted with chaff/flare dispensers under the tailboom and IRCM jammers (with the exception of the last two aircraft, 585 and 586, which came with fuselage-mounted triple dispensers). 586 was also unusual in having more convex canopies.

Polish Mi-24s were delivered in the sand/brown colour scheme. Starting in 1988, several aircraft overhauled in Hungary (Budapest) and at the PWL's overhaul plant No. 2 in Bydgoszcz received a new grey/green camouflage. Mi-24V '735' was unusual in having a large shark-mouth. Some time earlier (in 1986) the original two-digit serials matching the 'last two' of the c/n had been replaced with three-digit serials matching the 'last three' of the c/n for more accurate identification (though the original serials 'bled through' on some aircraft).

As with any type and any air arm, there were accidents, including some strange ones. Mi-24D '013' crashed on 13 September 1988, 13 hours after its latest overhaul. The aircraft was subsequently rebuilt and named 'Zabka' (froggie).

Not having any Mi-24DUs, the PWL had to use Mi-24Ds for training purposes. Mi-24D '458' was apparently lost due to pilot error when a young warrant officer making his first flight in the type caused the helicopter to become airborne prematurely while taxiing, then lost control; the 'Hind' rolled to port and fell on its side, seriously injuring instructor pilot Andrzej Maszenda who was in the WSO's seat. The trainee and the technician escaped with minor injuries.

By early 1995 the PWL reportedly had only 29 Mi-24s in service. However, 18 surplus Luftwaffe Mi-24Ds were acquired in late 1995/early 1996 and refurbished by the PWL's overhaul plant No. 1 in Lodz. Four more were to follow in early 1998. Originally, the PWL planned to establish a third Mi-24 regiment with these helicopters but plans were subsequently abandoned and the

Above: Special markings were applied to this 3 Eskadra, 56 PSB Mi-24V for a 1991 exercise.

Right: The scorpion badge of 8 Eskadra, 49 PSB is prominent on the nose of this Mi-24D.

aircraft were delivered to 49 PSB. Twelve of the 18 originally delivered were in service by June 1997.

The Poles seem to have given the helicopter a nickname of their own. A Polish brochure on the Mi-24D in the Przeglad konstrukcji lotniczych (Aircraft design analysis) series published in 1991 was subtitled 'Ognisty rydwan z Afganistanu' (chariot of fire from Afghanistan).

Serial	C/n	Version	Delivery date	Remarks	Serial	C/n	Version	Delivery date	Remarks	Serial	C/n	Version	Delivery date	Remarks	Serial	C/n	Version	Delivery date	Remarks
013	A1013	Mi-24D	20-9-78	Delivered as 13. Damaged 13-9-88 but repaired	269	340269	Mi-24D	1997	Ex-96+12, stored Lodz 6-97	732	410732	Mi-24V	1986	
014	A1014	Mi-24D	20-9-78	Delivered as 14	270	340270	Mi-24D	1997	Ex-96+13	733	410733	Mi-24V	1986	
015	A1015	Mi-24D	20-9-78	Delivered as 15	271	340271	Mi-24D	1997	Ex-96+34, stored Lodz 6-97	734	410734	Mi-24V	1986	
016	A1016	Mi-24D	20-9-78	Delivered as 16	272	340272	Mi-24D	1997	Ex-96+29	735	410735	Mi-24V	1986	
156	110156	Mi-24D	1997	Ex-96+01	276	340276	Mi-24D	1997	Ex-96+37	736	410736	Mi-24V	1986	
163	110163	Mi-24D	1997	Ex-96+06	277	340277	Mi-24D	1997	Ex-96+38, stored Lodz 6-97	737	410737	Mi-24V	1986	
167	110167	Mi-24D	1997	Ex-96+31	456	410456	Mi-24D	11-84	Delivered as 56?	738	410738	Mi-24V	1986	
169	110169	Mi-24D	1997	Ex-96+09	457	410457	Mi-24D	11-84	Delivered as 57	739	410739	Mi-24V	1986	
170	110170	Mi-24D	1997	Ex-96+08	458	410458	Mi-24D	11-84	Delivered as 58. W/O Pruszcz-Gdanski 11-7-90	740	410740	Mi-24V	1986	
174	103174	Mi-24D	10-81	Delivered as 74	459	410459	Mi-24D	11-84	Delivered as 59?	741	410741	Mi-24V	1986	
175	103175	Mi-24D	10-81	Delivered as 75	460	410460	Mi-24D	7-85	Delivered as 60? Ground instructional airframe at Pruszcz-Gdanski	742	410742	Mi-24V	1986	
176	103176	Mi-24D	10-81	Delivered as 76	461	410461	Mi-24D	7-85	Delivered as 61?	743	410743	Mi-24V	1986	
177	103177	Mi-24D	10-81	Delivered as 77	584	220584	Mi-24D	1986		744	410744	Mi-24V	1986	
181	103181	Mi-24D	10-84		585	220585	Mi-24D	1986		745	410745	Mi-24V	1986	
182	103182	Mi-24D	10-84	W/O	727	410727	Mi-24V	1986		746	410746	Mi-24V	1986	
208	730208	Mi-24D	1997	Ex-96+16	728	410728	Mi-24V	1986		747	410747	Mi-24V	1986	
209	730209	Mi-24D	1997	Ex-96+14	729	410729	Mi-24V	1986		748	410748	Mi-24V	1986	
210	730210	Mi-24D	1997	Ex-96+15	730	410730	Mi-24V	1986		956	340956	Mi-24V	1986	
211	730211	Mi-24D	1997	Ex-96+17	731	410731	Mi-24V	1986	Crashed 10-7-97	none	B4004	Mi-24D	1997	Ex-96+23, used for spares
213	730213	Mi-24D	1997	Ex-96+19, stored Lodz 6-97						none	B4069	Mi-24D	1997	Ex-96+03, used for spares

Left: Decorated intake covers are a common sight on Mi-24s, such as the 'bug eyes' painted on this Mi-24D of 49 PSB during 1998.

Sierra Leone

The Sierra Leone Air Force (SLAF) included a single Mi-24V serialled AF 0010 (c/n 3532421622258) based at Freetown-Lungi airport. Judging by the Soviet-style c/n (i.e., different from those usually applied to export 'Hinds') and the fact that the helicopter was flown by Belarussian contract pilots, it was most probably acquired in Belarus. Parts of a second Mi-24 were also seen at Freetown-Lungi. The two helicopters were reportedly purchased for US$9 million.

Slovakia

The Slovak Air Force (Slovenské Vojenské Létectvo) has 19 'Hinds' (10 Vs, eight Ds and one DU) in service, operated by 4.Letecka zakladna in Presov. 1.vrtulnikova letka operates the Mi-24V, 2.vrtulnikova letka the Mi-24D (and the single DU). Slovakian Hinds are overhauled in Trencin, where they are being repainted in a new camouflage scheme, very similar to that of

Slovakian Su-22s. This scheme consists of four colours, two greens and two browns, and has been applied to Mi-24Vs 0707 and 0813. One Mi-24V (0787) is painted in three colours only; the pale brown is missing. The Mi-24DU was overhauled in Ukraine and its 'new' scheme is very similar to the original, but with richer colours.

There were no helicopter bases in Slovakia during the Czechoslovakian era. Russian Mi-24s were based only in Sliac (Slovakia, near Zvolen) and in Olomouc, Milovice and Mimon (Czech Republic).

Slovakia's small fleet of Mi-24D/Vs (and a single Mi-24DU trainer) is being slowly repainted in this four-tone green/brown scheme (below left). Like the Czech air force, Slovakia also maintains an Mi-24 display team (right).

Mi-24D		0223		340223	0708		730708
4009	M34009				0786		730786
0100	M340100	**Mi-24DU**			0787		730787
0101	M340101	6040		7306040	0813		730813
0149	M340149				0814		730814
0150	000150	**Mi-24V**			0832		730832
0215	340215	0704		730704	0833		730833
0222	340222	0707		730707	0927		730927

South Yemen

The South Yemeni Air Force (People's Democratic Republic of Yemen) operated 15 Mi-24Ds, delivered in 1980. After the 1994 civil war 12 aircraft were understood to be still in service, but nothing is known about their status.

Serbia

An unknown number of Mi-24s are in service with the 'Police Air Forces' of the Federal Republic of Yugoslavia, and have been filmed in action over Kosovo province, during 1998, by TV news crews.

Sri Lanka

Six well-worn 'green crocodile' Mi-24Vs (serialled CH 610 through CH 615) were obtained by the Sri Lanka Air Force (SLAF) in November 1995 from CIS (probably Ukrainian) surplus stocks to be used in the prolonged civil war against the LTTE rebels .

Three 'Hinds' equipped 9 Attack Helicopter Squadron at Minneriya-Hinnurakgoda, and their first operational flight took place on 14 November 1995. The other three (CH 613 through CH 615)

remained in storage at Katunayake until pressed into service in September 1996. CH 614 was apparently shot down into the Bay of Bengal off Mullaittivu on 19 March 1997. Another 'Hind' was damaged on 12 September and a third lost on 10 November.

Further deliveries from an unknown source (probably Ukraine again) followed the first batch of six aircraft. In total, Sri Lanka has received 13 'Hinds' (and was believed to be seeking a total of 16, at one time). Three aircraft were delivered in 1998, and four may have been delivered in 1997. During this period, three 'Hinds' were reportedly returned to their supplier (and three have been shot down), so by early 1999 the SLAF is understood to have seven operational Mi-24s.

Sri Lanka's 'Hind' force has seen constant combat since its introduction in 1995, and has suffered several losses.

Sudan

Up to 20 Mi-24s have been attributed to the Sudanese Air Force (al Quwwat al-Jawwiya as-Sudaniya), but there is no confirmation of this number. No Mi-24s could possibly have been delivered by the Soviet Union since Sudan did not have 'friendly nation' status (unlike Libya, Algeria, etc.) and it is highly

improbable that so many could have been captured from the LARAF in 1983-1987 and retained.

Syria

Fifty Mi-24Ds, at least some of which were ex-Soviet Army aircraft, were handed over to the Syrian Air Force (al Quwwat al-Jawwiya al Arabiya as-Suriya). Only one aircraft serialled 2808 has been identified to date.

UK

In the late 1980s, an ex-Libyan Mi-25 was obtained via France and evaluated by the Rotary Wing Test Squadron of the Aeroplane and Armament Experimental Establishment (A&AEE). It was also later sighted at the West Freugh facility.

United States

The US Army has long had a requirement to train its personnel in tactics to be used against Soviet military hardware in the event of a war. While a few Soviet tanks, APCs and IFVs were obtained via international sources (mostly as war booty), Soviet combat helicopters – which were regarded as a serious threat – were harder to obtain. The US Army's training centres originally had to make do with synthetic 'Hinds' – radio-controlled models developed by the US Army Missile Command (MICOM), Bell JUH-1Hs crudely converted into Mi-24D look-alikes and Orlando Helicopter Airways QS-55s which were a more accurate imitation of the 'Hind-D'.

The US Army still made every effort to acquire genuine Mi-24s. A Libyan Mi-25 captured in Chad was reported to have been delivered to the US via France for evaluation, but its fate is unknown. The US Army's Operational Test and Evaluation Command (OPTEC) established in November 1990 – or, more precisely, the OPTEC Threat Support Activity (OTSA) at Biggs Army Air Field, Fort Bliss, Texas – does have three 'Hinds', none of which is apparently of Libyan origin.

Two of the helicopters were acquired from the German Luftwaffe on 12 April 1991. This became the easiest way to obtain 'Hinds', since German reunification made Soviet military equipment operated by the former LSK/LV readily available to the West for detailed inspection. Mi-24D (Mi-25) 96+30 (c/n 110166) was serialled 88-0616 and Mi-24P (Mi-35) 96+51 (c/n 340341) became 92-2270. Originally flown in East German two-tone green camouflage with small 'US Army' titles, by 1996 the Mi-24D was repainted in a glossy dark green/dark earth paint job reminiscent of Czech Air Force 'Hinds' and named 'Wild Thing' (with

This line-up of OTSA 'Hinds' at Biggs AAF in mid-1997 includes the Mi-24P 'Patience' and 'Wild Thing', the Mi-24D, before it was repainted.

appropriate 'Tasmanian Devil' nose art). By October 1998, however, 88-0616 had been repainted again in a tan/pale green camouflage similar to that worn by Soviet Mi-24s. Mi-24P 92-2270 (named 'Patience') appears to have retained its factory finish. Unlike some other OTSA aircraft which wear spurious 'bad guy' markings (a red star within a red circle), 88-0616 and 92-2270 have no insignia except tiny 'US Army' titles and small serials on the tail.

Some modifications were made to both helicopters. The Mi-24D has two large non-standard blade aerials on the tailboom and an American anti-collision strobe light replacing the standard rotating anti-collision beacon. In 1996 the YakB-12,7 machine-gun was replaced with a 20-mm M197 cannon from an AH-1S Mod and several MILES sensors were attached to the fuselage sides and engine cowlings (to register 'hits' with training lasers). However, these had been removed by October 1998 and the original armament reinstated. The Mi-24P has one large blade aerial installed in place of the L-166V-11E IRCM jammer and an American strobe light.

A third 'Hind', another Mi-25 reportedly named 'Warlord', was captured in near-perfect condition in Iraq during the Gulf War (only the missile director pod for the 9M17P ATGMs appeared to be missing when the aircraft was put on show in the US). The helicopter had appropriate yellow/olive drab camouflage with pale grey undersurfaces but had no Arabic serial and wore Iraqi flags on the fuselage rather than the triangular Iraqi Air Force insignia, so the markings may be non-authentic. The US Army serial 93-2472 was allocated but not worn visibly.

OTSA Mi-24s have aso operated from Fort Polk, Louisiana; Nellis AFB and Indian Springs Air Force Auxiliary Field, Nevada; Fort Bragg, North Carolina; Fort Rucker, Alabama; Fort Irwin, California; and MCAS Yuma, Arizona. With the other OTSA aircraft, they are widely used to represent the Red Force during various exercises such as Red Flag, Green Flag and Roving Sands.

This Mi-24D, 88-0616, appears to be the 'Hind-D' previously marked as 'Wild Thing', repainted in 1997/98 in a more anonymous scheme.

Vietnam

The Vietnam People's Air Force (VPAF) has been reported to operate 30 Mi-24As and Ds delivered in the mid-1980s, some of which were later transferred to the Cambodian Air Force. The helicopters are operated by the 916th regiment 'Ba Vi' at Hoa Lac AB near Hanoi; the unit is named after a hill near the town of Son Tay. Only one Vietnamese 'Hind' has been identified

so far, an Mi-24A serialled 7430 which is one of the exhibits of the VPAF Museum in Hanoi. The serial obviously has nothing to do with the aircraft's c/n.

This is the Mi-24A on show at the VPAF museum. It is most likely a combat veteran of the Cambodian invasion.

Future operators

Bosnia

In December 1998, the commander of the Bosnia and Herzegovina Federation Army (Vojska Federacije, VF), General Rasim Delic, was quoted in the local press as saying that the VF had purchased an initial batch of five Mi-24 'Hinds'. According to the general, these aircraft were then in a "friendly country", awaiting delivery. The VF

is building up its air arm, and took delivery of 15 ex-US Army UH-1Hs in 1998/99. The Hueys join approximately 10 Mi-8 'Hips' already in Bosnian service.

Malaysia had expressed its intention to buy six 'Hinds', and **Myanmar** (Burma) was interested in buying enough Mi-35s to equip a squadron 'subject to acceptable credit agreements'. Given these country's financial situations, these purchases now seem extremely unlikely to proceed.

A photo feature by
SrA Greg L. Davis
1st Combat Camera Squadron, USAF

The USAF's On-call Air Expeditionary Force
366th Wing

The United States Air Force is completely reorganising the way it deploys its combat forces. Under the Expeditionary Aerospace Force (EAF) concept, groups of squadrons – and their support elements – now train to operate as Air Expeditionary Forces (AEFs), for rapid deployments and sustained out-of-area operations. AEFs work at wing level with distinct fighter, attack, and combat support assets, working together as a single team to provide rapid, responsive air power. The 366th Wing is the USAF's first such unit.

The 366th Wing 'Gunfighters', based at Mountain Home AFB, Idaho, was originally established as a rapid-deployment 'super wing' and, as such, it pioneered today's EAF concept. The 366th was the first USAF unit to combine fighter, bomber and refuelling squadrons into a cohesive organisation that trained to deploy as one. As a result, the 366th Wing became the first AEF – and will be the only standing AEF, as all others will be integrated on an 'as required' basis. The USAF plans to establish 10 AEFs, which will be fully operational from 1 January 2000 onwards.

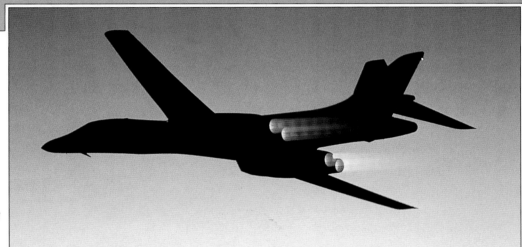

Opposite, above: This 'Gunfighter' formation includes aircraft from all the 366th Wing's component squadrons: the 34th BS 'Thunderbirds' (B-1B), 389th FS 'Thunderbolts' (F-16CJ), 390th FS 'Wild Boars' (F-15C), 391st FS 'Bold Tigers' (F-15E) and the 22nd ARS 'Mules' (KC-135R).

This page: The most specialised aircraft in the 366th's inventory are its B-1Bs. In 1994 the 'Bones' replaced the B-52Gs previously assigned to the squadron and the unit moved to Mountain Home. Before this the 34th BS had been based at Castle AFB. The arrival of the B-1Bs at last made the 366th a fully-integrated 'air intervention' wing.

Opposite, below: The F-15Cs of the 390th FS would provide air cover for any 366th Wing operations. These Eagles are late-production Block 41 standard aircraft with the APG-70 radar and F100-PW-200 engines. They are camouflaged in the two-tone grey Mod Eagle air superiority scheme.

Above and right: *This F-15C is carrying a diverse mix of air-to-air weapons, including two AIM-9L Sidewinders on the outboard underwing shoulder pylons, four AIM-7M Sparrows on the recessed stations under the fuselage and two AIM-120A AMRAAMs on the inboard shoulder pylons. This range of missiles allows the Eagle pilot to engage any target at any range, while using a weapon whose value matches the importance of the threat. For example, the active-radar AMRAAM would be kept for a very high-priority BVR target or an advanced close-in threat, such as a MiG-29 with agile missiles and a helmet-mounted sight.*

Left: *An AGM-130-armed F-15E of the 391st FS waits on a rain-swept ramp.*

Below: *The 366th's organic SEAD capability is provided by the Block 50 F-16Cs – or F-16CJs – of the 389th FS. The ability to suppress or destroy enemy air defences would be an essential capability for any AEF deployment. No realistic combat operations can be undertaken against a modern enemy without permanent SEAD support. In any future conflict, F-16CJs would work hand-in-hand with the USN/USAF expeditionary EA-6B Prowler squadrons.*

The term Expeditionary Aerospace Force (EAF) is applied to the USAF's newly defined concept of taking geographically dispersed units from the active Air Force, Air National Guard and Air Force Reserve and tying them together as unified combat forces ready for deployment. The EAF concept should ease the problem of no-notice and long-term deployments overseas for personnel, as having an 'order of battle' of 10 Air Expeditionary Forces (AEFs) will make supporting rolling commitments such as Southern Watch or Deny Flight easier to schedule. Barring all-out war, each AEF should now have 15 months' notice that it is scheduled to deploy, somewhere in the world. Air Expeditionary Force is the term used to describe each of the 10 Air Expeditionary Wings (AEWs) which are now being defined, each of which will have a host unit/base but will be made up of dispersed squadrons. An AEW will always include air-to-air, air-to-ground and SEAD assets – and usually tanking support – but might also include C-SAR or other specialist skills. The role of an AEF will be to rapidly deploy at 72 hours' notice to reinforce theatre forces anywhere in the world and conduct a range of missions from combat to humanitarian relief.

Above: Along with the 4th Wing at Seymour Johnson, the 366th Wing is actually outside the official EAF structure. This is simply because the 366th already existed as a de facto AEF, before the EAF concept was introduced. As such, it needs little or no reorganisation to act as an AEF and still operates as a 'ready-to-go' single deployable force – just as the 10 newly-established AEFs will.

The 366th 'owns' a mix of F-15Cs (left) and F-15Es (below). The F-15Es combine all the air-to-air skills of the F-15C with a long-range, precision-strike capability all their own. These tiger-striped Strike Eagles of the 391st FS are armed with four AIM-120s, AIM-9s and AGM-130 stand-off weapons.

Above and below: The 'Albino' Eagles of the 390th FS would be crucial in protecting any larger 366th Wing force packages. APG-70-equipped F-15Cs (and earlier upgraded MSIP-II Eagles) have a highly-classified NCTR (Non Co-operative Target Recognition) capability that allows the Eagle pilots to firmly identify targets on their radar, without relying on IFF, AWACS support or other radars. Once positively 'ID-ed' those targets can then be killed at maximum range by the AIM-120.

Right: Though the B-1B has a longer range and a heavier warload than the F-15E, the Strike Eagle can carry a much wider range of weapons, including specialist PGMs (such as the GBU-28 'bunker buster'). Having both aircraft on call gives force commanders far more tactical options.

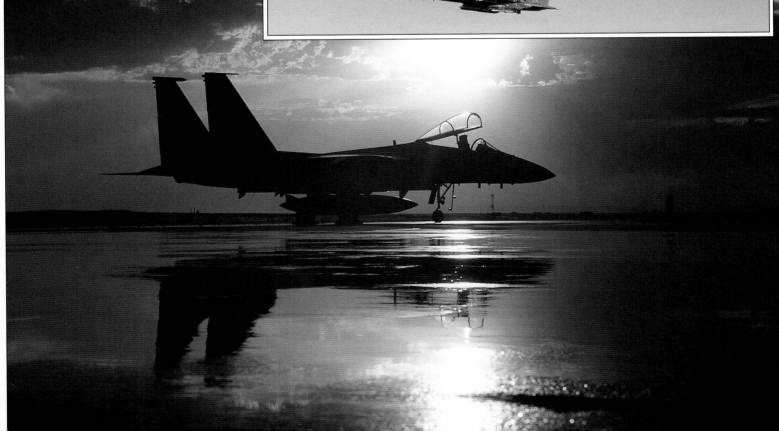

Mirage 2000
Variant Briefing

Returning to the delta wing, albeit with fly-by-wire controls which eliminate many of the disadvantages associated with the configuration, Dassault has produced a worthy successor to its earlier Mirage families. Assured of a solid home market, the Mirage 2000 has also achieved significant exports in an era of falling fighter sales.

Above: New life has been breathed into the Mirage 2000 by the second-generation Dash 5 family, which introduces a new radar, completely revised cockpit and the MICA missile, available in both IR and active radar (illustrated) versions.

Below: Representing Dassault's heavy/light fighter family, the sole Mirage 4000 poses with the second prototype Mirage 2000. The 2000 now undertakes all of the missions originally envisaged for the larger aircraft.

Puccini's 'Mimi', the consumptive heroine of his opera *La Bohème*, had a short and unfulfilled life. Dassault's 'Mimi' ('Mini Mirage'), admittedly less melodious, is today the matriarch of a large and diverse family; its descendants are instantly recognisable as the Mirage 2000 in its various guises. However, slightly different circumstances could have consigned this aeronautical namesake to equally premature oblivion.

It is as much a measure of the rapid evolution of avionics as of the Dassault company's expertise that the sophisticated and immensely complex warplane that is the Mirage 2000-5 was developed as a cheap alternative to a design which would have had a fraction of its potential – albeit nearly two decades earlier. The story of the Mirage 2000 is woven from many threads, one of which, perversely, originates at exactly the juncture at which the United Kingdom's TSR.2 strike aircraft met an abrupt, political ly-inspired end.

In May 1965, one month after the cancellation edict, another UK government statement revealed the launch of a venture known as AFVG: Anglo-French Variable Geometry. This interceptor and strike/attack aircraft overlapped the General Dynamics F-111Ks to which the RAF committed as a TSR.2 replacement and – fatally, as it transpired – posed a threat to the variable-geometry Mirage G which Dassault was developing. As in all the best French farces, the British Aircraft Corporation and Groupement Avions Marcel Dassault suddenly found themselves sharing the same bed as the unwitting victims of a misunderstanding.

The crux of that muddle was that while the RAF and Royal Navy wanted strike/attack capability, the Armée de l'Air (AA) then said it was looking for an interceptor, and there seemed no way of combining the requirements in one airframe with recourse to the technologies available at the time. In June 1967 France withdrew from AFVG, releasing a joyful Dassault to proceed unencumbered with its Mirage G (which had been rolled out the month before) and the UK, eventually, to fall in with West Germany and Italy on the aircraft that became the Panavia Tornado.

Looking like an enlarged, swing-wing Mirage F1, the Mirage G was further developed as the twin-engined G8, and from there into the fixed-geometry, Mach 3 Mirage G8A strike/interdictor, which the AA nominated as its Avion de Combat Futur (ACF) and planned to fit with a pair of the new SNECMA M53 engines, then on the drawing board. Procurement of 200-250 examples, redesignated Mirage F8, was envisaged, yet, before the prototype could be completed, the disproportionate cost of the programme proved its downfall: the same expenditure could have secured 500-625 Mirage F1s.

Chaired by Prime Minister Valéry Giscard d'Estaing, a National Defence Council meeting of 18 December 1975 took the not-unexpected step of terminating the ACF when the prototype was almost complete. In many countries, that

would have prompted a call of 'back to the drawing board', but the designated replacement had been taking shape in the Dassault design offices for several years and was ready for immediate adoption.

Simple fighter

Despite working on ever more complex versions of Mirage, Dassault had shown foresight in keeping alive the concept of a simpler fighter. Patriotic fervour may have been the driving force, but a cynical observer might point to the ACF's virtually non-existent export potential. During the early 1970s, several concepts of a 'Mimi' – Mini Mirage – had been examined under the direction of Jean-Jacques Samin and a team of engineers led by Jean-Paul Emoré and including François Dessirier, Christian Decaix and Jean-Maurice Roubertie. As the aircraft looked like the first-generation Mirage, it was alternatively known as Super Mirage III and later gained the alternative epithets of Delta 1000 and 2000.

By December 1975, Super Mirage 2000 was the generally accepted name for the aircraft which the Defence Council immediately nominated as the ACF's successor. This appeared a curious move, as the F8 was optimised for penetration missions with an Aérospatiale ASMP stand-off nuclear weapon and had secondary interception roles, whereas the 2000 was seen as an interceptor (what the AA wanted

a decade earlier) with some ground attack potential. A deciding factor in this *volte face* was undoubtedly the promise of 200 Delta Mirage 2000s at a total price of Fr15,000 million, compared with Fr18,000 million for a cut-down fleet of 100 ACFs.

While it was possible for the single-engined Mirage 2000 to adopt the M53 engine from its stillborn predecessor, a suitable intercept-optimised radar presented more of a problem. Thomson-CSF, the natural source, had no development programme under way in late 1975 and estimated that eight years would be needed to have an advanced pulse-Doppler system ready for service. Dassault was more sanguine regarding its own capabilities, predicting that a prototype Mirage 2000 could be flying within 18 months and be in service by 1982. These dates were to slip, and although it was 27 months before No. 01 took to the air, this still remarkably short time indicated how much work had been undertaken on the venture while the F8 was still supposedly the priority programme.

The impetus behind the Mirage 2000 was clearly apparent from the viewpoint of December 1975. Six months earlier, four NATO nations had rejected Dassault's offer of an M53-engined Mirage F1 in favour of the (then) General Dynamics F-16 and rubbed salt into the wound by making their announcement during the Paris air show. The ageing but still

dynamic Marcel Dassault spoke scathingly of the F-16's performance – particularly in claiming that its fixed air intakes restricted operational speed to Mach 1.7 – but had to concede that its fly-by-wire (FBW) design was a generation ahead of the F1. In the Mirage 2000, France planned to embrace the new technology of what was then called the combat-configured vehicle (CCV) or relaxed-stability design. Target operational speed for the Mirage 2000 was Mach 2.5, somewhat higher than actually achieved. Today, 'clean' speed is claimed to be Mach 2.2 for the Mirage and 2.0+ for the F-16C.

Dassault made no secret of the fact that the Mirage 2000 was intended to better the F-16 in all aspects except range, this deficiency being a consequence of superior US engine technology. It may seem curious that, in order to achieve its aim, the company resorted to an old configuration which it had seen fit to discard for the second (F1) generation of Mirages. However, that would be to underestimate the advantages of FBW control which enables a delta configuration to accentuate the positive while going some way towards eliminating the negative features inherent in this shape.

A different delta

In some (admittedly mainly British) accounts, it was the potential of the record-breaking Fairey FD2 which persuaded Dassault to abandon the stubby Mystère Delta (or Mirage I) in favour of the larger, single-engined, area-ruled Mirage III. With the prevailing technology, the delta had much to commend it at a time when the driving forces behind fighter design were ever-increasing speed and ceiling. Benefits include high internal volume, low wave drag and a simplicity of construction, reflected in

Having been deployed to Saudi Arabia for the 1991 Gulf war, Mirage 2000Cs remained on station in the country as part of Operation Alysse (Southern Watch), suspended in December 1998 after the US/UK Desert Fox air raids. This EC 3/2 aircraft ('4', seen over Iraq) was the first to be delivered to the Armée de l'Air.

Throughout the fighter world the Mirage 2000 is renowned for its excellent handling, making aerobatics a joy to those pilots lucky enough to fly the 'Mimi'. Low-speed manoeuvrability is on a par with the F-16 and MiG-29.

reduced costs. In part, this is because a tailless delta has fewer control surfaces than the more conventionally shaped aircraft and does not need the additional structural strength required to carry a horizontal tail. Furthermore – though few bothered about it at the time – the delta exhibits lower radar reflectivity at many angles. In short, it can fly fast in a straight line and carry a reasonable volume of internal fuel.

On the opposite side of the balance sheet, a low aspect ratio reduces the sustained turning rate, while having the aircraft's centre of gravity ahead of its aerodynamic centre means that the rear-mounted elevons have to work hard to produce any effect. Taking off, the initial attempt to rotate the aircraft with elevons up merely forces it harder down onto the runway, necessitating a larger airfield. Landing must be correspondingly fast (typically 184 kt; 340 km/h; 211 mph), with the additional complication of a high nose-up angle. In either circumstance, the moving trailing-edge surfaces are unable to act as flaps – as they would on a tailed aircraft – to reduce the speed required. The conventionally controlled delta needs a long runway and is at a disadvantage in a turning fight.

Relaxed stability

By contrast to the Mirage III, the 2000 has 'Karman fairings' at the wingroot which produce a more aerodynamically efficient blend with the fuselage with increased internal volume, but the minimum of additional drag. Less obvious, but essential to the aircraft's greater capabilities, is the relaxed stability design which moves the centre of gravity to behind the aerodynamic centre. An automatic flight control system and FBW controls are required because of this negative longitudinal stability, placing the Mirage 2000 in an entirely different class to its predecessor. Manoeuvrability is increased and landing speed decreased (to a typical 140 kt; 260 km/h; 162 mph). Rotation is achieved by lowering the elevons, thus increasing lift and pivoting the aircraft.

Slower speeds are made possible by the full-length leading-edge slats which also characterise the later delta. In two segments on each wing, the slats increase lift and are deployed in close combat, their use being restricted at other times to obviate the drag penalty. Wing span is 9.13 m (29 ft 11½ in), sweep is 58° on the leading edge and area is 41.0 m² (441.3 sq ft), giving a comparatively low loading for a fighter. The entire trailing edge is taken up with two-segment

elevons. Structure is mainly of metal, but with carbon-fibre composites elevons and fin. Strakes on the air intakes generate vortices at high angles of attack to maximise directional control. Door-type, carbon-fibre airbrakes above and below each wing are borrowed from the Mirage III.

Five hardpoints beneath the fuselage and two under each wing are available for the variety of weapons and tanks carried by the different Mirage 2000 versions. To free these positions for their best use, defensive aids are largely internal and result in antennas on the fin, wing tips and base of the rudder. Elements of the protective suite are common to most versions of the aircraft, the more recent having increased automation. A detachable refuelling probe is fitted ahead of the windscreen, offset to starboard. Two-seaters suffer a slight reduction in internal fuel capacity and, at 14.55 m (47 ft 9 in) in length (including nose probe), are 0.19 m (7½ in) larger than the single-place aircraft. Occupants are provided with an SEMMB (Martin-Baker licence-built) Mk 10 zero-zero ejection seat.

The 2000B sacrifices internal cannon and some fuel capacity for the second seat. This is the prototype, seen during carriage trials for the ASMP nuclear missile intended for the 2000N.

other testbeds had contributed over 4,100 sorties to the programme, as summarised below:

Aircraft	Quantity	Sorties	Task
Caravelle	1	17	M53 engine
Falcon 20	7	2,376	nav/attack system (incl. radar) and ECM
Meteor	2	93	radar altimeter, transponder and IFF
Mirage III	3	602	autopilot
Mirage F1	2	56	engine and cannon
Noratlas	1	32	navigation systems
Nord 260	4	62	TACAN
Vautour II	5	865	radar, Super 530 AAM
Totals	**25**	**4,103**	

Interceptor into service

A mere three years after development had been authorised, the prototype Mirage 2000 made its initial flight and the first small batch of production aircraft was approved for the AA. In each of the two following years (1980 and 1981), enough were ordered to equip 1½ squadrons, giving France the basis of its initial three-squadron wing. Such priority may be contrasted with that afforded to the current Dassault Rafale, which managed to garner only three AA (and 12 naval) orders 13 years after first taking to the air. Admittedly, that relaxed timetable is partly the product of reductions in East-West tensions, although the Mirage 2000 order book was also to suffer as a result of these. Plans for 372 of several versions were pared to 315, within which were minor variations of quantity as some interceptors were swapped to the attack contract.

It was as an interceptor that the aircraft first entered service, designated Mirage 2000C. There were four prototypes, flown from 10 March 1979 onwards, of which the first three required minor aerodynamic modifications before the production standard was reached. The single-seat 2000C has an empty weight of 7500 kg (16,534 lb) and a maximum take-off mass of 17000 kg (37,480 lb), including up to 3160 kg (6,967 lb) of internal fuel and 6300 kg (13,890 lb) of external stores (of which drop tanks are one option). Service ceiling is 54,000 ft (16460 m) and range on internal fuel is 1,000 nm (1852 km; 1,151 miles). G limits are +9 to -4.5.

Flying from Istrana until April 1995, and then from Cervia, Mirage 2000Cs, Ds and Ns have been active over Bosnia as part of the NATO peacekeeping force, the French contribution being known as Operation Crécerelle. A pair of 2000N-K2s took part in the raid on Udbina airfield on 21 November 1994, while one was lost to a SAM on 30 August 1995 during Operation Deliberate Force. This EC 3/5 2000C, seen peeling away from the tanker over the Adriatic, displays the typical long-endurance CAP configuration, consisting of two 2000-litre tanks and two Magic AAMs. Fitment of the large tanks precluded the carriage of Super 530D missiles, although aircraft armed with these weapons were held on alert at Cervia. For a time the 2000Cs carried two 250-kg or 500-lb bombs on the forward fuselage pylons.

New engines can take longer to develop than the aircraft they power, so it was as well that the SNECMA M53 was flying by the time that the Mirage 2000 was ready to do the same. Airborne trials had begun on the starboard side of a Caravelle on 18 July 1973 and continued in the previously mentioned Mirage F1E from 22 December 1974 onwards. A simple, modular,

Since the retirement of the Mirage IVP and S-3 missiles, the 2000N is the only strike asset assigned to the Forces Aériennes Stratégiques. The hitherto nuclear-only 2000N-K1s have been upgraded to have full conventional capability.

single-spool design, the afterburning M53 has three low-pressure turbine stages, five high-pressure stages and two turbine stages. Mirage 2000 prototypes had early M53-2 versions, but production has centred on the -5 and, later, more powerful -P2.

That was not the only engine planned for Dassault's third-generation Mirage. A pair of Turbo Union RB199 reheated turbofans (in other words, the Panavia Tornado powerplant) was revealed in 1978 as being intended for the international collaborative Mirage 3000. Nothing came of this proposal for an aircraft that would have pre-empted the Eurofighter, but more promise was initially shown by another twin-engined variant, the Mirage 4000. Announced by Dassault as a private venture in December 1975 (immediately after the Defence Council approved the Mirage 2000), this 33 per cent scaled-up 2000 employed a pair of M53s and bore the same relationship to its smaller brother as did the Mirage IV and III. It was less successful, and though the prototype aroused the interest of Saudi Arabia, it ended its days as a trials aircraft for the Dassault Rafale.

The effort to develop the Mirage 2000 also involved many other types, and by the end of 1993, when work was virtually complete, 25

Powerplant

Rated at 64.3 kN (14,462 lb) thrust dry and 95.1 kN (21,385 lb) with afterburning, the SNECMA M53-P2 is a continuous-bleed turbojet (low bypass ratio turbofan). It has a single shaft mounting two compressors, the first of which (low-pressure) handles a slightly larger amount of air to give a bypass ratio of 0.4. Total mass flow is 86 kg (190 lb) per second at a running speed of 10,600 rpm. Engine weight is 1500 kg (3,307 lb) and length is 5.07 m (16 ft 7½ in).

Cockpit

The pilot sits on a licence-built Martin-Baker F10Q zero-zero ejection seat. The Sextant TMV-980 display system consists of a VE-130 HUD and VMC-180 HDD. There is also a VCM-65 cockpit display for the Serval RWR.

Camouflage

Most 2000s deployed to Saudi Arabia retained their two-tone blue scheme, but this aircraft had a temporary experimental desert scheme applied over the top.

Dassault Mirage 2000C-S4-2
Escadron de Chasse 2/5
Operation Daguet
Al Ahsa AB, Saudi Arabia

The Armée de l'Air deployed 14 Mirage 2000Cs for Operation Daguet, the Armée de l'Air contribution to Desert Storm. All were S4 standard aircraft, and were drawn from all three escadrons of EC 5. Serials, including those of additional aircraft deployed on rotation, were as follows: 39, 47, 65, 72 and 73 from EC 1/5; 40, 45, 51, 59, 61, 63, 66 and 70 from EC 2/5; and 57, 58, 62 and 74 from EC 3/5. The first four aircraft deployed on 3 October 1990, although air defence missions in Saudi airspace did not begin until 12 December. The Mirage 2000s were initially restricted to CAPs over Saudi Arabia or short escort missions into Kuwait. From 24 January the 2000s flew with Jaguars and Mirage F1CRs into southern Iraq, without making contact with any enemy fighters. French Mirage 2000s flew a total of 340 CAP missions and 172 escort sorties. Abu Dhabi Mirage 2000EADs flew their first defensive missions on 16 February, performing a total of 58 by the war's end. Six reconnaissance missions were also flown, using 2000RADs, on 23/24/25 February.

Flight controls

The fly-by-wire system and SFENA autopilot control two-section wing elevons which travel 16° up and 25° down. The inboard leading-edge slats droop through 17° 30' while the outboard sections deploy to a maximum 30° deflection. Small airbrakes are located above the forward part of the wing.

Weapon stations

Nine attachment points are provided, with five under the fuselage. The centreline station is stressed for 1800 kg (3,968 lb), as are the inboard wing stations. Outboard wing stations are stressed for 300 kg (661 lb) while the remaining four fuselage stations are stressed for 400 kg (882 lb). The maximum external stores load is 6300 kg (13,889 lb).

Undercarriage

The landing gear is made by Messier-Bugatti. The mainwheel tyres are pressurised to 15 bars (217 lb/sq in) while the nosewheel is at 8 bars (116 lb/sq in). The nosewheel steers through ±45°, but can be disconnected for free castoring during ground towing.

Internal fuel

The total internal fuel capacity of 3978 litres (875 Imp gal) is carried in wing (1480 litres/326 Imp gal) and fuselage (2498 litres/549 Imp gal) tanks. Capacity in the two-seaters is 3904 litres (859 Imp gal).

Radar

The 2000C-S4 introduced the Thomson-CSF/Dassault Electronique RDI radar with high-PRF (above 100 kHz) Doppler function. In the final S4 aircraft (designated S4-2) the radar was initially the J2-4 version. The radar is optimised for air superiority work, in conjunction with the AD26 seeker head of the MATRA Super 530D missile. The radar's flat slotted plate antenna has an integrated IFF antenna. Weight of the 11 LRUs which make up the radar is 255 kg (562 lb).

Countermeasures

Early 2000Cs carry the manually operated Eclair (Alkan LL5062) chaff/flare system under the rear fuselage. ECM is provided by a Dassault Electronique Sabre in the fairing at the base of the fin.

Mirage 2000 Variants

The two-seat strike/attack variants outnumber the single-seat fighters in French service. Based on the 2000B trainer but with airframe strengthening to cope with the rigours of low-level buffet, the 2000N (above) and D (left) have a new weapon system with Antilope 5 or 53 radar providing various ground mapping functions and terrain avoidance (terrain following in D). The nav system has two radar altimeters and two INS sets. The 2000D also has an embedded GPS.

Normally, the 2000C uses only a small proportion of its weapons weight allowance to carry MATRA Magic and Super 530 AAMs. However, a fuller load of ground attack weaponry can be fitted to both the 2000C and its multi-role export counterpart, the 2000E. The two aircraft have the same weights and performance, two DEFA 554 30-mm guns mounted internally (125 rounds each), and also share the same type of radar as far as early French 2000Cs are concerned. Previously mentioned, it was the absence of intercept-optimised pulse-Doppler radar which resulted in the first 37 AA Mirage 2000Cs having a multi-role set, the Thomson-CSF RDM. Known at first as Cyrano 500 (following Cyrano II and IV in the Mirages III and F1), RDM was first tested in a Vautour in January 1980 and a Falcon 20 the following June. In November of that year, the third prototype Mirage 2000 was also equipped.

Thomson-CSF and Dassault collaborated on the definitive RDI radar, which still had a useful surface capability despite being optimised for interception. Delivered to squadrons from mid-1987, it lagged three years behind RDM in this respect. Technology remains sensitive, and no RDI aircraft have been exported. With the advent of RDI, the AA was able to use its Super 530D missiles instead of the Super 530Fs (the Mirage F1C's weapon) issued to squadrons flying the first 37 aircraft.

Military testing

Prior to air force service, early Mirage 2000s were evaluated by the Centre d'Essais en Vol (CEV) at Brétigny-sur-Orge and outstations including Cazaux and Istres. The first military user was the Centre d'Expériences Aériennes Militaires (CEAM) at Mont-de-Marsan. CEAM also received a small initial batch of all new major versions and sub-versions in order to formulate operating procedures and, in some cases, train the first user squadron. CEV's role was initially to evaluate the airframe and confirm airworthiness, but it now has a few Mirage 2000s for pure research. In some cases, CEAM has also trained foreign pilots for Dassault's export customers.

The AA marked its 50th anniversary – 2 July 1984 – by commissioning the first squadron of Mirage 2000Cs. Escadron de Chasse 1/2 'Cigognes', the famous 'Storks' squadron, was based at Dijon where, by early 1985, it had achieved full strength with 15 aircraft, including three trainers. Co-located EC 3/2 'Alsace' followed in March 1986 and EC 2/2 'Côte d'Or' equipped from June 1986 onwards, taking responsibility for pilot training with an appropriate share of the two-seat fleet.

Two more wings were outfitted with the definitive Mirage 2000C sub-variant, characterised by RDI radar (and Super 530D AAMs)

The primary weapon of the 2000Ds of EC 3 is the Aérospatiale AS30L laser-guided missile, with designation provided by the PDLCT FLIR/laser pod or ATLIS II TV/laser pod. Like the Super 530D air-to-air missile, AS30Ls are flight-time limited and are carried sparingly for training.

and M53-P2 engines. Whereas the Dijon aircraft replaced Mirage IIIEs, the remaining five interceptor squadrons had formerly flown Mirage F1Cs: EC 1/5 'Vendée', EC 2/5 'Ile de France' and EC 3/5 'Comtat Venaissin' all at Orange/Caritat, plus EC 1/12 'Cambresis' and EC 2/12 'Picardie' both at Cambrai/Epinoy. Defence cuts resulted in the third Cambrai squadron (EC 3/12 'Cornouaille') disbanding before re-equipment, further reductions bringing the disappearance of EC 3/2 in 1993 and EC 3/5 in 1997. Incorporated in the Force Aérienne Tactique, Mirage 2000Cs are assigned both to home defence and overseas intervention, the Orange squadrons specialising in the latter. Accordingly, it was aircraft of that wing which deployed to Al Ahsa, Saudi Arabia, for operations Desert Shield and Desert Storm in 1990/91, marking the Mirage 2000's combat debut – in the sense that it participated in a war, but encountered no enemy aircraft. Abu Dhabi, part of the United Arab Emirates, also committed

Exports of first-generation Mirage 2000s accounted for 157 aircraft for five air arms. India (below) was the second to order, but the first to receive aircraft, including a few early machines with M53-5 engines. Greece (below right) bought 40, primarily for the defence of Athens. They have been considerably upgraded, and some now have a secondary Exocet anti-ship capability.

its Mirage 2000s to the conflict. They included the 2000R reconnaissance version, unique to that customer, which relies entirely on external pods to acquire its information.

Fifth and last of the Mirage 2000 prototypes was the two-seat 2000B trainer, weighing 7600 kg (16,755 lb) empty and having a slightly diminished internal fuel capacity of 3100 kg (6,834 lb). All three fighter wings have operated at least a handful of 2000Bs for continuation training, with the previously mentioned EC 2/2 at Dijon acting as OCU for the interceptor force as well as a type conversion unit for pilots destined to fly strike/attack Mirage 2000s. On 1 July 1998, that role passed to EC 2/5 at Orange.

Strike and attack

In putting the Mirage 2000C into service as an interceptor, the AA had only covered the cancelled ACF's secondary role; there remained the question of a new low-level nuclear interdictor to replace the Mirage IVA, this having been the ACF's *raison d'être*. France had formed its own strategic force from 1964 onwards, eventually fielding an operational total of 36 (from 62 built) Mirage IVAs, each with a nuclear bomb semi-recessed in the belly. The carrier aircraft was no more than a scaled-up, twin-engined Mirage III, originally optimised

Ushering in a new era for the 2000D is the MATRA/BAeD APACHE 'stealthy' munitions dispenser. This weapon has a stand-off range of 140 km (87 miles), cruising at 150 m (500 ft) in mid-course before descending to 50 m (165 ft) for the terminal, active radar-guided phase.

for high-altitude missions and only later adapted to the low-level role with corresponding modification of the 65-kT weapon as the AN22. Additionally, having foregone the US-owned tactical nuclear arsenal for its North American F-100 Super Sabres upon withdrawal from NATO's military structure in 1996, France had built a replacement air arm from April 1973 onwards, based on the Mirage IIIE, SEPECAT Jaguar and the AN52 22-kT bomb.

Appreciating the limitations of free-fall bombing, the AA decided that the next generation of strike aircraft would carry a stand-off bomb, to which the designation ASMP (Air-Sol Moyenne Portée – Air-to-Ground Medium Range) was assigned. ASMP remained a priority after the demise of the ACF, the programme accelerating in 1976 when Aérospatiale and MATRA were commissioned to undertake parallel studies into turbojet- and ramjet-powered solutions, respectively. Aérospatiale's design was accepted and began development in 1978, remaining simply 'ASMP' to this day.

Left: Peru's Mirage 2000Ps are arguably 'top dog' in South America. This unusual formation sees a pair being led by a Chilean Mirage 50 and followed by an Argentinean IA-63 Pampa.

Below: A Peruvian 2000 refuels an earlier generation of Dassault delta, a Mirage 5P. The Peruvians use the same Intertechnique 231-300 refuelling pod as the Armée de l'Air.

Bottom: Oilfield defender – Abu Dhabi (UAE) has become an important customer for the Mirage 2000, and the only purchaser of the 2000R reconnaissance sub-variant. In association with a recent order for the 2000-9, Abu Dhabi is upgrading its existing Mirages to a similar standard, which includes the ability to launch Black Shaheen, an export version of Storm Shadow/SCALP.

Fitted with either a TN80 warhead of 150 kT or a 300-kT TN81, ASMP is broadly in the class of the Boeing AGM-69 SRAM, having a range of 43 nm (80 km; 50 miles) after low-altitude release from a platform flying at between Mach 0.6 and 0.95. Upon launching, ASMP is accelerated to Mach 2 by a powder propellant packed into the rear chamber of a ramjet. At the end of this five-second phase, blanks covering air intakes on each side of the missile are discarded and the ramjet begins operating on kerosene fuel. ASMP is 5.38 m (17 ft 8 in) long and weighs 900 kg (1,984 lb). It has no wings, relying instead on dynamic lift generated by the angular air intake trunks. Neither is it an 'intelligent' weapon in the sense of the current generation of terrain-following, radar-equipped, GPS-guided stand-off dispensers. However, having an inertial navigation system, it is programmed to fly a predetermined path (which can be varied until just

before launch) that makes use of terrain masking and avoids high-risk areas.

Notwithstanding the fact that the Mirage IIIE and Jaguar were single-seat aircraft, the AA decided from the outset that their replacement would have both pilot and WSO for maximum efficiency in all-weather interdiction. A two-

seat Mirage 2000, as ordered for training of interceptor pilots, was viewed as the ideal solution. Two prototypes were put on contract in 1979, initially designated 2000P (for Pénétration), but soon changed to 2000N (Nucléaire). Dimensions and weights are generally as for the 2000B – no more specific details

France is acquiring second-generation 2000-5s by conversion rather than new-build aircraft. Funding has been allocated so far for 37 for service with EC 2, the first entering service in 1998. The RDI radars released by the conversion process are being retrofitted to early machines which still have RDM. The Dash 5 conversion takes approximately six months per aircraft.

In common with most current fighters, the Mirage 2000 has undergone a radical cockpit modernisation. Compared to the 2000C (left), the 2000-5 (right) has a vastly improved workspace. The Sextant TMV-980 data display system (one head-up display and one head-down display) has been replaced by the Sextant Comète system, which employs a wide-angle HUD (not illustrated here: this is the original VE-130), three HDDs and a head-level display below the HUD. The only traditional dial-type instrument is the clock to the left.

have been released – and lo-lo-lo range is 500 nm (925 km; 575 miles). As for all Mirage 2000 variants, maximum permissible weight is 17 tonnes (16.7 tons).

The Mirage 2000B airframe required some local strengthening for its new mission in the turbulent lower air and, naturally, a navigation suite optimised for high positional accuracy. Key elements include a Dassault/Thomson-CSF Antilope 5 nose radar and twin inertial platforms, plus appropriate instrumentation in the rear cockpit. In its original form, Antilope 5 provides terrain-avoidance capability which is generally stated to be effective down to 61 m (200 ft), although AA operating squadrons appear to regard 91 m (300 ft) as the lower limit.

'Pre-strategic' force

Mirage 2000Ns with ASMP were issued to two former Mirage IIIE squadrons and one that previously operated Jaguars, all three transferring in September 1991 from the AA's tactical command to the Forces Aériennes Stratégiques (Strategic Air Forces), operator of silo-launched S-3 missiles and a depleted Mirage IV fleet also rearmed with ASMPs. (Both these accompanying systems were stood-down in 1996.) Despite the nominal change of status, the ASMP force is officially regarded as 'pre-strategic', leaving the

SLBMs of the French Navy as the weapons of ultimate recourse.

EC 1/4 'Dauphiné' worked up under the guidance of CEAM before transferring back to its home base at Luxeuil/St Sauveur on 30 March 1998. It became operational on 12 July, its aircraft at first restricted to carrying ASMP. EC 2/4 'La Fayette' achieved IOC on 1 July 1989, also at Luxeuil and also nuclear-only. Later Mirage 2000Ns were able to mount conventional weapons as an alternative to nuclear strike and they first went to EC 1/4 to allow surplus aircraft to reform EC 3/4 'Limousin' (previously the Jaguar-equipped EC 4/7) at Istres on 1 July 1990. Retrospective modification has now given all Mirage 2000Ns the conventional option.

Because of delays with the Rafale programme, the AA's requirement for Mirage 2000Ns was increased from 110 to 180, not all of which needed to be ASMP-armed. A version without the ASMP interface was at first mooted as the 2000N', then redesignated 2000D, the opportunity being taken to upgrade the navigation and attack system and more clearly separate the duties of the pilot and WSO. After some changes to requirements, the eventual buy was 161 aircraft, comprising 75 2000Ns and 86 2000Ds. The latter was intended primarily for precision attack with self-designated laser-guided weapons (AS30L missiles and LGBs), but can also deliver ordnance such as cluster bombs and rockets which require a closer approach to the target. Additional security from

Spirale

Fitted to late 2000Cs, 2000N-K2s and 2000Ds during production, and being retrofitted to 2000N-K1s, the MATRA Spirale system is an automatic countermeasures suite designed specifically for the Mirage 2000, and is integrated into the airframe. Chaff dispensers are mounted in the rear of the Karman fairings either side of the rear fuselage, while in the fuselage itself are eight-round flare dispensers. SAMIR missile plume warning receivers are mounted in the rear of the outboard missile pylons. Earlier Mirage 2000s use the Dassault Electronique Eclair chaff/flare system.

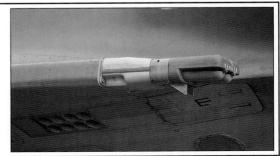

the defences will be obtained shortly, upon service entry of the MATRA/BAeD APACHE stand-off weapons dispenser.

Although nuclear delivery had long been the province of the tandem-seat Mirage IV, two-place conventional attack was a new concept to the AA. To assist in development of operational techniques, a squadron's worth of Mirage 2000Ns was assigned to Tactical Air Command, where it was declared operational on 30 August 1991 as the Nancy/Ochey-based EC 2/3 'Champagne'. EC 2/3 liaised widely with similarly-tasked squadrons in other air forces as it built up experience prior to the arrival of the first Mirage 2000Ds. Furthermore, in June 1992, as part of a reorganisation which resulted in all front-line units increasing from 15 aircraft in two flights to 20 in three, it was assigned a third escadrille. Various methods were used by different squadrons to ensure that the three badges were fairly distributed among their aircraft's fins.

First of the 2000D squadrons, EC 1/3 'Navarre' underwent conversion from Mirage IIIEs at CEAM, Mont-de-Marsan. At the earliest possible juncture, six aircraft, known as the Cellule Rapace (Rapacious Cell), were declared operational there on 29 July 1993, armed only with laser-guided weapons.

'Navarre' later returned to Nancy to become fully operational on 31 March 1994, but not before Cellule Rapace had been deployed to Cervia, Italy on 19 February 1994, along with 2000Ns of 'Champagne' squadron, to reinforce the Mirage 2000C element stationed there for NATO policing of former Yugoslavia. EC 3/3 'Ardennes' was the second Mirage 2000D squadron, becoming operational on 21 August 1995 and sending a detachment to Cervia nine days later. Two 2000Ds from each unit made the type's combat debut on 5 September that year when they used AS30Ls as part of a NATO attack on Serbian forces in Bosnia.

EC 2/3 began receiving Mirage 2000Ds in mid-1996, its conversion taking two years because of a reduced rate of deliveries. By then, all French Mirage 2000s except the ASMP force were contained within a new command, the Air Combat Force (Commandement de la Force Aérienne de Combat) which had replaced Tactical Air Command in March 1994 and assumed responsibility for interception as well as attack. It is in the former role that CoFAC is currently receiving a further boost with the beginning of deliveries of the latest Mirage 2000-5.

Major upgrade: the -5

During the second half of the 1980s and into the following decade, export sales of the Mirage 2000 slumped alarmingly as the aircraft was unsuccessful in several fighter competitions. Dassault urgently required an updated version to reinvigorate the interest of potential buyers and proposed to fit Thomson-CSF RDY radar, the equally new MATRA (now MATRA/ BAe) MICA air intercept missile and a cockpit modernised with technology from the Rafale

Orders for the Dash 5 were led by Taiwan, which has acquired 60 as part of its major revamping of its fighter forces. Magic 2 and MICA missiles were included in the deal, and the 2000-5EIs are tasked with air defence missions. Like the aircraft for Qatar, the Taiwanese Dash 5s have the full ICMS Mk 2 electronic countermeasures suite.

programme. The separate elements were test flown from 1988 onwards and the whole came together on 24 October 1990 when the much modified prototype Mirage 2000B flew as the first 2000-5. A single-seater followed on 27 April 1991.

Foreign interest was evinced in the Mirage 2000-5, although the home air force was reluctant to bestow its stamp of approval by making a purchase for the purpose of encouraging other buyers. After some behind-the-scenes lobbying, the AA announced in October 1992 that it did, after all, have "an operational need" for this aircraft, albeit as a conversion, rather than new-build. Taiwan then quickly placed a substantial order, followed by Qatar and Abu Dhabi/UAE. The first Mirage 2000-5s to attain IOC were those of a squadron of the 2nd TFW at Hsinchu, Taiwan in November 1997.

Apart from a length of 14.65 m (48 ft 0 in), the single-seat 2000-5 is similar in dimensions and weights to the 2000C/E. Dassault quotes an improved service ceiling of 60,000 ft (18290 m), declining to explain how this is achieved with the same engine and airframe. Extreme operational range in the air defence role – four MICA and two Magic AAMs, three external tanks jettisoned when empty, five minutes' combat at 30,000 ft (9145 m) – is 780 nm (1445 km; 898 miles). The Mirage 2000-5 can be equipped for attack missions, its most recent sub-variant having appropriately modified radar and the ability to launch a stand-off weapon.

In France, the 2000-5F interceptor reached CEAM in April 1998 and is now being prepared for service entry with EC 1/2 and EC 2/2. In a roundabout manner, Mirage 2000Cs

The Dash 5's RDY radar can provide ground mapping functions for attack missions. Qatar has purchased a wide range of precision ordnance to equip its multi-role 2000-5DDA/EDAs, including AS30L and Black Pearl, an export version of the APACHE stand-off munitions dispenser.

French Mirage 2000s carry bombs of both US and French origin. Shown above left are US Mk 82s, while above are SAMP Type 25 250-kg (551-lb) weapons. SAMP (Société des Ateliers Mécaniques de Pont-sur-Sambre) manufactures a range of low-drag bombs, with varying warheads (between 50- and 400-kg), noses and fin kits.

Left: Mirage 2000Cs are increasingly seen carrying air-to-ground weaponry in the form of bombs or rockets. This EC 2/5 aircraft carries a MATRA F4 18-round pod for 68-mm TDA Multi-Dart rockets. A variety of warheads is available, including kinetic energy darts, illumination rounds and inert trainers.

from the Orange-based squadrons are being upgraded for the Dijon wing, whose old aircraft are having their RDM radar replaced by RDI sets taken out of the Mirages before reissue to EC 1/5 at Orange. Following two prototype conversions at Istres, upgrades are being undertaken at Bordeaux, including the complete dis-assembly and transfer of fuselages to the Argenteuil plant for modification.

Preparation of the operating squadrons was launched in January 1998, when EC 1/2 began giving up its aircraft and temporarily replacing them with Alpha Jets (dismissively called 'Gadgets', but painted in full squadron markings) to enable pilots remaining at Dijon to maintain their flying hours. At the same time, EC 2/2 started running down its fleet of trainers and re-equipping with Mirage 2000Cs from Orange (RDI radar). This achieved, it was assigned to regular air defence duties from 1 August 1998 onwards. After working up at Mont-de-Marsan, the first dozen Mirage 2000-5Fs were due to gain IOC with EC 1/2 in April 1999, followed by EC 2/2 in 2000.

The Mirage 2000 story is far from finished, but the unusual absence of an aircraft at the 1998 Farnborough show could imply the end of the beginning, suggesting that marketing emphasis has shifted to the Rafale. Eight customers have contracted for 574 Mirage 2000s, not including 70 being upgraded to -5 or equivalent standard. Compared with over 1,400 Mirage III/5s and half that number of Mirage F1s sold, the third-generation Mirage has slowed the steeply downward trend in Dassault fighter sales, in spite of being far more sophisticated – and costly – than its predecessors. No longer a 'Mini Mirage', it is, perhaps, a Mirage Magnifique.   **Paul Jackson**

Developed by TBA, now TDA, the BAP-100 is a runway-cratering munition. The rear section contains a retarding parachute (below) while the main body consists of a booster rocket to accelerate the weapon towards the runway, and a warhead which is designed to explode beneath the concrete, lifting the surface. The weapon strikes the runway at around 230 m (755 ft) per second. A special carrier is required (right), which releases the weapons at a preselected time interval.

Left: An important family of weapons being developed for the air-to-ground role is the MATRA/BAeD APACHE and SCALP EG. Based on the same stealthy body, these are stand-off weapons with a small turbofan engine, pop-out wings and a range of about 150 km (93 miles). APACHE is a sub-munitions dispenser employing Prométhée millimetre-wave radar for terminal guidance. SCALP EG is a unitary warhead version with GPS/TERPROM guidance and imaging infra-red terminal guidance. Here a 2000N releases a test APACHE.

Mirage 2000 Variants

General note: Dassault fighter sub-designations are not allocated in alphabetical order, but derive in many cases from historical precedent originating in the 1960s. For example, there has been no Mirage 2000A because the Mirage IIIA appellation was restricted to a pre-service development batch. In the case of the initial two letters of the alphabet to be employed, usual aerospace practice is reversed, in that the two-seat trainer version is assigned the first available character. Elementary French supplies the rationale: 2000B for Biplace; 2000C for Chasse (Fighter).

Thereafter, other suffix letters are assigned according to role (N: Nucléaire) or customer (AD: Abu Dhabi). Some in the second category are more cryptic, such as M for Misr (Egypt) and H for Hindi (India), and it is usual for them to duplicate the designations of Mirage IIIs/5s or Mirage F1s in the case of countries which are long-term Dassault customers. The following data

	Single-seat	Trainer	Attack
Prototypes	2000-01/03	B 01	N 01/02
	2000-04		D 01/02
First generation	2000C (S1/S3)	2000B (S1/S3)	2000N
	2000C (S4/S5)	2000B (S4/S5)	2000N'
	2000E (EM, H, P)	2000BOB	2000D
	2000E (EAD, EG)	2000ED	2000S
	2000R (RAD)	'2000DA'	
	2000X (trials)	2000BX (trials)	
	2000-4	2000-3	
	2000-8		
Second generation	2000-CY	2000-5B 01	
	2000-5 01	2000-5D	
	2000-5F		
	2000-5E		
	2000-9		

therefore deal with Mirage 2000 variants in logical sequence of their development, not in alphabetical order. As an aid to reference, the table attached outlines the main 'families'.

The Mirage 2000 has emerged as a true multi-role aircraft, although it has evolved into two distinct sub-families. They are optimised for either air defence or attack and are represented here by a 2000D, carrying a PDLCT FLIR/laser designator pod, leading a 2000B fighter.

Single-seat fighter variants

Mirage 2000-01/03

The initial authorisation to proceed with the Mirage 2000 programme included three prototypes which, in Dassault fashion, were to be hand-built in the company's St Cloud experimental workshops near Paris. In earlier times, they would have been carried by road the short distance to Melun/Villaroche for final assembly and flight test, but the Dassault trials base had recently moved south to the better weather of Istres, and it was from here that development flying was undertaken. Reinforcing a previous break from French tradition, the trio was not numbered upwards from 001, but began with 01 – the series more properly used by pre-production aircraft.

Early trials demonstrated the need for a fin of increased chord and modification of the wing trailing edge/fuselage junction. Consequently, 01, 02 and 03 were the only Mirage 2000s to have the narrower fin with its distinctive curved leading edge, although they were later modified to production standard. Contributions of the aircraft to the development programme were as follows:

Mirage 2000-01: First flown at Istres on 10 March 1979 by Jean Coureau, achieving Mach 1.02 on dry thrust and Mach 1.3 with afterburner during a 65-minute sortie powered by the M53-2 engine. Initial official evaluation was a flight with a pilot from the CEV on 29 May 1978 (14th sortie), following which 01 was exhibited at Farnborough in September by Guy Mitaux-Maurouard, who demonstrated the aircraft's exceptional low-speed handling when only some 60 hours had been accumulated. No. 01 was modified at Cazaux between October 1978 and April 1979 with the larger fin, plus

2000-02 heads this prototype line-up, which includes one aircraft (probably 01) with the production fin. The patriotic paint scheme was applied for air show appearances.

straight-edged air intake splitter plates, and the Karman fairings at the wing trailing edge extended rearwards.

The internal cannon were first fired on 12 December 1979 (142nd flight) over the range at Cazaux, while between November 1980 and March 1981 Mitaux-Maurouard and Jean-Marie Saget cleared the aircraft for all flight manoeuvres from 0 to 800 kt (1480 km/h; 920 mph). By now with an M53-5 powerplant, it was handed over to SNECMA at Istres for engine trials, taking the M53-P2 aloft for the first time on 1 July 1983 (flight 580). No. 01's 1,202nd and final flight, in 1988, was to Le Bourget for exhibition in the Musée de l'Air et de l'Espace, having achieved a total of 1,149 hours 3 minutes of flying time.

Mirage 2000-02: First flown at Istres on 18 September 1978 by Guy Mitaux-Maurouard. Completed 125 sorties in the original configuration before receiving fin, trailing edge and air intake modifications. No. 02 concentrated on stores trials, including the RPL 501 and 502 1700-litre (374-Imp gal) drop tanks, and on its 164th sortie conducted the Mirage 2000's first aerial refuelling. The aircraft's 188th flight was delivery to the CEV for ordnance trials over the Cazaux ranges with bombs, cluster bombs and rockets. Flight 278, on 9 March 1981, saw the first launch of a dummy MATRA Magic AAM, while the first MATRA

Super 530 followed on 27 May the same year. Further modification was effected with fibre optic actuation of control surfaces, the aircraft returning to the air for its 479th flight on 3 November 1983. No. 02 was a few metres short of completing its 513th flight, on 9 May 1984, when fuel contamination caused a flame-out on the approach to Istres. Jean-Marie Saget ejected successfully from 75 m (250 ft), but the aircraft was almost completely destroyed by fire, having flown 399 hours 40 minutes.

Mirage 2000-03: First flown at Istres on 26 April 1979 by Mitaux-Maurouard. Fitted with a black radome, initially covering no more than ballast, it did not fly with RDM radar until 13 November 1980, becoming the first Mirage 2000 to do so. Equipped with navigation/attack avionics and modified with the new fin shape and related aerodynamic changes, it was based at Cazaux in 1982 for trials with Magic and

Super 530F AAMs. Whereas the two earlier aircraft had flown initially in natural metal finish before receiving an overall white paint scheme with red and blue trim, No. 03 was soon given a coat of air defence blue and light grey.

RDI radar was fitted (as was a camouflaged radome) during 1983 for trials of the Super 530D, the first launch of this variant following on 26 October 1984. The final flight (No. 647) took place on 31 August 1988 and was a ferry from Cazaux to Istres, bringing airborne time to 648 hours 4 minutes. After a period of storage, the third prototype was transferred on 20 May 1992 to the air force technical school (Ecole des Mécaniciens) at Rochefort/St Agnant.

2000-03 was the main RDM radar testbed, although it has yet to be fitted here. The aircraft was painted in this air defence scheme.

The second prototype is seen in the configuration and paint scheme in which it originally flew. Initially at least, 2000-02 differed in only minor detail from the first aircraft. As with the other prototypes, it was rebuilt with the revised fin.

Mirage 2000-01 initial configuration

Initial RWR fairing configuration

Tall fin initially, later retrofitted with production shape

One blade aerial on spine

No Karman fairings at rear of wing/fuselage junction

No radar – slimmer nose profile

Vane and pitot tube under nose

M53-2 engine

Mirage 2000-04

A fourth single-seat Mirage 2000 prototype was ordered in 1976. Powered by an M53-2, No. 04 first flew at Istres on 12 May 1980, piloted by Mitaux-Maurouard, achieving Mach 1.5 on this flight and Mach 2.0 on its third sortie. It was the first Mirage 2000 to be constructed to the definitive aerodynamic configuration, apart from being initially unpainted, with a 'solid' nose.

Once RDM radar was installed (black radome), No. 04 became representative of the initial production aircraft and, as such, was heavily involved in trials including missile and cannon firing, night refuelling and static tests in an anechoic chamber of the radar and self-defence jamming system. As part of the Mirage 2000-5 programme, No. 04 was modified to carry MICA missiles, flying so-equipped for the first time on 15 March 1990, its 732nd sortie. By 1991, it had a camouflaged radome, but was later withdrawn from flying.

As originally flown, 2000-04 had the new fin, Karman fairings and representative radome shape from the outset. The aircraft worked hard on weapon system development.

In its last useful role, 2000-04 tested the MICA missile. Here both EM and IR versions are carried.

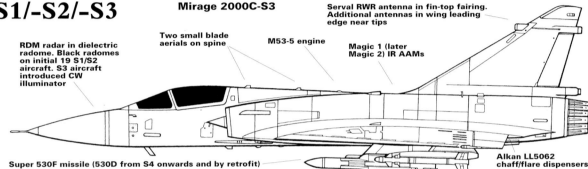

Mirage 2000-04 initial configuration

Small pitot forward of windscreen · Two aerials on spine · Cooling outlet · Production fin shape · No radar fitted – slimmer nose profile and equipment hatches · Air data vane under nose · M53-2 engine · Lengthened Karman fairings at rear of wing/fuselage join · Sabre jammer at base of fin

Mirage 2000C-S1/-S2/-S3

During the second and third financial years (1980 and 1981) of Mirage 2000 production procurement, France funded 22 and 15 2000Cs, respectively. As early production aircraft, they were to a lower standard of equipment than those which followed – particularly in view of the unavailability of the definitive M53-P2 engine and RDI radar. Provision was therefore made to equip these machines with the M53-5 and RDM, so as not to delay entry into service.

In the traditional French manner, production aircraft were numbered upwards from No. 1, the first two batches being Nos 1 to 37. These identities are serials, rather than constructor's numbers (c/ns), in that a single manufacturer's sequence was used for all Mirage 2000 types. For example, Mirage 2000C No. 22 (the last 1980-funded aircraft) has the c/n 68.

Later Mirage 2000Cs, which conformed to the intended production configuration, retained the same designation. However, just as 'F-16A' covers Fighting Falcons from Blocks -1, -5, -10 and -15, Mirage 2000s are given Standard sub-marks to differentiate minor changes in internal equipment. For the RDM/M53-5 aircraft these were as under:

Nos 1 to 15	Mirage 2000C-S1
Nos 16 to ?	Mirage 2000C-S2
Nos ? to 37	Mirage 2000C-S3

All were subsequently upgraded to S3s.

RDM radar is produced by Thomson-CSF and derives its designation from Radar Doppler Multifonctions (Multi-Role Doppler Radar). It had always been intended that Mirage 2000C-series exports would be equipped with RDM because of export restrictions on RDI, so integration in the first 37 French 2000Cs caused little additional work. The radar is a coherent, digital, frequency-agile system operating in I/J-bands (US military X/Ku) with modes for air interception and surface attack – both land and sea.

In the air-to-air role, RDM can look both up and down while searching, track while scanning (TWS), provide continuous tracking, generate aiming signals for combat, and compute attack and firing envelopes. Look-down was poor in early versions, requiring an in-service update before an acceptable standard was achieved. Over land, RDM supplies real-beam ground-mapping, navigation updates, contour mapping, terrain avoidance, blind let-down, target ranging and ground moving

Mirage 2000C-S3

RDM radar in dielectric radome. Black radomes on initial 19 S1/S2 aircraft. S3 aircraft introduced CW illuminator · Two small blade aerials on spine · M53-5 engine · Serval RWR antenna in fin-top fairing. Additional antennas in wing leading edge near tips · Magic 1 (later Magic 2) IR AAMs · Super 530F missile (530D from S4 onwards and by retrofit) · Alkan LL5062 chaff/flare dispensers

The first production Mirage 2000C was used for a series of avionics tests, including fitment of upgraded radars. The black radome gave way to grey for these trials.

target indication. Lastly, as an overwater radar, it gives long-range search and TWS, and additionally can designate targets for active radar homing missiles. Other mode options include Doppler beam-sharpening and continuous wave (CW) illumination of aerial targets.

The Mirage 2000 employs a SNECMA M53 low-bypass-ratio reheated turbojet developed for its predecessor, the stillborn ACF. Whereas the four single-seat prototypes initially used pre-production M53-2s rated at 83.34 kN (18,739 lb) thrust (although they were re-engined from 1980 onwards), the 2000C-S1/S2/S3 received an M53-5, providing 88.24 kN (19,842 lb) at full power and 53.92 kN (12,125 lb) in dry power on a bypass ratio of 0.32. Essential features of both variants include a three-stage fan, five-stage compressor, annular

combustion chamber, two-stage turbine and multi-flap variable nozzle. Digital engine control gives carefree handling throughout the Mirage 2000's flight envelope, and the modular powerplant, comprising 12 elements, simplifies repair and upgrading.

Self-defence aids of the early Mirage 2000C comprise a Thomson-CSF Serval RWR with antennas at each wingtip and on the trailing edge of the fin; a Dassault Sabre

jammer at the rear base of the fin with its detector in the fin leading edge; and a Dassault Eclair manually-operated chaff/flare system comprising Alkan LL5062 dispensers in the lower rear fuselage.

Mirage 2000C-S1: Production aircraft assembled and flown at Bordeaux. No. 1 first flew on 20 November 1982 (Guy Mitaux-Maurouard) and was delivered to

Aircraft '4'/2-EA was the first machine to be delivered to an operational unit, EC 1/2. Although carrying Super 530s here, the early S1 aircraft did not have the radar illuminator needed to guide them.

Left: An early weapon to be cleared was the MATRA ARMAT anti-radiation missile, seen here carried by a 2000C-S1. Both Egypt and India bought the ARMAT.

Right: Built as a 2000C-S2, this aircraft has been brought up to S3 standard with the grey radome.

CEV at Istres for development work, including trials of avionics for S3, S4-2A and S5 versions. No. 2 first flew 21 January 1983 and was assigned to SNECMA at Istres for trials of the M53-P2 engine and Dassault for navigation/attack avionics development. Nos 3 (flown 15 March 1983), 4, 5 and 6 went to CEAM at Mont-de-Marsan for service development work. Nos 7 (flown 14 December 1983) to 15 were delivered to first operational squadron, EC 1/2.

This first service variant was externally similar to prototype No. 04. Radomes were black, but gave way to grey when aircraft were upgraded to S3 standard. Principal feature of the S1 was the RDM Batch 1

radar which lacked an illuminator for a semi-active radar homing AAM. Accordingly, the Super 530 missile could not be fired and only the IR-guided Magic 1 was available for air combat.

Mirage 2000C-S2: Improved radar look-down capability characterised the S2 sub-variant, which was otherwise as its immediate predecessor. No. 16 was the first aircraft, but the quantity delivered has not been revealed. It is conceivable that all up to No. 37 were so-delivered and were uprated at a later stage to S3s. Grey radomes were introduced on the production line from No. 20. Most of the batch up to No. 37 had been delivered to EC 3/2 by

early 1987, although a few joined the mainly two-seat complement of EC 2/2, the OCU.

Mirage 2000C-S3: Addition of a CW target illuminator to the RDM radar gave compatibility with the Super 530F medium-range AAM, considerably increasing the Mirage 2000C's combat potential. Super 530 was developed from the first generation R.530, used by earlier generations of Mirage and readily recognised by its large, pointed fins. Long-chord fins, extending half the length of the missile body, identify this version, which entered service in December 1970 with the Mirage F1C interceptor, thus gaining the 530F designation. French Mirage 2000Cs have a secondary attack capability with free-fall bombs and MATRA F4 pods of 68-mm rockets.

Mirage 2000C-S3 Upgrade: By 1998, 26 of the original 37 RDM/M53-5 Mirage 2000Cs remained in AA service and a further two were with the CEV. As part of the Mirage 2000-5 programme, these aircraft are to receive redundant RDI radars from later production Mirage 2000Cs which are being converted to -5s.

Mirage 2000C-S4/-S5

RDI radar and M53-P2 engines were available for installation in Mirage 2000Cs purchased with 1983 and subsequent funds. An initial nine aircraft were funded in that year and the total had increased to 99 by 1989, or 136 Mirage 2000Cs in all. That figure was later reduced to 124 by a combination of transfers of orders to other variants and funding cuts. Production was as below:

Nos 38 to 48	Mirage 2000C-S4
Nos 49 to 63	Mirage 2000C-S4-1
Nos 64 to 74	Mirage 2000C-S4-2
Nos 75 to 124	Mirage 2000C-S5

Thomson-CSF developed RDI radar in conjunction with Dassault's electronics division, its initials signifying Radar Doppler à Impulsions (Pulse-Doppler Radar). Optimised for the air-to-air role, RDI has a flat, slotted plate antenna and operates in I/J (X/Ku) Bands. Range is some 90 km (56 miles) in look-down mode against a flying target. The radar has air-to-air search, long-range tracking/missile guidance and short-range tracking/identification facilities for air

combat, but can also provide ground mapping, contour mapping and air-to-ground ranging.

The Dassault Super AD26 missile seeker head is compatible with Doppler signals emanating from RDI, and when installed in the nose of a Super 530 missile changes its designation to Super 530D. This version of weapon is standard equipment of the main production batch of Mirage 2000Cs, matching the radar's better discrimination of targets to an improved interception capability. Slightly longer than the Super 530F and having an improved rocket motor, Super 530D can 'snap-up' to targets 40,000 ft (12200 m) higher than the launch aircraft and deliver a 30-kg (66-lb) fragmentation warhead at a maximum speed of Mach 4.6 to a hostile aircraft up to 21.6 nm (40 km/ 24.8 miles) away.

Since 1984, the Magic 2 IR-guided missile has also been available. Effective at distances between 320 m (1,050 ft) and 5.4 nm (10 km/6.2 miles), the Mk 2 has an improved proximity fuse for the 12.5-kg (28-lb) warhead and a seeker which can be directionally slaved to the RDI's antenna.

Above: EC 5 began to equip with the S4 variant in 1987 to become the first user with a fully operational aircraft. Super 530D and Magic II missiles were available from the start, greatly enhancing the aircraft's lethality.

Below: The S5 variant was the definitive fighter version, embodying full-spec RDI radar and M53-P2 engines. Both S4s and S5s have undergone upgrades, including the addition of HOTAS controls.

Increased aircraft performance is obtained from a considerable improvement in thrust available from the -P2 engine. Dry power is 64.32 kN (14,462 lb) – up 19 per cent – and full thrust is boosted by 8 per cent to 95.11 kN (21,385 lb) as a consequence of improvements including a bypass ratio raised to 0.40, a new low-pressure compressor and new fan. This version of engine is not directly related to the -2, having originally been designated -7. It is installed in all export Mirage 2000s, and will remain so following withdrawal of SNECMA's offer to provide a 98.05-kN (22,046-lb) thrust version, designated M53-P20, for later Mirage 2000s.

Mirage 2000C-S4: Initial standard of RDI/M53-P2 aircraft, delivered from July 1987 onwards. Total of 11 produced, of which the first three went initially to CEAM for service trials and the remainder began equipping EC 1/5. Radar in this version was RDI Series J1-1.

Mirage 2000C-S4-1: Improved J1-2 radar installed in the next 15 aircraft, which were delivered to EC 1/5 and EC 2/2. S4s were retrofitted to this standard.

Mirage 2000C-S4-2: RDI J2-4 radar in 11 production aircraft, comprising five for CEAM and six for 5 Wing.

Mirage 2000C-S4-2A: Update to all earlier S4 aircraft between Nos 38 and 74, adding RDI J2-5 radar and a modified throttle with HOTAS-type controls.

Mirage 2000-S5: Final 50 production aircraft to definitive standard with J3-13 radar. Delivered between late 1990 and June 1995; aircraft up to No. 93 went to CEAM or 5 Wing, majority of remainder to 12 Wing. No. 93 and subsequent aircraft were fitted with automatic MATRA Spirale

chaff/flare dispensers in the Karman fairings, replacing Eclair.

Mirage 2000-S5-2C: Retrofit introduced in 1995, initially on aircraft of EC 1/12, to provide RDI radar with improved anti-jamming circuitry. At the same time, Mirage 2000Cs operating over Bosnia on peacekeeping duties were fitted with an SAT SAMIR missile plume detector in the rear of a Magic launch pylon. In April 1994, these aircraft had gained a 'swing role' with Mk 82 bombs for attacking targets of opportunity while on Bosnian patrols. Some were designated as buddy tankers with an Intertechnique hose pod on the centreline and two non-standard 2000-litre (440-Imp gal) tanks on the inboard wing pylons.
Conversion is in hand of 34 (of 35 remaining) Mirage 2000C-S4-2As and three (of 48 remaining) S5s to Mirage 2000-5F standard, as detailed later.

Mirage 2000C-S5 early production

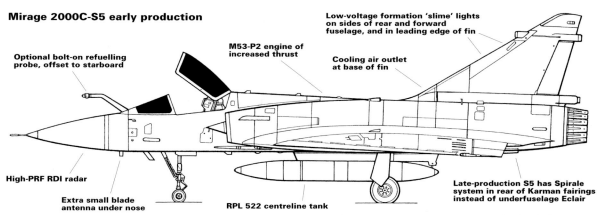

- **Optional bolt-on refuelling probe, offset to starboard**
- **M53-P2 engine of increased thrust**
- **Low-voltage formation 'slime' lights on sides of rear and forward fuselage, and in leading edge of fin**
- **Cooling air outlet at base of fin**
- **High-PRF RDI radar**
- **Extra small blade antenna under nose**
- **RPL 522 centreline tank**
- **Late-production S5 has Spirale system in rear of Karman fairings instead of underfuselage Eclair**

RPL-541/542 tanks of 2000-litre (440-Imp gal) capacity are increasingly common on 2000Cs. The aircraft above is seen on a mission over Bosnia, complete with Mk 82 bombs, while the pod-equipped aircraft below carries them for its tanking task. The refuelling pod is the Intertechnique 231-300.

Mirage 2000E (EM, H and P)

Mirage 2000EM (Egypt)

Two series of multi-role Exportation Mirage 2000s have been produced, not including the current 2000-5. The first of these comprised aircraft for Egypt (M), India (H) and Peru (P), all of which have basic self-defence suites and M53-P2 engines. Radar is RDM, fitted with a CW illuminator which allows it to operate with the Super 530 AAM. Differences from early 2000Cs (equipment in parentheses) include two main computers with expanded memory, a modified digital databus, a ULISS 52D inertial platform (52E), a TRT AHV-9 radar

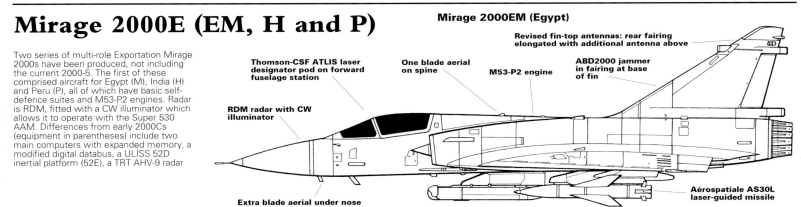

- **Thomson-CSF ATLIS laser designator pod on forward fuselage station**
- **One blade aerial on spine**
- **M53-P2 engine**
- **Revised fin-top antennas: rear fairing elongated with additional antenna above**
- **ABD2000 jammer in fairing at base of fin**
- **RDM radar with CW illuminator**
- **Extra blade aerial under nose**
- **Aérospatiale AS30L laser-guided missile**

Egypt's 2000EMs (this is the first aircraft) were delivered with a range of weaponry that included AS30L missiles, together with ATLIS II laser designation pods.

altimeter (AHV-6) and provision for a wide variety of weaponry, including air-to-ground. The VE-130 HUD and VMC-180 head-down displays remain unchanged on the 2000C. Self-defence can be provided by either ABD2000 (an export version of the 2000C's Sabre) or Thomson-CSF Remora (DB-3141 low-band or DB-3163 high-band) and CT-51J Caiman jamming pods. Each operator has also acquired compatible two-seat trainers, described under the Mirage 2000ED heading.

Mirage 2000EM: Egypt was the first export customer for the Mirage 2000, but the second recipient. The contract placed in December 1981 included 16 single-seat 2000EMs, the first of which flew in December 1985. Deliveries began in June 1986, the aircraft serialled 101-116. A unique feature of the 2000EM is a single, rear-facing antenna above the Serval DF unit high on the fin trailing edge. Based at Berigat, the aircraft are in a colour scheme of medium grey upper surfaces (with a black radome, however) and light grey undersides. Armament includes Magic, Super 530, ARMAT ASMs and AS30L ASMs with an ATLIS laser designator.

Mirage 2000H5 Vajra: India placed an order for 40 Mirage 2000s in October 1982, including 36 single-seaters. To expedite deliveries, the first 26, serialled KF101 to KF126, were produced with M53-5 engines and carried a '5' in their designation. KF101 flew on 21 September 1984 and, after pilot training in France, the first batch of seven

was delivered by air between 20 and 29 June 1985. The local name Vajra loosely translates as 'Thunderbolt'.

Mirage 2000H Vajra: Ten final aircraft from the first Indian contract (KF127 to KF136) and a follow-up batch of six (KF137 to KF142), ordered in March 1996 and delivered by October 1988, were supplied with M53-P2 engines. The earlier 26 were upgraded to this standard in India. Configuration and colour scheme (black radome) was as for the French 2000C but, by 1993, at least KF101 and KF104 had received mid-brown and dark green upper

Below: Confusion surrounds India's 2000Hs, which may be fitted with the attack-optimised Antilope V radar instead of RDM.

surface camouflage, suggestive of low-level tasking. IAF Vajras have always had a dual role, being able to carry MATRA ARMAT anti-radar missiles, Durandal anti-runway bombs and Belouga cluster bombs as alternatives to Magic and Super 530. However, at the arrival ceremony for the first seven aircraft, it was stated that the 2000H has an Antilope 5 radar and a second ULISS 52 INS, implying it to be a single-seat version of the 2000D interdictor. This apparent contradiction has never been fully resolved. Operating squadrons are Nos 1 and 7 at Gwalior.

Mirage 2000P: Peruvian Air Force version. Intent to order 14 aircraft was announced in December 1982 and renegotiated in July 1984 as a consequence of financial problems. An eventual total of 10 was delivered to Escuadrón 412 at La Joya from December 1986 onwards, together with Thomson-CSF ATLIS laser designators, 1000-kg (2,205-lb) MATRA guided bombs, MATRA AS30L missiles and a selection of free-fall bombs.

Peru's Mirage 2000Ps have a dual-role tasking, and are often seen armed with bombs. They also have the ability to fit ATLIS for the designation of AS30L missiles and MATRA BGL bombs.

Mirage 2000E (EAD and EG)

Improved self-defence equipment, extra computing power and additional air-to-ground armament options are to be found in the second series of export Mirage 2000s supplied to Abu Dhabi (part of the United Arab Emirates) (EAD) and Greece (EG).

Mirage 2000EAD: Between May 1983 and 1985, Abu Dhabi ordered 22 Mirage 2000EADs, which were numbered between 731 and 752. Acceptance was delayed by the customer's dissatisfaction with the standard of equipment installed, and not

until November 1989 were the first flown to the Middle East. Self-defence aids include Spirale chaff/flare dispensers in the Karman fairings and Elettronica ELT/158 radar warning receivers and ELT/558 jammers in place of the standard French equipment, the new fit being known as SAMET. A further unusual feature is the adaptation to carry AIM-9 Sidewinder AAMs as alternatives to Magic (which is also used). In common with Greek 2000EMs, there is a Chelton spade aerial under the forward fuselage in place of the usual swept-back blade antenna. Nos I and II Squadrons fly Mirage 2000s at Maqatra. In November 1998 it was announced that the aircraft will be upgraded to 2000-9 (2000-5 Mk II) standard as part of the UAE's deal to purchase new aircraft.

Mirage 2000EG-SG1: The Greek Mirage 2000 has extensive self-defence aids, more akin to the later 2000-5. The Mk 1 version of ICMS (Integrated Counter Measures System), developed jointly by Dassault, Thomson-CSF and MATRA, is based on the Mirage 2000C system, but with an additional pair of superheterodyne (superhet) antennas on the fin-tip, secondary DF receivers scabbed to the main DF pods at each wingtip, and Spirale dispensers in the Karman fairings.

Serialled 210 to 245, Greece's 36 Mirage 2000EGs were ordered in March 1985 and were delivered from March 1988 onwards to 331 and 332 Squadrons at Tanagra for air defence duties with Super 530D and Magic 2 AAMs. The exact version of radar is

Greek Mirage 2000EGs fly from Tanagra, with the air defence of Athens their primary tasking. However, at least some of the aircraft have been modified to launch the AM39 Exocet anti-ship missile.

Mirage 2000EG-SG1 (Greece)

One blade aerial on spine in forward position

Revised fin-top arrangement with additional small antennas above enlarged Serval units. Associated with ICMS Mk 1

M53-P2 engine

RDM radar with CW illuminator

Revised blade aerial under forward fuselage

Additional wingtip RWR antennas added to standard Serval units

Airfield emergency arrester hook

Spirale chaff/flare system in rear of Karman fairings

reported to be RDM3, which initially was covered by a black radome, later changed to grey.

Mirage 2000EG-SG2: Upgraded Greek aircraft, configuration undisclosed, but possibly connected with an update to ICMS which was declared operational in August 1995.

Mirage 2000EG-SG3: Modification to Greek Mirages to permit carriage of the 670-kg (1,477 lb) Aérospatiale AM39 Exocet anti-ship missile.

Abu Dhabi received 22 Mirage 2000EADs to equip its interceptor squadrons. Like the Greek Mirages, the EADs have the Spirale chaff/flare system, and incorporate non-French EW equipment. Unique among 2000s, the EADs are Sidewinder-capable.

Mirage 2000R (RAD)

In contrast to some reconnaissance versions of combat aircraft, the Mirage 2000R has no obvious airframe changes to accommodate cameras. RDM radar is retained, and the aircraft is capable of flying attack or air defence missions in addition to its primary duty. The operator is able to tailor the Mirage 2000R to specific tasks by varying the sensor pod carried on the fuselage centreline. Those available include:

– Thomson-CSF Raphaël SLAR 2000 (570 kg/1,257 lb), providing all-weather surveillance capability at up to 100 km (62 miles) and capable of real-time transmission of data to a ground station.

– Dassault COR2 multi-camera pod (400 kg/ 882 lb), with sensors operating the visible and infra-red spectra. Contains a fan of four AP OMERA 35 cameras (114 x 114 mm format) with focal lengths between 150 and 600 mm; an AP OMERA 40 panoramic camera (240 x 47 mm); and an SAT Super Cyclope infra-red linescan. Speed and altitude limitations are 600 kt (1100 km/h; 690 mph) and 11600 m (38,000 ft).

– Dassault AA-3-38 HAROLD long-range optical camera pod (680 kg/1,499 lb) containing a single AP OMERA 38 (114 x 114 mm) fitted with a 1700-mm telephoto for oblique photography of targets up to 100 km (62 miles) distant with a resolution of 1 m (3.3 ft). To assist aiming, the pod (which has the same shape as the COR2) also contains an Inspectronic CCD TV camera with a 30 to 300-mm zoom lens.

Only one customer has purchased the Mirage 2000R.

Mirage 2000RAD: Abu Dhabi's contracts included eight of this version, serialled 711-718, which were built in 1987. Configuration and equipment is as for the Mirage 2000EAD, except for the obvious provision for carrying reconnaissance pods. Furthermore, these are the only Mirage 2000 exports with the confirmed ability to fit the detachable refuelling probe available to French versions, although it may be presumed that Mirage 2000s of other operators have the option, if not the probes. In the case of Abu Dhabi, the tanker support would come from other Mirage 2000s fitted with a 250-kg (551-lb) Intertechnique 231-300 buddy hose-pod on the centreline. The 2000RADs are due for upgrade to 2000-9 (now 2000-5 Mk II) standard.

Below left: Seen in 1991 during Desert Storm, this 2000RAD sports the original desert camouflage and refuelling probe.

Below: The RADs have received a new grey camouflage. All reconnaissance sensors are carried externally, in pods on the centreline.

'Mirage 2000X' (single-seat)

The 2000 X7 is seen here with AS30L missiles, ATLIS pod and various test camera installations, including inward-facing cameras in place of the outboard pylons. Note the vestige of desert camouflage.

Not an official designation, this is a convenient label for various experimental Mirage 2000s which have appeared with non-standard identities for both short- and medium-term trials with the manufacturer. Two-seat aircraft in this category are discussed separately. Most, if not all, have been delivered to a customer at the end of their experimental use, but in many cases it has not been possible to determine their eventual identity.

Mirage 2000 X7: First flown on 9 November 1987 and marked '2000 X7' on the nose, carrying 2 Wing badges on the fin, this 2000C was used by Dassault for weapon trials including the AS30L and 1990, X7 gained this unit's badge on the fin and 'X7' applied immediately above, in the place normally occupied by the AA serial. Main trials use was as a launch aircraft for the MATRA/BAe MICA AAM, replacing prototype 04. It has also been seen in publicity photographs for the MATRA/BAe Apache stand-off weapons dispenser. Changes from the norm included a camera in place of the forward-facing jammer antenna in the fin leading edge and a rear-facing camera pod scabbed to the underside of the forward fuselage, both being used to record weapon separations. (The aircraft is possibly a rebuild of 2000C No. 7, which was damaged at Solenzara in June 1985.)

Mirage 2000 X7

Forward oblique camera mounted in former RWR fairing

Large blade aerial on spine

Early production 2000C with M53-5 engine

Black radome for RDM radar

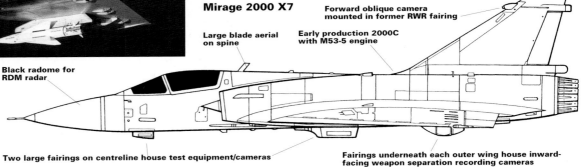

Two large fairings on centreline house test equipment/cameras

Fairings underneath each outer wing house inward-facing weapon separation recording cameras

Mirage 2000 Variants

Mirage 2000P X34: One Peruvian aircraft was used for 1000-kg bomb qualification in 1987.

Other export aircraft have been noted on flight test wearing their production numbers (for example, H37 on a 2000H) prior to application of serial numbers.

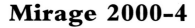

Left: Devoid of any pylons or test equipment, X7 is seen at the CEV. The flags are those of the (then) Mirage 2000 customers.

Above: Another photograph of X7 during AS30L trials shows the aircraft wearing a two-tone desert-style scheme.

Mirage 2000-4

This designation was allocated to one of the two stages by which the Mirage 2000-5 was evolved from the 2000C. Cockpit modifications of the Mirage 2000-3 are recorded in the section on two-seat trainer aircraft, the -4 stage being integration of the MATRA (now MATRA/BAe) MICA AAM. The first guided flight of MICA against a target drone was conducted on 9 January 1992 from the Mirage 2000 X7 (see above).

The Dash 4 designation covered integration of the MICA missile. Here an EM (radar-guided) version of the weapon is fired by the 2000 X7, while another missile is carried on the port pylon. The X7 retained the test camera installations from earlier trials.

No further aircraft were built to the -4 configuration, all other MICA-capable Mirage 2000s having the revised cockpit and other changes.

Mirage 2000-8

Dash 8 is the designation given to the export variant which became the Mirage 2000EAD, RAD and DAD for Abu Dhabi. It is conceivable that other export aircraft shared the -8 configuration.

Two-seat fighter variants

Mirage 2000B-01

In 1976, Dassault decided to increase the number of Mirage 2000 prototypes on order to five with the addition of a company-funded two-seat aircraft. In the usual manner, this was known as the 'B' version, but its duties extended far beyond conversion training, and it became both a valuable testbed and a useful demonstrator. Fifth to fly, it conducted its maiden sortie on 11 October 1980 in the hands of Michel Porta, powered by an M53-5 engine. Initially painted in house colours of white overall with red and blue trim, B-01 was the platform for the first Mirage 2000 flights with a dummy ASMP stand-off missile (8 July 1981, flown by Hervé Leprince-Ringuet) and ATLIS laser designation pod.

A live ASMP launch followed at CEV Cazaux in 1982, as did firing of the Dassault CC-630 765-kg (1,687-lb) twin 30-mm DEFA M554 cannon pod (25 October 1985) which compensates for the two-seater's lack of internal armament.

Early flights were with a white 'solid' nose, but the aircraft gained a black radome and RDM radar (following No. 03) in 1981. When displayed in 1985 it was in air defence camouflage and marked 'SNECMA M53-P2'. It then became the Mirage 2000B Y2, as described later.

Equipment, configuration and capabilities are as near as possible to the 2000C, apart from loss of internal cannon and some fuel. Integral wing capacity of 1480 litres

(326 Imp gal) is unaffected, but the 2000B loses 74 litres (16 Imp gal) from the fuselage tank, for a revised capacity of 2424 litres (533 Imp gal). A slightly raised spine results in the 2000C's aft-facing, raised engine air bleed outlet immediately ahead

The first two-seater was unpainted for its initial flights. It subsequently received a white scheme.

of the fin being replaced by a pair of flush rectangular doors in each side.

Mirage 2000B

France has not been the only nation to order two-seat trainer versions of combat aircraft almost as an afterthought, but that sin of omission was not committed in the case of the Mirage 2000. In 1979, the first year of production funding, just four new Mirages were ordered – all of them 2000Bs. The figure had increased to 22 by 1986 and 32

by 1990, the last two suffering cancellation. Of the 30 built, two are with CEV on long-term trials and two have been lost in accidents.

Mirage 2000Bs have been allocated both to an OCU and to individual squadrons, the latter requiring commonality with the sub-version of 2000C which they operate. In the case of conversion unit aircraft, it will be noted that some have an engine/radar combination which does not parallel any single-seat machine. Production details are:

Nos 501 to 514	Mirage 2000B-S3
Nos 515 to 520	Mirage 2000B-S4
Nos 521 to 522	Mirage 2000B-S4-2
Nos 523 to 530	Mirage 2000B-S5

All Mirage 2000Bs were delivered in standard blue and grey upper surface camouflage, the first 15 with black radomes, the remainder grey.

Mirage 2000B-S3: The first production 2000B flew on 7 October 1983, and thus

followed 2000C No. 6; Nos 502 and 503 were supplied to CEAM for service trials and the balance went to the three squadrons of 2 Wing, including the OCU, EC 2/2. All have M53-2 engines and most have RDM radar, the exceptions being No. 501, used by CEV as a trials vehicle for RDI radar and, later, the Rafale's RBE2; and No. 503, delivered to CEAM in March 1987 with the sixth RDI prototype. No. 504 was converted to a testbed, as described under the Mirage 2000BOB heading. Some early

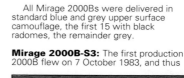

Mirage 2000Bs mirror the Cs in production standards, which largely concern the radar. The black radomes (above) identify early S1/S3 aircraft with RDM, while grey radomes (right) distinguish later S4/S5 aircraft with RDI radar.

aircraft were built to S1 and S2 radar standards (see Mirage 2000C) before modification to S3.

Mirage 2000B-S3 Upgrade: Surplus RDI radars will be installed in some previously RDM-equipped aircraft in parallel to the similar programme being undertaken on early Mirage 2000Cs.

Mirage 2000B-S4: In 1987-88, six further aircraft were supplied to CEAM (one) and 5 Wing with RDI J1-1 radar, but retained the -5 engine. Two, Nos 516 and 517, were later nominated for transfer to 2 Wing and thus were modified in 1990 with RDM radar.

Mirage 2000B-S4-2: The next two trainers, supplied in 1990, both had RDI J2-4 engines, but No. 521 was powered by an M53-5 and went to 5 Wing, while No. 522 had a -P2 for use at CEAM.

Mirage 2000B-S5: Eight remaining aircraft were mostly issued to 12 Wing in the first instance and were to the full 'early

S5' standard with RDI J3-13 radar and -P2 engines, although no Spirale self-defence dispensers were installed. The last was delivered in December 1994.

Mirage 2000Bs are assigned throughout the air defence units for continuation training duties, with a larger number concentrated in the training unit. Until 1998 the OCU was EC 2/2 'Côte d'Or' at Dijon-Longvic, with which this 2000B-S4-2 served. Now the training task is undertaken by EC 2/5.

Mirage 2000B-S3

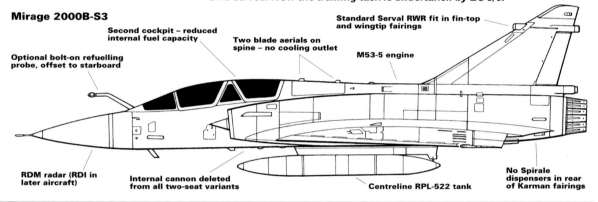

Optional bolt-on refuelling probe, offset to starboard

Second cockpit – reduced internal fuel capacity

Two blade aerials on spine – no cooling outlet

Standard Serval RWR fit in fin-top and wingtip fairings

M53-5 engine

RDM radar (RDI in later aircraft)

Internal cannon deleted from all two-seat variants

Centreline RPL-522 tank

No Spirale dispensers in rear of Karman fairings

Mirage 2000BOB

The Banc Optronique Biplace (Two-seat Optronic Testbed) is operated by the CEV at Brétigny-sur-Orge on behalf of the defence ministry and aerospace industry, specialising in military electro-optic trials. After four years with 2 Wing, No. 504 was delivered to Brétigny on 5 August 1988 and underwent modification for its new duties, flying again on 28 June 1989 with pilots Claude Saget and Philippe Limacher. An upgrade to S3 standard was completed when the aircraft returned to the air on 19 September 1989, ready for its duties to begin.

Equipment tested has included the Thomson-TRT Rubis FLIR pod, Sextant VEH 3020 holographic HUD (for the Mirage 2000-5, replacing the standard VE-130) and

Sextant night vision goggles. Among non-visual tests have been those of an onboard oxygen-generating system for the Rafale. Externally, the 2000BOB differs little from the air force version, now having a grey radome and fixed refuelling probe. Unusually for a 2000B, it is often flown with a pair of RPL 541/542 2000-litre (440-Imp gal) external tanks, more commonly seen on the 2000N/D.

The Mirage 2000BOB is a permanent test vehicle for various equipment trials. Here it is seen outside the famous hangars of the CEV at Brétigny.

Mirage 2000ED (BG, BM, DAD, DP and TH)

Originally built as a 2000TH5, this Indian two-seater was subsequently re-engined to full 20000TH standard.

Although never assigned to a specific customer, 2000ED is the general designation for exported Mirage 2000 trainers. In fact, customers for the first-generation trainer have been given 2000B and 2000D designations, those for India adopting the English convention of T for trainer.

Aircraft configurations reflect those of the main single-seat purchase by each operator, all having RDM radar and M53-P2 engines, except where stated otherwise.

Mirage 2000BG: Greek version; four aircraft delivered in 1988, serialled 201 to 204. ICMS Mk 1 self-defence system, including second pair of fin antennas and Spirale dispensers.

Mirage 2000BM: By chance, Egypt also assigned the numbers 201 to 204 to its four trainers supplied in 1986.

Mirage 2000DAD: Six aircraft, 701 to

706 for Abu Dhabi, delivered 1989-90. In contrast to the EADs and RADs supplied simultaneously, they have light blue and light grey upper surface camouflage (plus black radomes). In common with the other Abu Dhabi Mirage 2000s, they will be upgraded to 2000-9 configuration.

Mirage 2000DP: Peru's trainer order was reduced to two aircraft, serialled 193 and 195 (194 being current on a Mirage 5). The first was handed over at the Paris air show on 7 June 1985.

Mirage 2000TH5: Four, KT201 to KT204, accompanied the first batch of Indian single-seat aircraft, all powered by -5 engines to ensure early delivery. They were retrofitted with M53-P2s in India and became 2000THs.

Mirage 2000TH: Three more Indian trainers were KT205 to KT207, of which the last was delivered on 7 October 1988. The first four were converted to this standard.

Left: Six 2000DAD two-seaters were included in Abu Dhabi's first batch, finished in a grey scheme. The aircraft have Spirale installations but retain RDM radar.

Below: Peru was initially to have acquired three two-seaters, but this was cut to two 2000DPs when the planned purchase was reduced. They serve with Escuadrón de Caza-Bombardeo 412 at La Joya.

Above: Greece operates four two-seaters, fitted with full mission equipment, including ICMS Mk 1.

Below: Coincidentally, Egypt's four 2000DM two-seaters have the same serials as the Greek machines.

'Mirage 2000X/Y' (two-seat)

As previously noted under single-seat variants, some aircraft were assigned special designations for trials leading up to the Mirage 2000-5.

Mirage 2000B X1: First production Mirage 2000B No. 501 was transferred to Dassault for trials and demonstration flying. Marked 'BX1' on the fin, and with national insignia removed, it first flew in its new guise on 13 February 1987 and has since been occupied in trials and demonstration flying. By 1990 it was marked 'Mirage 2000-5' and sported dummy MICA missiles, a grey radome and superhet fin-tip antennas in addition to the usual larger ECM protrusions.

Mirage 2000B Y1: Two-seat prototype B01 was renumbered BY1 and on 10 March 1988, with Patrick Experton in command, took to the air for the first time with a 'glass' cockpit from the Rafale, as described under Mirage 2000-3. In May 1988 it added RDY radar, but was still marked only as 'Mirage 2000' when shown statically at Paris in June 1989, wearing a transparent radome and superhet antennas. It later became BY2.

Mirage 2000B Y2: Further modification of BY1 with MICA AAMs resulted in this new identity, which was being worn by 1990, together with the title 'Mirage 2000-5'. It reverted in the following year to B01, as described later.

Left: This aircraft, built as the two-seat prototype, has had a long career as a Dassault testbed. Here it is seen at the 1989 Paris air show, marked as 'BY1' and with a transparent radome for ground display of the RDY radar. It had already received a glass cockpit as part of the Dash 3 upgrade. Today it is the 2000-5B demonstrator.

Right: 'BX1' is seen carrying four dummy MICA missiles. This aircraft is another Dassault Dash 5 demonstrator, formerly the first production two-seater and a regular sight at trade shows.

'Mirage 2000DA'

Joint references to French Air Force Mirage 2000Cs and 2000Bs sometimes use this unofficial designation to indicate the Défense Aérienne (Air Defence) role to which they are assigned.

Mirage 2000-3

The -3 project number was assigned to a private venture upgrade with five multifunction screens transferred from the Dassault Rafale programme. Replacing the earlier-generation instruments, the 'glass' cockpit was dubbed Advanced Pilot System Interface (APSI) by Dassault and first flew in BY1, as mentioned above. With RDY radar, a new central processing unit and VEH 3020 holographic HUD, the -3 is raised to -5 configuration.

Two-seat attack variants

Mirage 2000N 01 and 02

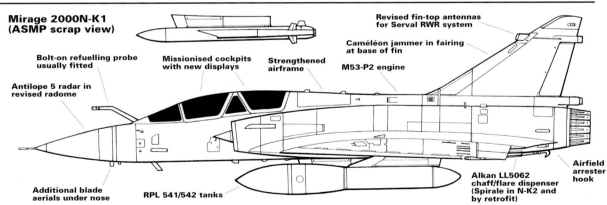

Using the two-seat 2000B as a basis, Dassault produced a nuclear strike version of the Mirage 2000 to carry an Aérospatiale ASMP stand-off missile. Changes to the airframe were restricted to local strengthening to combat the additional stresses of prolonged flight at low level. More than compensating for the two-seater's slightly reduced internal fuel capacity of 3904 litres (859 Imp gal), RPL 541 and 542 external tanks of 2000 litres (440 Imp gal) each were developed as an alternative to the 2000B/C's RPL 501 and 502. On ferry flights, an RPL 522 tank of 1300 litres (286 Imp gal) can be installed on the centreline.

Avionics underwent considerable change, beginning in the nose with installation of a Dassault/Thomson-CSF Antilope 5 radar. Optimised for air-to-ground

missions and scanning in J (Ku) Band with a flat-plate antenna, this terrain-avoidance radar surveys the ground out to 12 km (7 miles) ahead and generates steering commands for the pilot when at altitudes as low as 90 m (300 ft) and at speeds up to 600 kt (1112 km/h; 691 mph). Other modes available are air-to-air (30 km; 19 miles), ground search (same range), ground mapping and surface target ranging. When desired, the terrain-avoidance and mapping modes can be interleaved, the radar rapidly switching between the two to provide these functions simultaneously.

In the rear seat, the WSO is provided with two SAGEM ULISS 52P inertial platforms, two TRT AHV-12 radio altimeters and a duplicate of the pilot's Sextant VMC 180 three-colour head-down display of radar information. Further assistance in navigation

comes from the Antilope 5's partial terrain-reference capability which allows it to produce a position update from ground height variations. The 2000C's SFENA 605 autopilot is replaced by a 606.

Mirage 2000N 01: First of two aircraft ordered in 1979, No. 1 first flew at Istres on 3 February 1983, piloted by Michel Porta

For its first six flights, the prototype 2000N was unpainted. The radarless nose carried a small air data vane.

(the second seat, normally occupied by Bruno Coiffet, being empty on that occasion). Powered by an M53-5, the aircraft was initially unpainted, with a 'solid' nose, but green and grey low-level disruptive pattern camouflage was applied before the seventh sortie. It first carried an inert ASMP on its 34th flight, during trials at Cazaux. N01 was delivered to the CEV in October 1983 for preliminary assessment, yet it was not until later in the year that it received Antilope radar and a black radome (as did all later 2000Ns) for intensive trials in the low-level regime. After its 615th flight, on 2 March 1990, N01 underwent conversion to the prototype Mirage 2000D.

Mirage 2000N 02: Porta was the pilot for N02's first flight on 21 September 1983. Like the 12 Mirage 2000s which preceded it, No. 2 relied on an M53-5. Camouflaged and with full avionics, it remained at Istres for development work including ECM system, ASMP carriage and later modification with Spirale dispensers in the Karman fairings. It conducted 493 sorties as a 2000N – the last on 26 April 1990 – before being reworked as the second 2000D.

Still lacking radar, N01 is seen here during early ASMP trials. Note the undernose bulge and underwing fairings housing test cameras.

Mirage 2000N

A batch of 15 Mirage 2000Ns was included in France's 1983 defence budget, and by 1987 the full total of 75 had been funded. Two production standards emerged:

No. 301	Mirage 2000N
Nos 302 to 331	Mirage 2000N-K1
Nos 332 to 375	Mirage 2000N-K2

By 1998, seven had been lost in accidents and another two were on long-term assignment to the CEV.

The Mirage 2000N/ASMP combination replaced Mirage IIIEs armed with AN52 free-fall nuclear bombs, an initial squadron being declared operational on 12 July 1988. Normal operational fit is RPL 541/542 tanks

Mirage 2000N-K1 (ASMP scrap view)

- Revised fin-top antennas for Serval RWR system
- Caméléon jammer in fairing at base of fin
- M53-P2 engine
- Bolt-on refuelling probe usually fitted
- Missionised cockpits with new displays
- Strengthened airframe
- Antilope 5 radar in revised radome
- Additional blade aerials under nose
- RPL 541/542 tanks
- Alkan LL5062 chaff/flare dispenser (Spirale in N-K2 and by retrofit)
- Airfield arrester hook

Below: Capable of ASMP carriage only, Mirage 2000N-K1s served exclusively with EC 4. The fleet has been upgraded to N-K2 standard, with all 2000Ns now concentrated in the wing, at Luxeuil.

Right: Prior to deployment of 2000Ds, EC 2/3 received N-K2s which operated in the conventional role. This bomb-carrying example is seen on Bosnia patrol, its temporary camouflage beginning to wear off.

February 1987 and later to CEV (also at Istres) for development work, in the course of which it was upgraded to K2 standard with provision for conventional weaponry and Spirale dispensers. It also took on the external appearance of a Mirage 2000D in having the nose probe deleted and, later, superhet antennas added to the fin-tip.

Mirage 2000N-K1: The initial production standard concerned 30 aircraft which lacked Spirale dispensers and, less visibly, were unable to launch conventional weapons. The first three were supplied to CEAM (including No. 303, later to CEV for APACHE launch trials) and the remainder issued to EC 1/4 and EC 2/4. From 1990 onwards, they were upgraded with limited conventional attack capability and now equip EC 3/4 and part of EC 2/4. Upgrading to K2 standard was due for completion by the end of 1998.

Mirage 2000N-K2: Able to operate with ASMP or conventional weapons (although not those with precision guidance), the final 44 aircraft were delivered between July 1988 and late 1993, the first four initially for CEAM. Spirale dispensers – or, at least, the appropriate mountings – were installed from the outset. The balance of the batch re-equipped EC 1/4, but 18 were delivered directly to EC 2/3, where only their conventional abilities were employed until the squadron converted to Mirage 2000Ds from mid-1996 onwards. They are now being transferred to the three other Mirage 2000N squadrons to reassume a nuclear deterrance role.

Mirage 2000N'

N Prime (N Apostrophe) was a 'non-nuclear nuclear' Mirage 2000N, foreseen as a Mirage IIIE replacement because of delays with the Dassault Rafale programme. To avoid contradiction and confusion, the version was redesignated Mirage 2000D in 1990, before any had been built.

on the inboard pylons, Magic self-defence AAMs outboard and ASMP on the centreline. Defensive avionics are similar to those of the Mirage 2000C, including Serval RWR, but with a Dassault Caméléon jammer replacing Sabre in the fin-root position. Two Alkan LL5062 16-shot flare dispensers are located in the lower rear fuselage.

Despite their nuclear role, some Mirage 2000N squadrons maintain a secondary capability with conventional weapons such as BAP 100 and BAT 120 bomblets, Belouga CBUs and 68-mm rocket pods.

Mirage 2000N No. 301: Unusually for a 'production' machine, No. 301 was built at Istres, from where it first flew on 3 March 1986, crewed by D. Chenevier and Bruno Coiffet. It was delivered to CEAM on 19

Mirage 2000D 01 and 02

In producing a conventional attack version of the Mirage 2000N, Dassault took the opportunity to install later versions of some equipment to upgrade the aircraft's capabilities. External differences between the two include deletion of the nose pitot; addition of ICMS Mk 2 countermeasures, betrayed by a second pair of small (superhet) antennas on the fin-tip; a spine antenna for GPS (which is integrated with

the ULISS 52P INS); and cockpit transparencies covered in gold film to reduce radar reflectivity.

Internally, the ASMP interface is removed and Antilope radar upgraded to 53C/D standard, adding a terrain-reference system to provide terrain-following capability down to 300 ft (90 m) at the usual penetration speed of 520 kt (963 km/h; 598 mph). The central computer is now a

Dassault 2084 XR, and the autopilot, a SFENA 607. 'Have Quick 2' radios provide secure, jamming-free communications and lighting is compatible with night vision goggles. Differences in the crew's positions are profound, with the 2000D having more integrated HOTAS controls and being well on the way to a 'glass' cockpit. The pilot has a second large screen in the left of the instrument panel and the Officier Système d'Armes (WSO) gains two more screens of a similar size to add to the one (mounted centrally) inherited from the 2000N. Among several functions, these new screens can

display images from FLIR pods and laser designators. Whereas the pilot of the 2000N has some responsibility for navigation, the 2000D's WSO is entirely in charge of the nav/attack system. With the benefit of inputs from GPS, average navigational accuracy is increased from the 80 m (260 ft) of the 2000N to 8 m (26 ft).

Dassault proudly proclaims the 2000D designation to stand for the aircraft's Diversifié (diversified) potential; French Air Force squadrons operating other, less heavily laden fighters call it the '2000 Diesel'.

Mirage 2000D 01: Following conversion from 2000N 01 at Istres, the prototype returned to the air on 19 February 1991, flown by Chenevier and Coiffet and wearing D01 on the fin. Conversion also included an M53-P2 engine, but the black radome colour was retained and superhet antennas were not fitted to the fin. After use in weapons and nav/attack system trials, D01 is believed to have been withdrawn from use.

Mirage 2000D 02: Previously 2000N 02, the aircraft was reflown at Istres on 24 February 1992 by Chenevier and Brunet. D02 had extra features more representative of the production aircraft which followed it, in the form of superhet antennas, a dark green radome and the standard grey and green camouflage applied to undersides as well as upper surfaces. It, too, appeared to have completed its trials by 1998.

Mirage 2000D

Funding of the 2000D began in 1988 with 18 aircraft and ended with the 75th in 1991 but, following a reappraisal of needs, the French Air Force cancelled 15 air defence aircraft and reordered them in 1994 as 2000Ds. A 1996 defence review amended the total again, resulting in a final figure of 86. Since 1996, the 2000D has been the only version in production (as opposed to under conversion) for France. Planned variants are:

Nos 601 to ?*	Mirage 2000D-R1
Nos ? to 686	Mirage 2000D-R2

*The final delivery of 1997 was No. 651; the last in 1998 was due to be No. 659; and No. 686 is scheduled for 2001. One has been lost and another is assigned to CEV.

Key to much of the Mirage 2000D's extra potential is precision attack weapons is the 340-kg (750-lb) Thomson-CSF PDLCT TV/thermal imaging pod carried on a pylon beneath the starboard air intake. This Pod de Désignation Laser à Caméra Thermique (Laser Designation Pod with Infra-Red Camera) is effective day or night and is used to direct either a 520-kg (1,146-lb) Aérospatiale AS30L missile or 990-kg (2,183-lb) MATRA/BAe BGL 1000 bomb (a weapon rejoicing in the marketing name of Arcole). AS30L delivers 240 kg (529 lb) of

explosive at Mach 1.2; the Bombe à Guidage Laser is 850 kg (1,874 lb), including casing, before pop-out rear fins and guidance unit are attached.

One missile or LGB is carried on the starboard inner wing pylon, balanced by an RPL 541 tank and having an RPL 522 on the centreline. Two laser weapons and an RPL 522 are possible on shorter missions, or when aerial refuelling is available. Additionally, as an economy measure, ATLIS designation pods from the diminishing SEPECAT Jaguar force are being refurbished as ATLIS II and issued to Mirage 2000D squadrons. Other ordnance used by French Air Force units comprises:

– MATRA/BAe BAP 100 anti-runway bomblets in two packs of nine on centreline

– MATRA/BAe BAT 120 anti-personnel/anti-armour bomblets, similarly stored

– MATRA/Thomson-Brandt BLG 66 Belouga cluster bombs, maximum of seven, each 305 kg (672 lb)

– 250-kg (551-lb) (conventional shape or SAMP BL EU2 low-drag) or US Mk 82 500-lb (227-kg) bombs, in several positions

– MATRA/BAe F4 68-mm (2.7-in) rockets in 18-round pods, one per wing

From 2000, the MATRA/BAe APACHE-AP stand-off weapons dispenser will be available. The 1230-kg (2,712-lb) Arme Propulsée A CHarges Ejectables – Anti Piste (Powered Weapon with Ejected Load – Anti Runway) has pop-out wings, a small turbojet, an INS and its own radar to enable

Left: This 2000D is in typical precision attack fit for a longer-range mission, carrying only one AS30L missile (or BGL 1000 bomb). The PDLCT (illustrated) is the primary designation pod but the ATLIS II is also available. The latter is a daylight-only pod.

Derived from the 2000N, the 2000D has a further enhanced electronic warfare suite and numerous other refinements, most notably in the cockpit. The WSO has screen displays for FLIR/TV imagery and the luxury of GPS for navigation.

it to attack airfields up to 140 km (87 miles) from the release point. The first fully-representative long-range launch of an APACHE was by Mirage 2000N (No. 303) from the CEV base at Cazaux on 29 July 1994.

Mirage 2000D-R1N1L: The first six Mirage 2000Ds initially had the ability only to launch (with PDLCT) AS30L and BGL 1000, plus Magic AAMs. No. 601 was delivered to CEAM on 9 April 1993, and with the five following aircraft was used to work-up a flight of EC 2/3 known as Cellule Rapace. This gained IOC on 29 July 1993, giving the French Air Force an urgently needed potential with laser-guided weapons. By June 1995, all had been upgraded to full R1 standard.

Mirage 2000D-R1N1: From No. 607, an increased (but not complete) range of weapons could be carried. Possibly as few as four aircraft were supplied in this configuration.

Mirage 2000D-R1: Able to operate with all the conventional weapons detailed above, apart from APACHE and SCALP. First aircraft believed to be No. 611; all production has been for ECs 1/3, 3/3 and (from mid-1996) 2/3. A 1995 retrofit introduced the SAT SAMIR missile plume detector (DDM – Détecteur Départ Missile) in the rear of Magic launch rails of both 2000Ns and 2000Ds.

Mirage 2000D-R2: Production will be changed late in 1999 to this version, which adds the ability to launch APACHE; full automation of the self-defence suite by integration of SAMIR with chaff/flare dispensers and jammers; and provision for ATLIS II laser guidance pods.

Mirage 2000D-R3: A third production standard was originally proposed with provision for an APACHE development known as SCALP and a reconnaissance pod. Cancellation of R3 was announced in June 1996 as part of defence economies.

The 2000D is being produced in two main batches, later aircraft (R2 configuration) being able to carry the APACHE stand-off munitions dispenser weapon. Here the weapon is seen during tests using the seventh production aircraft, which was the first 2000D-R1N1. In the anti-airfield role, APACHE-AP dispenses 10 52-kg (115-lb) KRISS runway-cratering sub-munitions.

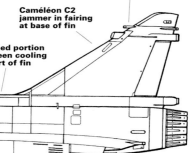

Mirage 2000D-R1

- Antilope 53C radar in green radome
- Radome probe deleted
- Additional blade aerials
- Bolt-on refuelling probe usually fitted
- PDLCT laser designator and AS30L missile
- Missionised cockpits with new displays
- GPS antenna
- Slightly fattened portion of spine between cooling outlet and start of fin
- ICMS Mk 2 EW system with additional antennas above main Serval units
- Caméléon C2 jammer in fairing at base of fin
- Spirale dispensers in rear of Karman fairings

Mirage 2000P

Proposals for an ASMP-carrying Mirage 2000 interdictor initially used this designation to denote Pénétration. In order to avoid confusion with the similarly-tasked Mirage IVP, it was soon changed to Mirage 2000N.

Mirage 2000S

Dassault used the 2000S designation for a non-nuclear interdictor to be offered for export. Essentially a parallel to the 2000D, it was quietly dropped from promotional literature in the mid-1990s before any could be sold. However, two Mirage 2000Ns had been marked with the '2000S' logo for air show exhibition: No. 314 in 1989 and No. 327 the following year.

Marked simply 'S' on the fin and carrying the legend 'Mirage 2000S', this aircraft is in fact a standard 2000N masquerading as the export version of the aircraft then known as the 2000N'. The aircraft is seen at the 1989 Paris air show, fitted with Magics, AS30Ls and a dummy PDLCT pod.

Second-generation variants

Mirage 2000CY

Development of the Mirage 2000-5 involved the contributions of several aircraft, including a single-seat Mirage 2000C assembled at Istres and numbered 'CY1'. By 1988, a 'CY2' and 'CY3' had been reported, perhaps being the same aircraft with progressive avionics upgrades. CY1 later became the first single-seat Mirage 2000-5 prototype.

Mirage 2000-5 01

The Mirage 2000-5 brings together Thomson-CSF RDY radar, the APSI cockpit, MATRA/BAe MICA missiles and the ICMS Mk 2 self-defence system in a major update of the original interceptor weapons system. This was first achieved in a two-seat aircraft, the single-place prototype being a conversion of CY1, which first flew on 27 April 1991, wearing '01' on the fin.

RDY (Radar Doppler Multicible – Multi-target Doppler Radar) initially went aloft in a Mystère (Falcon) 20 testbed in June 1987 and also underwent trials (of its air-to-surface modes) in a Sud-Ouest Vautour of CEV in 1989-90 and in Mirage 2000s No. 04 and X7. It is a multifunction X-band (I-band) Doppler radar, able to detect targets flying at low or high altitude, irrespective of their angle of approach. Performance is claimed to exceed that of current US radars such as the F-16's AN/APG-68 and F-15's AN/APG-70, air-to-air range being a maximum of 70

nm (130 km; 81 miles). High pulse-repetition frequency is employed for velocity search and for distant, low-flying aircraft; low PRF for high targets and air-to-ground modes; and medium PRF for all-aspect look-up/look-down detection.

Processing of data presents the pilot with a tactical threat analysis based on up to 24 potential target aircraft, of which a maximum of eight can be tracked while scanning continues and four are presented on the pilot's screen with annotated interception and firing data. The flat-plate antenna, scanning +/-60° in both azimuth and elevation, can contain four optional raised dipole aerials for IFF interrogation by the Thomson-CNI IDEE 1. Modes offered by RDY include others for surface attack, such as ground mapping, contour mapping, target ranging and moving target indication; sea target tracking; and Doppler beam-sharpening.

MICA, the Missile d'Interception, de Combat et d'Autodéfense, was developed by MATRA before its missiles division joined with that of BAe. Development began in May 1987, and it was first launched from a Mirage 2000C on 9 January 1992. Similar in shape to the Super 530 but, at 112 kg (247 lb), only slightly larger than a Magic, it supplants both weapons by virtue of having the choice of either (pointed) radar-guided or (rounded) infra-red seeker heads. Furthermore, the former version has

An important feature of the 2000-5 is the Sextant Avionique VEH 3020 combined HUD/HLD (head-up display/head-level display). The HUD can display FLIR imagery across a 14° x 10° field of view.

an AD4A head containing an active radar, making it a fire-and-forget weapon – unlike the Super 530, which needs target illumination by the parent aircraft throughout its flight. MICA qualification trials from a Mirage 2000-5 were satisfactorily completed in July 1996. Tests of air-to-ground ordnance continued until May 1997.

Internal aspects of the 2000-5 include uprating the engine-driven generators from 20 kVA to 25 kVA each and installing a VEH 3020 HUD (VEM 130) and head-level display for the pilot. Autopilot is a SFENA 608, INS a ULISS 52ES (incorporating GPS), central computer a Dassault XR13, and radar altimeter the TRT AHV-17. For export, the fully-automated ICMS Mk 2 improves upon the self-defence suite of the Mirage 2000D by adding a receiver/processor in the nose to detect missile command links; secondary DF antennas on the wingtip pods (as on Greek 2000EGs); and a third (LAM) antenna on the fin leading edge.

Originally 'CY1', this aircraft is the 2000-5 demonstrator, completed in export configuration with the ICMS Mk 2 EW suite.

Mirage 2000-5F

Originally indifferent to the private venture 2000-5, the French Air Force was eventually prevailed upon to allocate funding for the conversion of 37 existing airframes. Production approval was given on 25 November 1993 and the first was funded in the 1994 defence budget, followed by 10 in 1995, 23 in 1996 and three in 1997. It is envisaged (subject to prior attrition) that 34 will be former Mirage 2000C-S42As (i.e., between Nos 38 and 74), the balance of three to come from stocks of S5s (Nos 75 to 124).

Prototype conversions were undertaken at Istres of Nos 51 and 77, the first flying in its new configuration on 26 February 1996, and the second two months later. The initial 'production' conversion – at Bordeaux, but involving airframe refurbishment at Argenteuil – No. 38 was handed over at Istres on 30 December 1997 to meet contractual obligations, but did not transfer to CEAM to begin pilot conversions until April 1998. A further 11 deliveries were due in 1998, 22 in 1999 and the final three in 2000, to re-equip EC 1/2 and 2/2 at Dijon.

Mirage 2000-5F-SF1: The initial standard of conversions for the French Air Force differs slightly from the 2000-5 baseline as promoted for export, most notably in omission of the two superhet antennas from the fin (the single, small sensor being retained below the forward-facing jammer). The French standard of self-protection equipment (Serval, Sabre and Spirale) is retained, but with slight modifications.

Mirage 2000-5F

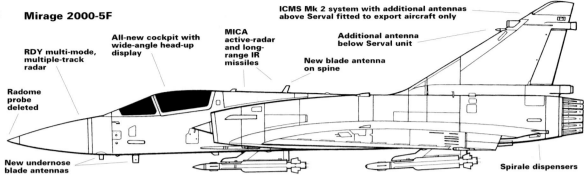

ICMS Mk 2 system with additional antennas above Serval fitted to export aircraft only

Additional antenna below Serval unit

MICA active-radar and long-range IR missiles

New blade antenna on spine

All-new cockpit with wide-angle head-up display

RDY multi-mode, multiple-track radar

Radome probe deleted

New undernose blade antennas

Spirale dispensers

Armament is optimised for the air defence role, the normal configuration being four MICAs on pylons beneath the wingroots and a pair of Magic 2s outboard. When available, the IR version of MICA will replace Magic. Use of the wingroot pylons frees the inboard wing positions for two large RPL 541/542 tanks and these, in conjunction with the usual RPL 522 tank on the centreline, increase endurance in the air defence role from 1½ to three hours.

Converted aircraft – of which the first also include Nos 38, 39, 73 and 78 – retain their original serial numbers. The first squadron is to be declared operational in April 1999.

Mirage 2000-5F-SF2: Projected French Air Force upgrade with GPS, a JTIDS-type datalink, compatibility with pilot's helmet sight and an unspecified long-distance identification aid – optical or radar-based.

Above: In maximum-range configuration the 2000-5F carries a centreline RPL 522 tank, wing-mounted RPL 541/542 tanks and a bolt-on refuelling probe. The leading-edge slats and Spirale dispensers show up well in this view.

Left: This 2000-5F (no. 51) wears the badge of CEAM, the air force test unit. The Dash 5 is readily identified by 'RDY' titles aft of the radome and by the lack of nose pitot.

Below: No. 77 was the one of the first two aircraft updated to Dash 5 standard. It carries the markings of EC 2/12, although the first service deliveries were made to EC 2/2.

Mirage 2000-5E (EDA and EI)

Exports of the Mirage 2000-5 were launched in November 1992, on receipt of a major order from Taiwan for 60. Qatar later announced a contract for 12 and Abu Dhabi (for the UAE) added 30 more to the order book, as well as funding an upgrade for 33 older aircraft. The UAE batch is described under the Mirage 2000-9 heading.

Mirage 2000-5EDA: Qatar's order (contract Falcon) of July 1994 included nine single-seat aircraft, serialled QA90 to QA98. They have the full ICMS Mk 2 defensive aids suite, including five fin antennas, secondary wingtip sensors and provision for Spirale, plus a GPS aerial in the spine. Air-to-air missiles are MICA and Magic 2, but the aircraft also have an air-to-ground role with the MATRA/BAe Black Pearl stand-off missile (which is an export adaptation of APACHE); AS30L and BGL 1000, with

appropriate designator; and BAP 100, Durandal and Belouga. A 400-kg (882-lb) Thomson-CSF ASTAC ground radar locator pod can also be carried. The first four Qatari aircraft (including some -5DDAs) arrived on 18 December 1997 after training in France.

Mirage 2000-5EI: MICA and Magic also are the prime armament of Taiwan's 48 single-seat aircraft, the first squadron of which gained IOC in November 1997. Numbered 2001 to 2048, the aircraft additionally carry their production numbers on the fin in the form EI01 to EI48, although some documentation has used the designation 2000-5Ei. Configuration is similar to the air defence-optimised -5F, apart from having all five fin antennas. Deliveries to Taiwan began with the arrival by sea on 5 May 1997 of the first five. There is a requirement for a second batch of 60.

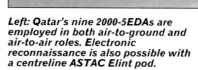

Left: Qatar's nine 2000-5EDAs are employed in both air-to-ground and air-to-air roles. Electronic reconnaissance is also possible with a centreline ASTAC Elint pod.

Above: Taiwan's 48 Mirage 2000-5EIs serve with the 2nd TFW at Hsinchu. Optimised for air defence duties, they were supplied with MATRA/ BAe Magic 2 and MICA missiles.

Mirage 2000-9 (2000-5 Mk II)

After a protracted competition, Abu Dhabi ordered 30 new Mirage 2000s in December 1997, requiring delivery to take place between late 1998 and late 2001. All 33 remaining Mirage 2000EADs, RADs and two-seat DADs will also be modified to this standard, originally named 2000-9 but

rechristened Mirage 2000-5 Mk II in 1999. The $3.4 billion deal was not finalised until November 1998, with an attendant slippage in delivery dates.

The -9 was specifically developed to satisfy Abu Dhabi's requirement for a long-range attack aircraft, which could also carry

six MICA missiles. Synthetic aperture and beam-sharpening modes have been added to the radar, now designated RDY7. Other new equipment includes an air-to-ground datalink, Thomson-CSF Detexis integrated EW suite, LCD colour displays plus provision for a laser-designation pod or Thomson Optronics Nahar navigation FLIR. The GEC-Marconi Hakim PGM-4 powered stand-off bomb was originally considered as the most likely air-to-ground weapon for the

2000-9, but in November 1998 it was announced that they would be armed with the MATRA/BAe Dynamics Black Shaheen, a development of the SCALP EG/Storm Shadow being developed for the RAF and Armée de l'Air. Despite US objections that it contravened international missile control agreements (due to its long range), the Black Shaheen/MICA deal has now been finalised between the UK and the UAE, and is expected to be worth around $2.1 billion.

Mirage 2000-5B 01

The original Mirage 2000B prototype served as an RDY radar testbed (BY1 and BY2) before being fully upgraded to become the first 2000-5. As such, it was flown by Patrick Experton on 24 October 1990, six months ahead of the single-seat prototype. It reverted to the identity 'B01' (marked on the fin) and was broadly representative of the export configuration, apart from lacking the third forward-facing fin antenna. By 1996, on completion of flight trials, B01 was stored by Dassault in anticipation of the opening of an aviation museum at Bordeaux/Merignac.

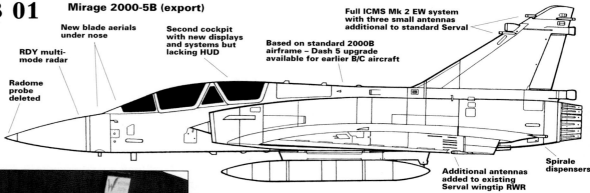

Mirage 2000-5B (export)

New blade aerials under nose

Second cockpit with new displays and systems but lacking HUD

Full ICMS Mk 2 EW system with three small antennas additional to standard Serval

RDY multi-mode radar

Based on standard 2000B airframe – Dash 5 upgrade available for earlier B/C aircraft

Radome probe deleted

Spirale dispensers

Additional antennas added to existing Serval wingtip RWR

Left: B01 seen at the 1992 Farnborough show, displaying the unusual staggered MICA carriage.

Below: In addition to trials work, the 2000-5B is used for export demonstrations and training.

Mirage 2000-5D (DDA and DI)

Export trainers with RDY radar have been supplied to two overseas operators of the Dash 5E.

Mirage 2000-5DDA: Qatar's three

aircraft, QA86, QA87 and QA88, are partners to nine 5EDAs. First to fly, late in 1995, QA86 was handed over in France (with two other aircraft) in a ceremony on 8 September 1997.

Mirage 2000-5DI: Taiwan has 12 of this version, 2051 to 2062 (production numbers DI01 to DI12), of which 2051 was the first export Mirage 2000-5 to fly, in October 1995. The initial aircraft was handed over in France on 9 May 1996.

Both Dash 5 export customers have acquired two-seaters, in full operational fit. The Qatari aircraft (below left) was the first to be delivered to the Gulf state.

Mirage 3000

Brief details were revealed in the spring of 1978 of a Mirage 2000 air superiority variant powered by two Turbo Union RB199s in

place of the single SNECMA M53. The aircraft was offered as the basis for a joint venture between France, (West) Germany and the UK, all of which were in the early stages of establishing programmes for their next combat aircraft (which eventually became the Rafale and Eurofighter).

French proposals were for its own industry to be responsible for the airframe, Germany for the armament and weapons system, and the UK to take charge of engine installation. No size or weight information was publicised – even if such parameters had been defined – but the

employment of two reheated turbofans totalling 131.99 kN (29,680 lb) of thrust would have provided an extra 50 per cent of power in comparison to the standard Mirage 2000. The Mirage 3000 proved unsuccessful as a viable joint venture project, no doubt due to its wholly French origins.

Mirage 4000

A private venture development, this one-third scaled-up Mirage 2000, with a projected maximum take-off weight of some 20 tonnes (19.68 tons), was announced by Dassault in December 1975 as the Delta Super Mirage. Most significantly, having two SNECMA M53 engines in place of one (the -P2 version was specified from the outset), it spanned 12.00 m (39 ft 4½ in), was 18.70 m (61 ft 4t in) long and had 73.0 m² (786 sq ft) of wing area. Systems and avionics were adapted from the smaller aircraft wherever possible, and though the aerodynamics were virtually identical, the 4000 did have variable-incidence canards (not strakes) and a proportionately shorter rear fuselage which obviated the need for extended Karman fairings as retrofitted to the first three Mirage 2000s. Including fin tanks, the 4000's internal fuel capacity was some three times greater than that of the 2000, in addition to which carriage was possible of up to three external tanks, each of 2500 litres (550 Imp gal). With this maximum fuel, combat radius with a reconnaissance pod was stated to be 1,000 nm (1850 km/ 1,150 miles).

Intended as a dual role combat aircraft able to undertake both air superiority and strike/attack missions, the Mirage 4000 would have been a parallel to the Boeing F-15 Eagle or Sukhoi 'Flanker' family had its full potential been realised. When the mock-up was revealed in December 1977, hints were dropped that Saudi Arabia was funding development, and by 1980, Defence Minister Prince Sultan Ubn Abdul Aziz was openly saying that procurement was being considered. Following a recommendation by the defence committee of what was then France's ruling party that 50 Mirage 4000s should be acquired to replace Mirage IVs, Defence Minister Yvon Bourges conceded that an order could be placed. However, these statements represented the nearest approach the Mirage 4000 made to a production line.

Initially unpainted, the prototype was flown by Jean-Marie Saget for the first time at Istres on 9 March 1979, achieving Mach 1.2 and 10975 m (36,000 ft) on the power of its two M53-2 engines. During the sixth sortie, on 11 April, it flew to Mach 2.04 and then demonstrated a 25° angle of attack. By June, No. 01/F-ZWRM (neither identity was carried externally) was performing impressive, slow-speed, nose-up flypasts at

the Paris air show, painted in house colours of white overall with red and blue trim, plus 'Super Mirage 4000' titles. During 1980, the aircraft was flown with two of the large underwing fuel tanks, ending the year with approximately 100 flying hours in the hands of five pilots, including one each from the CEV and French Air Force.

By 1981, it had received M53-5 engines, and at the following year's Farnborough show flew in interceptor and attack configuration on alternate days. In the latter guise it used all 12 hardpoints (including six beneath the fuselage) for two fuel tanks, two Sycamor jamming pods, two self-defence Magic AAMs, a laser designator, two AS30L ASMs, two 1000-kg LGBs and a podded Antilope radar. The production

Right: In original guise the 4000 was dubbed the 'Super Mirage'. It was powered by the M53-2 engines, subsequently receiving -5s.

Below: The desert scheme was applied for the 4000's reappearance in 1986. It is seen here carrying six Magic 2 missiles.

aircraft would also have been able to carry a nose radar with a scanner diameter of up to 80 cm (31.5 in). Also in 1982, construction was reported to be under way of a pre-production aircraft, fitted with a full navigation and attack system, but it failed to appear and No. 01 was eventually withdrawn from use.

This unique aircraft returned to the air in 1986 (now marked as plain 'Mirage 4000' on the cockpit sides) to undertake trials for

the Rafale programme, particularly the performance of a canard delta in turbulent air. Both aircraft were shown at Farnborough in 1986, but when the big Mirage appeared at Paris the following year, it had adopted desert camouflage on the upper surfaces. No. 01 was still in use with the CEV at Brétigny in 1989, but when it next appeared at Paris, in 1995, it was as a permanent exhibit outside the Musée de l'Air et de l'Espace.

Air Power Analysis

US Navy

As US naval aviation approaches the threshold of the 21st century the service holds a combat record second to none, and the potential of its combat power has influenced events worldwide. However, the Navy of the late 1990s is radically different to that of previous eras. Forced to do 'more with less', some within the Navy argue that it is now doing 'too much with too little'. The demands on US sea-based air power have not let up and, at times, the Navy is struggling with the resources available to it.

The end of the Cold War and the dissolution of the Soviet Union brought about political and public pressure to reduce defence budgets, but there has been no let-up in the need for Navy deployments – if anything, demand has increased. The strain of a high tempo of operations, declining budgets and the cancellation of some prominent aircraft programmes – such as the A-12 and the P-7 – has pushed the resourcefulness of US naval aviation to the limit. Promising new programmes such as CVX, the F/A-18E/F Super Hornet and the Joint Strike Fighter are encouraging for the future of naval aviation – but all have had their difficulties and are far from guaranteed, even now. The outlook for other programmes, such as

the new Common Support Aircraft (CSA) and the Maritime Multimission Aircraft (MMA), is even less certain.

The fall in defence spending from 1990 onwards accelerated the steepest decline in US naval aviation force structure since the end of World War II. In 1994 alone, 37 squadrons were disestablished, the greatest number in a single year since the 12 months preceding the outbreak of the Korean War. Since 1988, when the free-spending Reagan build-up levelled off and began to decline, 116 Navy squadrons have been disestablished; five more – VP-91, VQ-5, VQ-6, VXE-6 and possibly VQ-11 – are scheduled to be disbanded by 2000.

has determined the CVX should be a large-deck, nuclear-powered aircraft-carrier. The first CVX (CVX-1) will begin construction in 2006 and will replace the *Enterprise* in 2013. It will have a new nuclear plant that requires less manpower to operate and maintain, a new electrical power generation and distribution system and will continue efforts begun on CVN 77 to reduce onboard manning and total ownership costs (TOC). CVX-2 will feature the new topside to be designed for CVN 77 and the new nuclear plant to be designed for CVX-1 and will have an improved hull to provide the service-life margins needed to accommodate improvements and modernisations over the next century. Also to be included in CVX-2 are new aircraft launch (EMALS) and recovery (EARS) systems and new functional arrangements and distributive systems to further reduce onboard manning and improved maintenance and survivability features.

The fleet of other 'flat-tops', the amphibious assault ships dedicated to the US Marine Corps, has gone through extensive modernisation since 1990. With the exception of *Inchon*, the entire group of 'Iwo Jima'-class amphibious assault ships (LPHs) has been decommissioned: *Okinawa* in 1992, *Iwo Jima* in 1993, *Guadalcanal* in 1994, *Tripoli* in 1995, *New Orleans* in 1997 and *Guam* in 1998. As a response for the need for a dedicated mine countermeasures command ship (MCS) during the Gulf War, *Inchon* was converted from 1994 at Ingalls Shipbuilding in Pascagoula, Mississippi to MCS 12, a Naval Reserve Force ship now based at Ingleside, Texas. Major changes to the command, control, communications, computers and intelligence (C^4I) systems were incorporated, including upgrades to NAVMACS II, CIWS, SLQ-32, radars, etc. The addition of a number of new shops and upgrades to the capabilities of existing ships will enable the *Inchon* to respond promptly and efficiently to the need for emergency repairs in any theatre of operations. Ingalls completed the conversion on 28 May 1996. It will provide integrated mine countermeasures, command and control for aviation mine countermeasures (AMCM), surface mine countermeasures (SMCM) and explosive ordnance disposal mine countermeasures (EODMCM). *Inchon* made its first deployment in March 1997, with MH-53Es and HH-46Ds.

The Navy is approaching its goal of a force of 12 large-deck amphibious assault ships (LHAs and LHDs). The five 'Tarawa'-class LHAs (*Tarawa, Saipan, Belleau Wood, Nassau* and *Peleliu*) continue in service, but plans to put them through a service-life extension programme (SLEP) are now being superseded by a plan to build more 'Wasp'-class LHDs. Concern over the age and stability of the LHAs has brought calls from the Commandant of the Marine Corps for funding additional LHDs instead of extending the life of the LHAs. The FY 1999 budget includes advanced funding for LHD 8 (as yet unnamed). Six LHDs are now in commission (*Wasp, Essex, Kearsarge, Boxer, Bataan* and *Bonhomme Richard*), the latest of these commissioned in 1998. LHD 7 (*Iwo Jima*) is scheduled for commissioning in February 2001.

LHAs and LHDs now embark two HH-46Ds for rescue and utility work, in addition to their Marine aircraft. The HH-46Ds are assigned as detachments from HC squadrons, a change of practice during the early 1990s from the assignment of a UH-1N directly to the ship.

Primary aviation vessels

Today's carrier battle groups are focused less on open-ocean naval engagements and more on projecting power ashore along the littoral areas of the world. Carrier battle groups have evolved during the 1990s in several ways. The groups are smaller in terms of numbers of ships assigned; fewer escorts are assigned, in light of the reduced aircraft and submarine threat. CVBGs are now formed with permanently assigned ships, including submarines, under a battle group commander (a rear admiral, either a carrier group commander or a cruiser-destroyer group commander) and are officially designated with the name of the CVBG's flagship, e.g., Enterprise Battle Group. Continuing a trend that began in the mid-1980s, the carrier air wing commander is the strike warfare commander for the entire battle group.

The Navy's carrier force has declined in numbers from 14 to 11. Since 1990, eight carriers have been retired: *Coral Sea* (CV 43) in 1990, *Lexington* (AVT 16) in 1991, *Midway* (CV 41) in 1992, the entire 'Forrestal' class – *Saratoga* (CV 60) in 1994, *Forrestal* (AVT 59) in 1993, *Ranger* (CV 60) in 1993 and *Independence* (CV 62) in 1998 – and *America* (CV 66) in 1995. *Forrestal* was in conversion to replace *Lexington* as an aviation training ship (AVT) when it was promptly decommissioned. *Independence* replaced *Midway* as the carrier forward-deployed to Japan in 1991, but was itself replaced in 1998 by *Kitty Hawk* (CV 63). *Kitty Hawk, Constellation* and *John F. Kennedy* are the only non-nuclear powered carriers in service. *John F. Kennedy* – which completed a two-year

extensive overhaul in 1995 – is officially a part of the Naval Reserve Force, with a small portion of its crew composed of reservists, but has been maintained in the active force deployment rotation. The bulk of the force is formed by *Enterprise* (CVN 65), which was extensively overhauled and refuelled (for its second time) during the early 1990s and the eight 'Nimitz'-class nuclear-powered carriers. In June 1998 *Nimitz* (CVN 68) commenced a three-year refuelling and overhaul (that will extend its service life to 50 years) and will be followed by *Dwight D. Eisenhower* (CVN 69). *Carl Vinson* (CVN 70), *Theodore Roosevelt* (CVN 71) and *Abraham Lincoln* (CVN 72) presumably will undergo the same process in turn. Only three carriers, all 'Nimitz'-class, have entered service since 1990: *George Washington* (CVN 73) in 1992, *John C. Stennis* (CVN 74) in 1995 and *Harry S. Truman* (CVN 75) in 1998. The *Ronald Reagan* (CVN 76), whose keel was laid in February 1998, is scheduled to join the fleet in 2003.

CVN 77, a 'Nimitz'-class ship, will begin the transition to the CVX next-generation carrier. Congress included $50 million for CVN 77 in the FY 1998 budget and $124.5 million in the FY 1999 budget. Construction will begin in 2001 and CVN 77 will replace *Kitty Hawk* in 2008. A contract was awarded to Newport News Shipbuilding in September 1998 for construction of CVN 77, which will be the first ship of a three-ship evolution to CVX and will have a new topside. The Defense Acquisition Board Review (DAB) for CVX, conducted in September 1998,

Above: VF-2's latest markings are seen on this F-14D, which is also fitted with **BOL** launch rails for its AIM-9 Sidewinders.

Right: VF-11 'Red Rippers' flies F-14Bs. This aircraft wears the remnants of an NSAWC camouflage scheme.

Above: Seen on deployment at Twentynine Palms, this F-14A carries the markings of VF-14 'Tophatters'.

Right: The F-14Ds of VF-31 'Tomcatters' are currently attached to Air Wing 14 aboard the USS Lincoln.

Above left: VF-32 'Swordsmen' operates F-14Bs as part of CVW-3 attached to the USS Enterprise (CVN-65).

Left: Tomcats from VF-101 'Grim Reapers' have worn a progression of unit markings, and this F-14D wears the latest.

Above: VF-41 'Black Aces' F-14s became the first to drop bombs in combat, over Bosnia in 1995. The unit flies F-14As.

US Navy Carrier Air Wings

US ATLANTIC FLEET

CVW-1	**AB**	
USS John F. Kennedy (CV 67)		
VF-102	F-14B	AB1xx
VMFA-251	F/A-18C	AB2xx
VFA-82	F/A-18C	AB3xx
VFA-86	F/A-18C	AB4xx
VAQ-137	EA-6B	AB50x
VAW-123	E-2C	AB60x
HS-11	SH-60F, HH-60H	AB61x
VS-32	S-3B	AB7xx
VRC-40 Det	C-2A	ABxx

CVW-3	**AC**	
USS Enterprise (CVN 65)		
VF-32	F-14B	AC1xx
VMFA-312	F/A-18C	AC2xx
VFA-37	F/A-18C	AC3xx
VFA-105	F/A-18C	AC4xx
VAQ-130	EA-6B	AC50x
VAW-126	E-2C	AC60x
HS-7	SH-60F, HH-60H	AC61x
VS-22	S-3B	AC7xx
VQ-6 Det A	ES-3A	AC76x
VRC-40 Det	C-2A	ACxx

CVW-7	**AG**	
USS George Washington (CVN 73)		
VF-143	F-14B	AG1xx
VF-11	F-14B	AG2xx
VFA-136	F/A-18C	AG3xx
VFA-131	F/A-18C	AG4xx
VAQ-140	EA-6B	AG50x
VAW-121	E-2C	AG60x
HS-5	SH-60F, HH-60H	AG61x
VS-31	S-3B	AG7xx
VRC-40 Det	C-2A	AGxx

CVW-8	**AJ**	
USS Theodore Roosevelt (CVN 71)		
VF-41	F-14A	AJ1xx
VF-14	F-14A	AJ2xx
VFA-15	F/A-18C	AJ3xx
VFA-87	F/A-18C	AJ4xx
VAQ-141	EA-6B	AJ50x
VAW-124	E-2C	AJ60x
HS-3	SH-60F, HH-60H	AJ61x
VS-24	S-3B	AJ7xx
VRC-40 Det	C-2A	AJxx

CVW-17	**AA**	
USS Dwight D. Eisenhower (CVN 69)		
VF-103	F-14B	AA1xx
VFA-34	F/A-18C	AA2xx
VFA-83	F/A-18C	AA3xx
VFA-81	F/A-18C	AA4xx
VAQ-132	EA-6B	AA50x
VAW-125	E-2C	AA60x
HS-15	SH-60F, HH-60H	AA61x
VS-30	S-3B	AA7xx
VRC-40 Det	C-2A	AAxx

US PACIFIC FLEET

CVW-2	**NE**	
USS Constellation (CV 64)		
VF-2	F-14D	NE1xx
VMFA-323	F/A-18C	NE2xx
VFA-151	F/A-18C	NE3xx
VFA-137	F/A-18C	NE4xx
VAQ-131	EA-6B	NE5xx
VAW-116	E-2C	NE60x
HS-2	SH-60F, HH-60H	NE61x
VS-38	S-3B	NE7xx
VRC-30 Det	C-2A	NExx

CVW-5	**NF**	
USS Kitty Hawk (CV 63)		
VF-154	F-14A	NF1xx
VFA-27	F/A-18C	NF2xx
VFA-192	F/A-18C	NF3xx
VFA-195	F/A-18C	NF4xx
VAQ-136	EA-6B	NF50x
HS-14	SH-60F, HH-60H	NF61x
VS-21	S-3B	NF7xx
VQ-5 Det 5	ES-3A	NF76x
VRC-30 Det	C-2A	NFxx

CVW-9	**NG**	
USS John C. Stennis (CVN 74)		
VF-211	F-14A	NG1xx
VMFA-314	F/A-18C	NG2xx
VFA-146	F/A-18C	NG3xx
VFA-147	F/A-18C	NG4xx
VAQ-138	EA-6B	NG50x
VAW-112	E-2C	NG60x
HS-8	SH-60F, HH-60H	NG61x
VS-33	S-3B	NG7xx
VRC-30 Det	C-2A	NGxx

CVW-11	**NH**	
USS Carl Vinson (CVN 70)		
VF-213	F-14D	NG1xx
VFA-97	F/A-18C	NG2xx
VFA-24	F/A-18C	NG3xx
VFA-94	F/A-18C	NG4xx
VAQ-135	EA-6B	NG50x
VAW-117	E-2C	NG60x
HS-6	SH-60F, HH-60H	NG61x
VS-29	S-3B	NG7xx
VQ-5 Det C	ES-3A	NG76x
VRC-30 Det	C-2A	NGxx

CVW-14	**NK**	
USS Abraham Lincoln (CVN 72)		
VF-31	F-14D	NK1xx
VFA-115	F/A-18C	NK2xx
VFA-113	F/A-18C	NK3xx
VFA-25	F/A-18C	NK4xx
VAQ-139	EA-6B	NK50x
VAW-113	E-2C	NK60x
HS-4	SH-60F, HH-60H	NK61x
VS-35	S-3B	NK7xx
VRC-30 Det	C-2A	NKxx

Assignments current as of 1 December 1998. During 1998, fleet VAQ squadron modexes switched to 50x series from 62x. VQ detachments being disbanded over the course of late 1998 and early 1999 as ES-3A is retired; only three detachments remained deployed at the end of 1998.

NAVAL RESERVE FORCE

CVWR-20	**AF**	
VFA-201	F/A-18A	AF10x
VMFA-142	F/A-18A	MBxx*
VFA-203	F/A-18A	AF30x
VFA-204	F/A-18A	AF40x
VAW-78	E-2C	AF60x
HS-75	SH-3H, UH-3H	
NW610		
VAQ-209	EA-6B	AF62x**

Note: VF-201 redesignated VFA-201 on 1 January 1999 upon transition to the F/A-18A. HS-75 is administratively assigned to Commander Helicopter Wing Reserve.
* Presumably HS-75 and VMFA-142 would adopt CVWR-20 modex if mobilised.
**VAQ-209 has not yet adopted 50x modex.

Aircraft of the US Navy

To observers of military aviation, the current US military aircraft procurement environment, compared with that of the past, seems surreal. The US Navy has only one fixed-wing combat aircraft in production, the F/A-18E/F Super Hornet strike fighter. The only carrier support aircraft in production – the E-2 – is an upgrade of a design that first flew over 35 years ago. The only Navy helicopter in production is the CH-60S Knighthawk, a new development of a 20-year-old design. The T-45C Goshawk trainer is in full production and will be joined early in the next decade by the T-6A Texan II primary trainer. The A-12 and P-7 never made it off the drawing board and the P-3C Update IV and the EA-6B ADVCAP were cancelled in the prototype stages.

The picture is not as bleak as it first appears. Avionics upgrades, improved engines and new 'smart' weapons have maintained or improved the tactical effectiveness of the aircraft in service. Service-life extension programmes and even remanufacture programmes have kept ageing airframes flying. Reducing the number of types in service has lowered the costs of maintaining the support structure for naval aircraft. Nevertheless, the advancing average age of the Navy's aircraft fleet is of increasing concern to planners.

The first production Super Hornets will enter fleet readiness squadron service in 1999 and the following year will see the service entry of the CH-60S, the T-6A, the SH-60R Seahawk and, if all goes well, the Joint Strike Fighter (JSF). Two proposed programmes, the Common Support Aircraft (CSA) and the Multi-purpose Maritime Aircraft (MMA), have not yet been funded.

F-14 Tomcat/Super Tomcat

The F-14 Tomcat (Super Tomcat in the case of the F-14D), flown by the Navy's fighter (VF) squadrons, remains the most capable naval interceptor in the world, despite the relatively recent addition of strike missions to its roles. The Navy is accelerating the retirement of the initial long-serving Tomcat version, the F-14A, which is still powered by troublesome TF30 engines. The F-14B (initially designated F-14A+) featured F110 engines that resisted compressor stalls and markedly improved performance, increasing thrust by 30 per cent, thereby eliminating the need for afterburner on launch and greatly increasing engine life and time on station. Some 32 F-14As were converted to F-14Bs to augment production F-14Bs. A later batch of 14 F-14As was remanufactured into F-14Bs during the mid-1990s. A few F-14As and F-14Bs were modified into NF-14As and NF-14Bs for test work.

The last production version of the F-14, the F-14D Super Tomcat, features the F110 engine, the jam-resistant APG-71 radar, the Joint Tactical Information Distribution System and the dual Television Camera Set/Infra-Red Search and Track sensor. The last of 37 production F-14Ds rolled off the Grumman line on 10 July 1992. Another 18 F-14As were remanufactured into F-14Ds. The Super Tomcat entered service too late to participate in the Gulf War. A few F-14Ds have been converted to NF-14Ds for test work.

The Navy has steadily upgraded its F-14 fleet during the 1990s to keep it effective until its scheduled retirement in 2008. The most significant change was the addition of an air-to-ground attack capability latent in the F-14 since its initial design. The retirement of the A-6, the cancellation of the A-12 and the Navy's requirement for 50 strike aircraft in each carrier air wing led to the development of an F-14 strike capability. F-14s were fitted with the capability of dropping 'dumb' bombs, expanded to include laser-guided bombs. This air-to-ground capability was put into use in air strikes in Bosnia during 1995. Installation of the LANTIRN system, first deployed by VF-103 on USS *Enterprise* in June 1996, gave the F-14 the capability to laser-designate targets for its own GBU-24 LGBs. By April 1997, all deploying carrier battle groups carried a LANTIRN-equipped F-14 squadron. LANTIRN F-14s received upgrades including the ALR-67 radar warning system, BOL chaff dispensers, night-vision capability and GPS. LANTIRN-equipped F-14Bs were first used in combat by VF-32 during the Desert Fox strikes against Iraq in December 1998. Installation of the GPS began in 1995 on the F-14D and in 1996 on the F-14As and F-14Bs. (Plans to arm the F-14 with the AIM-120 AMRAAM have been cancelled.)

The first F-14 remanufactured under the F-14B Upgrade (formerly F-14A/B Upgrade) programme was delivered in 1997. These aircraft received a major computer upgrade, digital avionics and structural and survivability enhancements to make them comparable to the F-14D. The Navy is replacing the vertical display indicator group with a more reliable system that includes a HUD for the F-14B Upgrade. A plan to combine F-14B Upgrade and F-14D aircraft in the same squadrons was cancelled in 1997.

A major safety enhancement to the F-14 is the incorporation of a digital flight control system (DFCS) that will replace the existing analog one. The DFCS is designed to prevent departures from controlled flight, including spins that have resulted in the loss of several aircraft.

The Tomcat continues to perform photo-reconnaissance with the TARPS (Tactical Air Reconnaissance Pod System). A digital system – TARPS-DI – entered service in 1996 and was able to downlink near-real-time imagery for immediate threat and battle-damage assessment. TARPS-DI first deployed in November 1996 with VF-32. A further development, TARPS-CD, began testing in 1998 and included real-time electro-optical step-framing imagery. The Tomcat is being modified with a Fast Tactical Imagery (FTI) system, which will allow day/night stand-off imagery transmission and reception of any imagery source on the F-14 (LANTIRN, TCS, TARPS-DI). With the FTI system, the F-14 can use the LANTIRN system to provide GPS-quality target co-ordinates for targeting options and transmit them, with the imagery, to a carrier or to other FTI-equipped aircraft. The first FTI-equipped F-14s will deploy with VF-14 and VF-41 in April 1999.

As of mid-1998, 107 F-14As, 76 F-14Bs and 46 F-14Ds were in service in four active F-14A squadrons, five F-14B squadrons and three F-14D squadrons, as well as four NF-14A, one NF-14B and four NF-14D aircraft in permanent test roles. The Navy is accelerating the retirement of the F-14A, but planning to keep the F-14B Upgrade and F-14D aircraft in service until 2008. Two Tomcat squadrons will transition to the F/A-18E; the others will receive the F/A-18F.

F/A-18 Hornet

Production of the F/A-18C Hornet for the Navy is ending in 1999. The first production version of the Hornet – the F/A-18A – equips only one active-duty operational squadron, in addition to four Reserve squadrons, the two Hornet fleet readiness squadrons (FRSs) and the Naval Flight Demonstration Squadron ('Blue Angels'). The two-seat counterpart to the F/A-18A, the F/A-18B, serves in small numbers in the two Hornet FRSs, one reserve adversary squadron, with test squadrons and with the 'Blue Angels'.

The F/A-18C is the primary version of the Hornet in front-line carrier service, equipping all but one active-duty strike fighter (VFA) squadron, as well as the two Hornet fleet readiness squadrons (FRSs). The F/A-18C incorporates improved weapons in the form of the AIM-120 AMRAAM, the AGM-84E SLAM and the IR-imaging version of the AGM-65 Maverick. The AGM-154 JSOW (Joint Stand-Off Weapon) was introduced in late 1997. The longer-range AGM-84H SLAM-ER (expanded response) is entering service in 1999. F/A-18Cs produced from 1989 feature improved night-attack capabilities, including a FLIR pod, a raster HUD, night-vision goggles, cockpit lighting compatible with NVGs, a digital colour moving map and a multi-purpose colour display. Improved-performance engines were introduced in production F/A-18Cs during the mid-1990s. The F/A-18C fleet is steadily being upgraded with a tactical FLIR/laser designator pod, ARC-210 radios, GPS and a cockpit video recorder. Programmed upgrades to be completed by 2001 include the AGM-84H, AIM-9X Sidewinder, JSOW, Link 16 and ATARS (Advanced Tactical Air Reconnaissance System). By 2004, further upgrades will include advanced colour cockpit displays, satellite communications and the Block 6 version of the AGM-88 HARM.

The two-seat F/A-18D, counterpart to the F/A-18C, equips the two Hornet FRSs and some test squadrons. Unlike the Marine Corps, which uses the F/A-18D as a front-line combat aircraft, the Navy uses the aircraft only for pilot training and test work.

As of mid-1998, the Navy and Marine Corps had 252 F/A-18A, 32 F/A-18B, 414 F/A-18C and 127 F/A-18D aircraft in service, as well as two NF/A-18As, two NF/A-18Cs and three NF/A-18Ds serving in permanent test roles.

One poor F/A-18 characteristic is its range and/or endurance on certain strike-mission profiles. The latest lot of F/A-18C/Ds is far more capable than the first F/A-18A/Bs; however, by 1991 it was clear that avionics cooling, electrical and space constraints would limit future growth in capability. Additionally, as improvements increased the aircraft's empty weight, Hornets were returning to their carriers with less than optimal reserve fuel and/or unexpended weapons. Although the F/A-18C/D's growth is now limited, the Hornet will continue to fill

Above: The F-14Bs of VF-102 have begun to adopt this revised marking, without the traditional rattlesnake.

Right: VF-103, once the 'Sluggers', adopted the 'Jolly Rogers' identity of VF-84 when the latter was disbanded in 1995.

Above: The badge of VF-143 'Pukin' Dogs', as seen on this F-14B, actually shows a winged griffin.

Right: VF-154, the 'Black Knights', is today the only F-14 unit based outside the USA. Its F-14As operate from NAF Atsugi.

Left: VF-211 'Flying Checkmates' operated F-14Bs between 1989 and 1992, but has now reverted to F-14As.

Above: VF-213 'Black Lions' now flies F-14Ds as part of Air Wing 11 on the USS Carl Vinson (CVN-70).

Above: VFA-15 'Valions' transitioned to the Hornet in 1986 and is now based at NAS Oceana.

Below: VFA-27 'Chargers' is one of three Pacific Fleet strike fighter units stationed at NAF Atsugi, Japan.

The Hornets of VFA-22 'Fighting Redcocks' (above) are based at NAS Lemoore, alongside those of VFA-25 'Fist of the Fleet' (right).

VFA-34 'Blue Blasters' (below) and VFA-37 'Bulls' (below left) are both NAS Oceana-based squadrons.

carrier air wings for many years to come, slowly giving way to the larger, farther-reaching and more capable F/A-18E/F.

F/A-18E/F Super Hornet

The F/A-18E/F Super Hornet, an evolutionary development of the night-strike F/A-18C/D, is the highest priority programme in US naval aviation. The Super Hornet will be a strike fighter that has significant growth potential, more than adequate carrier-based landing weight and range, endurance and ordnance-carrying capabilities comparable to those of the A-6 and F-14 that the Super Hornet is replacing. The F/A-18E/F, considerably more survivable than the F/A-18C/Ds currently in service, is designed to be able to conduct unescorted strikes against highly defended targets early in a conflict.

The Super Hornet features two more stores stations and can carry the full array of new Navy air-to-ground ordnance, including the JDAM, the JSOW and the SLAM-ER. The Super Hornet's two F414 turbofans give it 44,000 lb (195.69 kN) of thrust – 12,000 lb (53.37 kN) more than that available to the F/A-18C/D – and give the aircraft the ability to land on a carrier with a load of expensive 'smart' weapons. Its carrier recovery payload is increased to 9,000 lb (4082 kg). The Super Hornet will be able to carry an aerial refuelling store.

Although a 41 per cent interdiction-mission range increase may be the most dramatic improvement in the Super Hornet, the ability to recover aboard a carrier with optimum reserve fuel and a load of precision strike weapons is of equal importance. The Super Hornet has the space, power and cooling capability needed to accommodate valuable but installation-sensitive avionics, such as an electronically scanned-array antenna, as they become available. While the F/A-18C/D has incorporated a modicum of low-observables technology, the Super Hornet was designed from the outset to optimise stealth and other survivability enhancements.

The first Super Hornet rolled out in September 1995 and flew for the first time in November 1995, ahead of schedule and 1,000 lb (454 kg) under specified weight. The Super Hornet successfully conducted its initial carrier trials in January 1997 aboard the USS *John C. Stennis* (CVN 74). By September 1998, the five F/A-18Es and two F/A-18Fs participating in the three-year flight test programme had flown over 2,300 flights and 3,500 hours. The first production aircraft (an F/A-18E) flew on 6 November 1998 and was delivered to VX-9, at Patuxent River.

The Super Hornet, which entered low-rate initial production in September 1997, is scheduled to become operational in 2001. The first Super Hornet fleet readiness squadron, VFA-122, was established at NAS Lemoore, California on 1 October 1998 and held a ceremony on 15 January 1999 to welcome the Super Hornet to the fleet. An East Coast Super Hornet FRS, VFA-174, is scheduled to stand up at NAS Oceana in 2003/04.

The 1997 Quadrennial Defense Review reduced the projected Super Hornet purchase from 1,000 to a minimum of 548. Twelve were funded in FY 1997; numbers increased to 20 in FY 1998 and to 30 in FY 1999 and are expected to reach a final maximum rate of 48 per year in FY 2001. Initially, production will favour the F/A-18F for transition training. Production

could increase to as much as 785, depending on the progress, or lack thereof, of the JSF. Navy plans project a production run that will equip each carrier wing with one F/A-18E and one F/A-18F squadron, along with two F/A-18C squadrons that will eventually acquire the JSF as the Hornets are phased out. The F/A-18F will replace the F-14 and fulfil its reconnaissance and forward air controller roles in addition to its interceptor and strike roles. A variant of the F/A-18F, designated F/A-18G, has been proposed as a replacement for the EA-6B.

Joint Strike Fighter

The Joint Strike Fighter (JSF) is envisioned as a stealthy replacement for the Hornet in the second decade of the next century. The programme, formerly known as JAST, Joint Advanced Strike Technology, is intended to field the next-generation strike aircraft for the Navy, Marine Corps and Air Force with an emphasis on affordability. One of four planned variants of the JSF, the Navy's carrier-capable version will be a single-seat, single-engined, supersonic fighter with an internal weapons bay and state-of-the-art avionics. The use of a single engine is a departure from the Navy's long-held insistence on two engines in tactical aircraft, for safety in overwater and combat operations.

In November 1996, designs from Boeing and Lockheed Martin were selected to compete against each other. Boeing is expected to fly its two X-32 concept demonstration aircraft (CDA) in mid-2000. The Lockheed Martin team, which includes Northrop Grumman and British Aerospace, is producing two X-35 CDAs. The X-32 and X-35 – which are demonstrators, not prototypes – will use different configurations of the Pratt & Whitney F119 engine. The first CDA from each company will represent the Air Force version; the second will be the Marine Corps STOVL version. Later, the Air Force version will be modified to perform as carrier-based aircraft. The winning design will be engineered into a full-scale JSF in the engineering and manufacturing development programme phase, to begin in 2001.

The UK is a full partner in the programme and anticipates purchasing 60 JSFs to replace its Sea Harriers. Overall production of the JSF is expected to reach 3,000 aircraft. The General Electric F120 engine will be an alternative engine option for JSF customers. The JSF is scheduled to enter service in 2008 and eventually replace the F/A-18 in at least two squadrons per carrier air wing. The Navy expects to acquire at least 480 JSFs.

Electronic attack

The Navy has operated the EA-6B Prowler electronic warfare aircraft since 1972. The carrier-capable EA-6B is capable of jamming enemy radars and communications and attacking radars with AGM-88 HARMs. The EA-6B has been upgraded through the years with the EXCAP (expanded capability) and ICAP (increased capability) I and II upgrades. ICAP II is now the standard fleet configuration.

The Prowlers are planned for upgrade to the Block 89A configuration, which includes an upgraded AYK-14 mission computer, an inertial navigation set integrated with GPS and two anti-jam ARC-210 radios. The Block 89A version first flew in June 1997. The first of 20 aircraft (modified from a Block 82 Prowler) was delivered to NAS Whidbey Island in December 1998.

In FY 1997 Congress increased, to $201.6 million, the president's EA-6B budget request of $100.6 million to enable the Navy to procure another 60 Band 9/10 transmitters and 10 of 20 new wing centre-sections, which are needed to replace sections subject to embrittlement and fatigue. Another major upgrade to the aircraft, ICAP III 'Warfighter Upgrade System', is intended to upgrade Block 89A EA-6Bs with the equipment needed to allow them to execute their missions through 2015. The upgrade will replace the ageing ALQ-99 receivers, integrate off-board connectivity, integrate the USQ-113 communications jammer and replace obsolete avionics. These upgrades may be accomplished using currently available avionics, contractor-off-the-shelf (COTS) equipment, non-development items (NDI) and/or government-furnished equipment (GFE). ICAP III development began in March 1998 with an engineering and manufacturing development (EMD) contract awarded to a team led by Northrop Grumman. The ICAP III is expected to fly in 2001 and enter service in January 2004.

The addition of the AGM-88 during the mid-1980s gave the EA-6B a weapon to supplement its impressive jamming capability and on 31 March 1998 the Navy's tactical electronic warfare (VAQ) squadrons were redesignated electronic attack (VAQ) squadrons. The Department of Defense decided in 1994 that the EA-6B would become the nation's prime electronic warfare aircraft; the USAF's EF-111As were retired in May 1998. The last of four joint expeditionary EA-6B squadrons, joining the 10 fleet EA-6B units, was established in October 1997. As such, the EA-6Bs now deploy overseas in Navy expeditionary units in support of USAF operations.

The EA-6B has been out of production since the last of 170 built rolled off the Grumman line on 29 July 1991 and the high level of defence commitments has strained the availability of this ageing aircraft, which is programmed to serve until 2015. Approximately 125 remain in service. No replacement has been identified, but a version of the F/A-18F Super Hornet (F/A-18G) has been mentioned as a possible option.

Airborne early warning

The Northrop Grumman E-2 Hawkeye first flew in 1961; the E-2C version first flew in 1971. The current variant's radar can detect targets anywhere in a 6-million cubic mile surveillance envelope and simultaneously track 2,000 targets. The five-man E-2C crew can control more than 20 airborne intercepts simultaneously.

The E-2C has been in service and in production so long that aircraft have been retired at the end of their fatigue lives even as new E-2Cs left production. The fleet has been progressively upgraded with improvements to mission avionics and communications equipment and has been produced in baseline, Group 0, Group I and Group II (with T56-A-427 improved engines, which extend time on station) versions.

E-2 procurement was to have ended with the last of the six aircraft funded in FY 1992. Subsequently, the Navy determined that it would be more cost-effective to buy new aircraft than to extensively upgrade existing models. Accordingly, four new E-2Cs were funded in FY 1995, three in FY 1996 and four each in FYs 1997 and 1998. An additional 21 aircraft will be procured during FY 1999-2003. The Navy's active inventory

VFA-81 'Sunliners' (above), VFA-82 'Marauders' (left), VFA-83 'Rampagers' (above right) and VFA-86 'Sidewinders' (right) are all Atlantic Fleet units, based at NAS Oceana (in the case of VFA-81 and VFA-83) and MCAS Beaufort.

VFA-87 'Golden Warriors' (left), VFA-105 'Gunslingers' (right) and VFA-106 'Gladiators' (below left) are all Atlantic Fleet units. VFA-113 'Stingers' (below right) is a West Coast unit, based at NAS Lemoore.

Above: VFA-115 'Eagles' (until 1996 VA-115) is a NAS Lemoore-based unit.

Below: VFA-125 is the West Coast FRS. Like all other FRSs, it is known universally as 'the RAG'.

VFA-137 'Kestrels' has been a Hornet operator since 1987. It is now based at NAS Lemoore.

VFA-146 'Blue Diamonds' operates as part of CVW-9 aboard the USS John C. Stennis. Its sister squadron in CVW-9 is VFA-147 'Argonauts' (below).

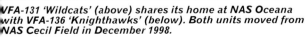

VFA-131 'Wildcats' (above) shares its home at NAS Oceana with VFA-136 'Knighthawks' (below). Both units moved from NAS Cecil Field in December 1998.

includes 78 E-2Cs, as well as two TE-2Cs for training E-2 pilots. An updated version of the E-2C, known as Hawkeye 2000, made its first flight in 1998. This upgrade includes an improved COTS-based mission computer upgrade, a new Advance Control Indicator Set (ACIS), a 12-ton vapour-cycle system, satellite communications and the Co-operative Engagement Capability (CEC). The Navy's ultimate goal is to eventually update the entire E-2C fleet to the HE2000 configuration.

All Group I variants have been retrofitted to Group II standard. By 2010 all production Group II aircraft will be upgraded to the Hawkeye 2000 standard. All Group 0 aircraft will be retired by 2004. A variant of the Common Support Aircraft is programmed to replace the E-2C.

Sea control

The S-3B Viking, which incorporated anti-surface warfare upgrades such as the APS-137 inverse synthetic aperture radar and the AGM-84 Harpoon as well as the UYS-1 Proteus acoustic sensor suite, completed replacement of the S-3A in the early 1990s. Mission emphasis has shifted away from ASW towards anti-surface warfare and land-attack missions. In September 1993 this was recognised when air anti-submarine (VS) squadrons were redesignated as sea control (VS).

The S-3's versatility, long range, high endurance and ability to carry stand-off weapons have resulted in a marked increase in its missions and flying hours. With the retirement of KA-6Ds, A-6Es and now ES-3As, S-3Bs are the sole organic refuelling platforms in carrier task forces and the number assigned to each air wing has been increased from six to eight. As of mid-1998, 114 of 119 S-3Bs converted remained in service.

The Navy now is conducting an S-3B Service-Life Assessment Program (SLAP) to identify structural components to be repaired and/or replaced in a Service-Life Extension Program (SLEP). A full-fatigue-article test is scheduled for FY 1999 as a part of this effort. Several upgrades are being installed on the S-3Bs (intended to serve through 2015), including GPS, carrier aircraft inertial navigation system II (CAINS II), a new autopilot and flight control system, new tactical displays, the AYK-23 central computer, satellite communications equipment and improved UHF/VHF radios.

The S-3B is planned for replacement by a variant of the Common Support Aircraft. However, in a surprise move in late 1998, the Navy decided to delete ASW as a mission for the S-3B, leaving anti-surface warfare as its primary mission, with overland strike support, mine warfare and aerial refuelling as secondary roles. In addition, half (four) of the aircraft in each squadron will become permanent tankers, a move that will result in their redesignation (KS-3B?). The S-3Bs will no longer carry an enlisted sensor operator and will normally fly with one pilot and one naval flight officer. In view of the tanker capability of the F/A-18E/F, it is possible that the S-3B eventually will be retired without replacement.

CV Sigint

The 16 ES-3A Shadows converted from S-3As during the early 1990s are being retired after less than a decade in service. The Shadows, which had filled the gap left by the withdrawal from service of the EA-3B Skywarrior, deployed with

each aircraft-carrier in two-ship detachments. There were fewer ES-3A airframes than are needed to support two 10-ship detachments and maintain a standard turnaround training schedule, so ES-3A airframes are transferred from one detachment to another to meet operational requirements. Like S-3Bs, ES-3As serve as tankers for the carrier air wing. The ES-3As proved exceptionally valuable over Bosnia in the reconnaissance role in support of NATO forces.

In mid-1998, the Navy made the decision to withdraw the ES-3A from service by mid-1999, without replacement. The aircraft's mission avionics suite, becoming obsolescent in the age of interconnectivity in the electronic battlefield, was deemed too expensive to upgrade. Carrier battle groups in the future will rely on land-based aircraft (such as EP-3Es and RC-135s) and space-based sensors to support Sigint requirements. It has not been determined if a CSA variant will return the Sigint role to the carrier air wing.

Carrier onboard delivery

For the specialised mission of delivering personnel, mail, spare parts and cargo to aircraft-carriers at sea, the Navy still relies on a fleet of Grumman C-2A Greyhound COD aircraft, derivatives of the E-2 Hawkeye early warning aircraft. Two fleet logistics (VRC) squadrons, one on each coast, deploy two-ship C-2 detachments on each aircraft-carrier. The 38 C-2As currently in service (plus one dedicated fatigue-test airframe), produced during the mid-1980s, replaced an earlier production run of 17 produced in the mid-1960s. A SLEP, delayed from 1994, is awaiting the assessment of a full-scale fatigue-life study. The SLEP will include installation of dual ARC-210 radios, full-face oxygen masks and an improved pitot-static system. Installation of the CAINS II inertial navigation system, funded under SLEP, began in FY 1998. No other major improvements are planned. The C-2A is planned for eventual replacement by a version of the Common Support Aircraft (CSA). However, Northrop Grumman has proposed a remanufacture programme for the C-2A in which the T56 turboprops would be replaced by turbofans.

Common Support Aircraft

A feasibility study concluded in November 1997 determined that a single airframe was technically and economically able to replace the E-2C, S-3B, ES-3A and C-2A by 2015. The aircraft is envisioned either to be produced in specialised variants or be equipped with modular mission suites. The Navy submitted a mission needs statement in early 1998, but Congress declined to provide any funding in the FY 1999 budget, encouraging the Navy to define further its requirement. Given the 1999 retirement of the ES-3A and the deletion of ASW as an S-3B role, the eventual character of the CSA programme, if it is ever funded, is likely to be somewhat different from its original vision.

Maritime patrol

The Navy has long operated the land-based Lockheed P-3 Orion maritime patrol aircraft for anti-submarine and anti-shipping roles, as well as for surveillance, reconnaissance, mine laying, drug-interdiction and search and rescue missions. Developed to counter the Soviet submarine threat, the P-3 force, greatly reduced since the

end of the Cold War, found itself in demand in the littoral warfare environment of the 1990s.

The current front-line version, the P-3C, first entered service in 1969 and has been upgraded frequently since, through Updates I, II, II.5 and III and is currently undergoing several programmes to extend the life of the airframe and improve its mission suite and armament. (The Boeing Update IV package, with a vastly improved mission suite and new engines, was cancelled in 1992, a victim of post-Cold War budget cutbacks.) The Navy is gradually upgrading most P-3Cs to an Update III Common Configuration that will be the fleet standard.

P-3C aircraft are continually being modernised with several improvement programmes to satisfy Navy and joint requirements through the early part of the 21st century. A roll-on counter-drug upgrade (CDU) sensor package, which included Cluster Ranger high-powered optical sensors, became available in the early 1990s and proved useful in NATO peace enforcement over Bosnia. Additional upgrades include installation of a modernised communications suite, GPS, common avionics improvements, modernised cockpit instrumentation and a new acoustic station sub-system display-and-control set that will permit integration of shallow-water anti-submarine warfare (ASW) sensors in the littoral environment. Retrofits of 25 older P-3Cs to the Update III common configuration via the Block Modification Upgrade Program (BMUP) are funded through FY 2000.

The Navy has moved the P-3C's operational emphasis to the littorals and is improving the anti-surface unit warfare (ASUW) capabilities of the P-3Cs. The Anti-surface Improvement Program (AIP), originally planned for 146 P-3Cs, incorporates enhancements in ASUW, over-the-horizon targeting and command, communications, control and intelligence (C^3I), plus survivability enhancements. These upgrades include anti-surface weapons (AGM-65F and AGM-84E); APS-137 (V)5 inverse synthetic-aperture radar; a stand-off electro-optics sensor; upgraded Elint detection and classification; DAMA, SATCOM and OTCIXS C^3I systems; and chaff and flare dispensers, a missile warning system and 'inerted' fuel tanks. The P-3C AIP development aircraft began testing in December 1996 and is currently in use by VP-30 for fleet introduction training. Twenty-eight AIP production upgrades are presently on contract; five had been delivered to the fleet by mid-1998. The AIP version was initially deployed in June 1998 by VP-9, which operated the aircraft in support of the Fifth Fleet in the Persian Gulf. The initial inventory objective is 56 AIP aircraft, well short of the goal of equipping each VP squadron with four AIP aircraft.

The Sustained Readiness Program (SRP) is underway to keep the P-3C airframe in service until 2015. The first P-3C to go through SRP returned to service in February 1998 and was delivered to the fleet in June 1998. Fifty SRP kits have been procured to date, with an inventory objective of 222 aircraft. An FY 1999 Service-Life Assessment Program (SLAP) will determine ultimate airframe life. Its product, a SLEP kit, will be added to the ongoing SRP process in FY 2002.

In recent years, P-3Cs have been valuable reconnaissance platforms, serving joint commanders on missions over Somalia, Haiti, Rwanda, Bosnia and Kosovo. Maverick-armed P-3Cs were also

VFA-151 'Vigilantes' (above) operates as part of CVW-2.
VFA-192 'The World Famous Golden Dragons' (right) is based at NAS Atsugi, along with VFA-27 and VFA-195 (below).

Above: VAQ-129 'Vikings' is the FRS for the Prowler community.

Below: Apart from the Japan-based units, all active-duty Navy EA-6B squadrons are based at Whidbey Island. This is a VAQ-130 'Zappers' aircraft.

Above: VAQ-128 'Fighting Phoenix' is one of the four joint USN/USAF expeditionary Prowler units.

Right: VAQ-131 'Lancers' operates as part of CVW-2 aboard the USS Constellation.

Below: This VAQ-132 'Scorpions' EA-6B is the squadron 'CAG bird'. VAQ-132 is attached to CVW-17.

Above: This VAQ-134 'Garudas' EA-6B is seen at Nellis AFB during a regular Prowler deployment to a 'Flag' exercise.

Below: VAQ-135 'Black Ravens' sail as part of Air Wing 11, aboard the USS Carl Vinson (CVN-70).

Left: VAQ-136 'Gauntlets' is the sole Atsugi-based EA-6B unit.

Above: VAQ-138 is one of the few Prowler units not to have seen combat.

Left: The badge of VAQ-137 'Rooks' features a stylised North American bird.

Right: VAQ-139 'Cougars' sails as part of CVW-14.

used to enforce sanctions in the Adriatic against the former Yugoslavia. The 12 active patrol squadrons (down from 24 in 1991) all operate the P-3C Update III version, as do three of the seven reserve patrol squadrons. A few P-3Bs and P-3Cs in service with patrol squadron special projects units are modified with specialised reconnaissance equipment.

As of mid-1998, 228 P-3Cs remained in service. Other variants of the P-3 still in service include one TP-3A pilot trainer (to be retired in February 1999), five VP-3A executive transports, five UP-3A/B utility transports, one NP-3C and 13 NP-3D (former EP-3A, RP-3A, EP-3B and RP-3D) RDT&E and oceanographic survey aircraft, six P-3B/C special projects aircraft and one EP-3J electronic aggressor aircraft.

Land-based Sigint

The Navy operates 11 Lockheed EP-3E Orion land-based electronic reconnaissance aircraft to intercept, collect, identify and exploit signals intelligence (Sigint) in support of joint theatre and fleet commanders. The unarmed EP-3E carries a large crew, mostly electronic warfare operators, communications intercept operators and linguists. The aircraft often fly missions off the coast of potentially hostile nations, monitoring their radar and communications activity. During the mid-1990s, 12 P-3Cs were converted under the CILOP (Conversion-In-Lieu-Of-Procurement) programme to EP-3Es with the ARIES II (Airborne Reconnaissance Integrated Electronic System II) mission suite. These aircraft replaced two EP-3B 'Bat Rack' and 10 EP-3E 'Aries I' (all P-3A conversions) in service with two fleet air reconnaissance (VQ) squadrons. The last EP-3E ARIES II aircraft was delivered in 1997. One VQ-2 EP-3E was damaged beyond economical repair in a September 1997 landing mishap at Souda Bay, Crete; a P-3C has been selected to receive the damaged EP-3E's mission suite and will be converted to an EP-3E.

The Sensor System Improvement Program (SSIP) upgrade, which features improvements to the EP-3E's communications and data automation capabilities, is nearing the end of combined developmental and operational testing at NAS Patuxent River, Maryland. Theatre deployment and fleet operational test and evaluation began in late 1998. All EP-3Es are scheduled for SSIP upgrade by FY 2000. One EP-3E modified beginning in December 1997 with the high-band Sigint prototype sub-system of the Joint Sigint Avionics Family (JSAF) is being operationally tested. The retirement of the ES-3A in 1999 will further increase fleet reliance on the EP-3E and Air Force RC-135 for Sigint support.

Strategic communications

Since the late 1960s, the Navy has operated strategic communications aircraft which linked the national command authority with the nuclear deterrent force's fleet ballistic missile submarines. Known by the programme name TACAMO (take charge and move out), 16 Boeing E-6A Mercurys had replaced the EC-130G/Q Hercules aircraft by 1992. The Mercury transmits very-low-frequency communications with 30,000-ft (9144-m) trailing-wire antennas. The E-6 continues to provide survivable and reliable command, control and communications (C^3) to US strategic forces. All E-6A aircraft are currently undergoing

a major mission systems upgrade to the E-6B configuration to better support the submarine communications role and serve as airborne command posts (ABNCPs) for the US Strategic Command. The E-6B retains all E-6A capabilities and is equipped with a battle-staff compartment and an airborne launch-control system capable of launching Peacekeeper and Minuteman ICBMs. Other upgrades include installation of GPS, the Orbit Improvement System (to increase antenna efficiency), a new mission computer system, UHF frequency division multiplexing, an LF transmit capability and a MILSTAR command post terminal. Planned upgrades include additional satellite communications capabilities, a new receiver terminal and new cockpit displays.

The first E-6B was delivered on 14 October 1997. E-6Bs flew their first operational missions in April 1998 and completely replaced the Air Force EC-135C Looking Glass aircraft in September 1998. The first test launch of an Air Force Minuteman III ICBM commanded by an E-6B took place on 24 June 1998. All 16 E-6As will have been modified to the E-6B series by 2000; six E-6Bs had been delivered by mid-1998. Fifteen of the Navy's 16 E-6s are divided into two operational squadrons (VQ-3 and VQ-4) assigned to Strategic Communications Wing One at Tinker AFB, Oklahoma City, Oklahoma; the 16th aircraft is used as a test platform. Despite the end of the Cold War, all 16 E-6 Mercury aircraft will be kept in service and be postured to provide C^3 through partial airborne coverage and ground alert. Two TC-18Fs, modified Boeing 707-320s, are used as cockpit trainers for E-6 crews.

Multi-purpose Maritime Aircraft

The Multipurpose Maritime Aircraft (MMA) programme is envisioned to replace the P-3, EP-3, E-6 and C-130 in naval service. An MMA definition study has been funded by the Navy and a technical and economic feasibility study is planned for 1999. P-3 fleet service is expected to expire by 2016, so Navy planners hope to initiate production of the MMA by 2010.

Tiltrotors

The production of the MV-22B Osprey tiltrotor is underway for the Marine Corps. The Navy envisions procuring 48 HV-22B rescue versions; however, no funding has been provided to date and service entry of the HV-22B is not likely before 2010.

ASW helicopters

The Navy has commenced the execution of its Helicopter Master Plan, which will ultimately reduce the eight different types of helicopters currently operated by the Navy to two H-60 variants, combining operational and cost effectiveness in meeting the burgeoning missions expected to be performed by fleet organic rotary-wing aircraft now and in the future. Three types currently in fleet service are the SH-60B LAMPS III, the SH-60F (CV-Helo) and the HH-60H. (The Marine Corps operates eight VH-60Ns in its presidential support fleet. Three UH-60As on loan from the Army are used by the US Naval Test Pilot School.)

Procurement of all existing Seahawk versions of the H-60 ended with funding for eight HH-60Hs in the FY 1994 budget. As of mid-1998, there were 165 SH-60Bs, 76 SH-60Fs and

37 HH-60Hs in the fleet inventory, as well as two NSH-60Bs and one YSH-60F in permanent test roles. Two follow-on types under development are the SH-60R and the CH-60S.

The SH-60B, which replaced the SH-2 Seasprite in the early 1990s, functions as an extension of the shipboard weapon system of the cruiser, destroyer, or frigate on which it is deployed. With radar, ESM, MAD, IR and sonobuoy sensors, the SH-60B can detect and track submarines and surface ships and attack with ASW torpedoes and anti-shipping missiles. Its secondary missions include SAR, medevac, VertRep, fleet support and communications relay. SH-60Bs routinely deploy on 'Ticonderoga'-class Aegis guided-missile cruisers, 'Spruance'-class destroyers and 'Oliver Hazard Perry'-class guided-missile frigates. An upgrade programme for 93 SH-60Bs, called Block I, will continue through mid-1999 and includes installation of the Mk 50 torpedo, GPS and AGM-119 Penguin anti-shipping missiles, as well as the AAS-44 infra-red sensor.

During FY 1997, eight SH-60Bs were armed with Hellfire missiles, and the arming of 24 active-duty and 18 reserve HH-60H aircraft with those missiles has started. Another 79 SH-60Bs will be armed with Hellfires, with fleet introduction planned for the second quarter of FY 1999. Eventually, 230 H-60 helicopters will be armed with Hellfire. However, until more missiles are procured, the arming programme will result in the Hellfire inventory level being reduced from 86 per cent to 73 per cent. By the end of FY 1999, 87 SH-60Bs will be able to launch Penguin missiles.

During the 1990s, the SH-60F (CV-Helo) replaced the SH-3H Sea King in all active-duty HS squadrons as the aircraft-carrier's ASW helicopter. Equipped with dipping sonar and armed with ASW torpedoes, the SH-60F provides inner-zone defence to a carrier battle group. (The AQS-22 dipping sonar will replace the current AQS-13F.) The SH-60F also serves in plane guard, rescue and logistics roles.

In HS squadrons, the SH-60F is augmented by the HH-60H strike rescue version that has the primary role of conducting combat SAR and insertion and extraction of special operations forces. The HH-60H, which replaced the HH-1K in the Naval Air Reserve, is armed with 7.62-mm machine-guns and Hellfire missiles.

SH-60R and CH-60S

The Navy is currently developing the SH-60R as a replacement for both the SH-60B and SH-60F. Most SH-60B, SH-60F and HH-60H airframes will be remanufactured into SH-60Rs, including 38 SH-60Bs originally scheduled for the Block I upgrade. The SH-60R will feature many improvements, including an increase in gross operating weight, two additional stores stations, a 1553 databus, an AYK-14 mission computer, improved cockpit displays, an AQS-22 light-weight low-frequency dipping sonar, a UYS-2 acoustic processor, a multi-mode inverse synthetic-aperture radar, an upgraded ESM system, an IR sensor and an integrated self-defence system. The MAD system will be deleted, but the SH-60R will retain the 7.62-mm machine-gun, the Penguin and Hellfire missiles and the Mk 46 and Mk 50 torpedoes as armament. Remanufacturing will commence in 1999, conclude in 2011 and extend

Above: VAQ-140 'Patriots' is attached to CVW-7 aboard the USS Washington (CVN-73).

Below: VAQ-142 'Gray Wolves' is one of the joint expeditionary EA-6B units, along with VAQ-128, VAQ-133 and VAQ-134.

VS-22 'Checkmates' (above) and VS-24 'Scouts' (below) are East Coast units attached to CVW-3 and CVW-8, respectively.

Above: VAQ-141 'Shadowhawks' played an important part in the Operation Deliberate Force strikes of August 1995.

Right: The S-3Bs of VS-21 'Fighting Redtails' each wear a Viking's head fin badge.

Below: VS-30 'Diamondcutters' are based at NAS Jacksonville, with all the Atlantic Fleet S-3s.

Left: VS-29 'Screaming Dragonflies' is based at NAS North Island, home of the Pacific Fleet S-3B force. Only VS-21 is based elsewhere, at NAF Atsugi.

Right: VS-32 'Maulers' deployed with Maverick-capable S-3Bs during its 1998 cruise as part of CVW-1.

Left: VS-33 'Screwbirds' pioneered the integration of the AGM-84 Harpoon with fleet Viking squadrons.

Right: This is the 'CAG bird' of VS-35 'Blue Wolves', the most recently established Viking squadron, which stood up in 1991.

Left: VS-38 'Red Griffins' sails as part of CVW-2, aboard the USS Constellation.

Right: A shamrock fin badge marks this S-3B as a VS-41 aircraft, the sole Viking FRS.

the service life of the airframe to 20,000 hours from the current 10,000 hours. The SH-60R is scheduled to enter service in 2002.

A proposed variant of the SH-60R, the SH-60R(V), is planned for HS squadrons as a less-expensive CV-Helo. This version is envisioned to be wired for all SH-60R systems but would not have all systems installed. A final decision on production has not been made.

Commencing in 1999, the Navy is procuring a second new H-60 variant, the CH-60S Knighthawk, to perform the combat logistics support, combat SAR, organic airborne mine countermeasures, vertical replenishment and utility missions. In late 1997, Sikorsky flew the YCH-60 development helicopter, fabricated from an Army UH-60L Black Hawk and a Navy SH-60F and demonstrated it in the VertRep role. Basically a Black Hawk with rotor, engines (T700-GE-401C), tail pylon, gear box, rescue hoist and automatic flight control system of a Seahawk, the CH-60 has dual large cargo doors, a cabin with reversible floorboards (one side with rollers to handle pallets) and an external cargo hook. The CH-60S was approved in 1998 for low-rate initial production and is planned for service as a replacement for the CH-46D, HH-46D, UH-46D, UH-3H, HH-1N, VH-3A and HH-60H. The CH-60's advantages over the HH-60H include the ability to carry a rigid inflatable boat internally; a Black Hawk-style tailwheel that allows steeper approaches to landing; and the external stores support system. The YCH-60 is being tested in 1999 as a mine-warfare platform and may yet prove to be a suitable replacement for the MH-53E by using remotely operated systems and laser detection systems.

Five CH-60Ss were funded in the FY 1999 budget; production is expected to increase to 18 per year until up to 185 have been produced. The CH-60S is expected to reach IOC in FY 2001. The procurement of all Navy H-60 variants is scheduled for completion by 2011.

Exit LAMPS I

The Kaman SH-2G Seasprite (LAMPS Mk I) remains in service with two reserve squadrons (HSL-84 and HSL-94). The SH-2G is the only Navy platform currently using the Magic Lantern laser mine-detection system (delivered in December 1996) and is expected to be retired from service by 2000. SH-2Gs deploy on reserve early-build 'Perry'-class guided-missile frigates (FFGs) not equipped to handle the SH-60B. With the pending retirement of the early 'Perry' FFGs, the SH-2Gs will no longer be required. Seventeen SH-2Gs remain in service.

Reigning Sea Kings

Another ASW helicopter, having been replaced on carriers by the SH-60F, is the Sikorsky SH-3H Sea King, one squadron of which provides ASW and rescue services for CVWR-30. Reserve squadrons HS-75 and HC-85 also operate the UH-3H, a utility version of the SH-3H (modified with a cargo hook and redesigned cabin) for rescue, torpedo recovery and other range services. The UH-3H is operated by VC-8, the Pacific Missile Range Facility and by several air station base flights. The Navy converted 53 SH-3Hs into UH-3Hs. Four former presidential transports, VH-3As, provide executive transportation in the Norfolk, Virginia area. A single

NVH-3A is used by the Rotary-Wing Aircraft Test Squadron as a test platform for the presidential fleet of 11 Marine Corps VH-3Ds. The UH-3H and the VH-3A are scheduled for replacement by the CH-60S Knighthawk.

Mine countermeasures

The Sikorsky MH-53E Sea Dragon, a derivative of the CH-53E Super Stallion assault transport, remains the Navy's sole dedicated mine countermeasures helicopter. Most of the Navy's 44 MH-53Es are operated by HM-14 and HM-15; these squadrons are manned by a 50-50 mix of active and reserve personnel. Five MH-53Es are used to train Navy Sea Dragon crews with the Marine Corps' CH-53E training squadron (HMT-302) at MCAS New River, North Carolina. One NMH-53E serves in a permanent test role. In 1994 the Navy transferred the last of its CH-53E vertical onboard delivery (VOD) helicopters to the Marine Corps and replaced them with MH-53Es, operated by HC-4 in the Mediterranean. MH-53E deliveries were completed in FY 1994. The installation of GPS has greatly increased the effectiveness of the MH-53E. Current plans call for the MH-53E to be operated well into the 21st century; as a consequence, the Navy is conducting a SLAP to determine requirements for a SLEP. Future plans call for the integration of an upgraded GPS capable of stand-alone navigation in national airspace and the installation of T64-GE-419 (versus -416) engines to allow for one-engine-out operation. If suitable mine countermeasures systems are developed, the CH-60S may be adapted to replace the MH-53E.

Vertical replenishment

An ageing fleet of Boeing Vertol H-46 Sea Knights – in their fourth decade of service – sustains the Navy's VertRep capability and provides rescue/utility detachments for the amphibious assault ships (LHAs and LHDs) and the single mine countermeasures support ship (MCS). The CH-46D, HH-46D and UH-46D are essentially similar and used interchangeably by the HC squadrons, with the HH-46Ds equipping the rescue detachments.

The Sea Knights are going through a dynamic component upgrade (DCU) to extend their operating life and to lift flight restrictions imposed by fatigue. In the early years of the decade, major funding was provided for modernisation of the aircraft, including night-flying improvements and dynamic-component upgrades (DCUs). The latter include a new rotor head, a new aft-rotor vertical shaft, a transmission upgrade and new flight controls. When the upgrades are complete, the aircraft will have been returned only to its original level of capability. Half of the H-46 fleet has received DCU rotorheads. However, only a few aircraft have DCU completely installed; those aircraft have improved corrosion resistance, increased fleet readiness and reliability, and have eliminated the need for recurring inspections. A total of 312 aircraft (this figures includes US Marine Corps CH-46Es) is scheduled to receive DCU modifications, with the last upgrade planned for 2002.

As of mid-1998, 42 HH-46Ds, 27 CH-46Ds and 11 UH-46Ds remained in service. The predicted shortage of H-46s will reach 48 aircraft by the turn of the century. The Navy is supporting procurement of the CH-60S to replace the H-46

fleet. An approved COEA has identified the CH-60S as the best alternative to replace the H-46Ds, with savings of $650 million anticipated over the life cycle of the programme. The Navy has experimented with the Kaman K-MAX helicopter and the Bell 212 (operated by Evergreen) in the VertRep role, but no commitment has been made.

Fleet logistics

The Navy has managed to maintain control over a sizeable logistics aircraft fleet ever since World War II. The current fleet is used to meet rapidly changing requirements in transporting personnel, mail, spare parts and other cargo to ports for transfer to ships at sea. Aircraft rotate on detachments to forward fleet operating areas such as the Mediterranean, Persian Gulf and the Western Pacific.

The McDonnell Douglas C-9B Skytrain II, a military version of the DC-9-32 airliner, has been in naval service since 1973. These aircraft have been augmented by second-hand DC-9-31s and later by DC-9-33s, which retained their civil designations. The 17 C-9B and 12 DC-9 aircraft have been operated by the Naval Air Reserve for almost two decades; they are currently going through an avionics upgrade in order to remain consistent with commercial aviation standards and FAA requirements. In 1997 Congress funded the procurement of two Boeing 737-700s, designated C-40A, to begin replacing the C-9 fleet. A third C-40A was ordered in 1998. The C-40A is scheduled to enter service in 2000.

During the early 1990s, the Navy retired its fleet of Lockheed C-130Fs and KC-130Fs (the latter borrowed from the Marine Corps). Twenty new C-130T transports were obtained for four Naval Air Reserve VR squadrons, the last two being delivered in late 1996. These aircraft equipped two new squadrons (VR-53 and -54) and replaced DC-9s in two others (VR-55 and VR-62). They routinely rotate on detachment to forward operating areas along with the C-9s, having assumed the fleet-support airlift role once performed by the now retired C-130Fs of VR-22 and VRC-50 and the KC-130Fs of VR-22. The modern C-130Ts have since been upgraded with ARC-210 radios and GPS. There are no plans to procure additional C-130Ts.

Phase-out in Antarctica

In 1998, the Navy began retiring its ski-equipped LC-130F and LC-130R Hercules transports used to supply the scientific research stations in Antarctica. The LC-130Fs of VXE-6 have been retired and the squadron's LC-130Rs are being transformed into LC-130Hs for the New York Air National Guard's 109th Airlift Wing, which has assumed the Antarctic support role and operates similar LC-130H aircraft. VXE-6's TC-130Q training aircraft also have been retired. The squadron retired its HH-1Ns in 1996, turning over helicopter services to contractors.

In December 1998, the Air Force transferred to the Navy the NC-130H, the former EC-130V drug-interdiction aircraft (with an E-2C radome and radar system installed) used briefly by the Coast Guard in the early 1990s. The aircraft has joined the Naval Force Aircraft Test Squadron at NAS Patuxent River, Maryland as a development platform for the Hawkeye 2005 radar system and associated support architecture.

The Navy's two ES-3A Shadow squadrons, VQ-5 'Sea Shadows' (above) and VQ-6 'Black Ravens' (below), will be disestablished in 1999 and the ES-3A withdrawn from service.

VAW-112 'Golden Hawks' (above), VAW-113 'Black Hawks' (left), VAW-116 'Sun Kings' (below left) and VAW-117 'Wallbangers' (below) are all West Coast E-2C Hawkeye squadrons, based at NAWS Point Mugu. A fifth Pacific Fleet Hawkeye unit, VAW-115 'Sentinels', is based at NAF Atsugi. VRC-30 is stationed at Point Mugu, alongside the E-2Cs.

Right: VAW-121 'Bluetails' is one of the very oldest of E-2 squadrons, having stood up in April 1967.

Below: VP-4 'Skinny Dragons', now based at MCAF Kaneohe Bay, is one of the six remaining P-3C squadrons attached to the two Patrol Wings of the Pacific Fleet.

Above: VAW-120, based at NAS Norfolk, acts as the FRS for the whole Hawkeye community.

Below: VAW-123 'Screwtops' is one of the six Atlantic Fleet E-2C units.

The US Navy's P-3 Orion force has, arguably, seen the greatest reduction in the Soviet-era threat it was designed to counter – and thus the greatest cuts in its overall strength. The Orion community is now evenly split between the active Navy and Reserve, with just 13 active-duty patrol squadrons remaining. These P-3Cs are from VP-5 'Mad Foxes' (above right) and VP-8 'Tigers' (right), both East Coast units from Patrol Wings 11 and 5, respectively.

Above: VAW-125 'Tiger Tails' is attached to Air Wing 17, aboard the USS Eisenhower.

Below: VAW-126 'Seahawks' is attached to Air Wing 3 aboard the USS Enterprise.

Gulfstream C-20D Gulfstream IIIs and C-20G Gulfstream IVs are operated by the Naval Air Reserve for a variety of rapid-response transport duties, but mostly for transportation of high-level Navy and Marine Corps military and civilian officials. The C-20Ds – both operated from NAF Washington, DC by Fleet Logistics Support Squadron 1 (VR-1) – are fitted with executive compartments with accommodation for five passengers and staff compartments with accommodation for eight passengers.

Four C-20Gs are operated (two each) by VR-48 at NAF Washington and VR-51 at MCAF Kaneohe Bay, Hawaii. The C-20G may be configured for cargo operations, passenger operations, or various combinations of the two. With passengers seats, removed the aircraft may be modified to the following configurations: three pallets/no passengers, two pallets/eight passengers and one pallet/14 passengers. With a full complement of seats installed, the aircraft can accommodate up to 26 passengers and a crew of four.

Base flights

Versions of the twin-turboprop Beech C-12 Huron (Super King Air) are still used extensively for base flight support aircraft, with a few specialised variants assigned the additional duty of range clearance and support. As of mid-1998, 44 UC-12Bs, 20 TC-12Bs, 10 UC-12Fs, 10 UC-12Ms, two RC-12Fs and two RC-12Ms remained in service. Most UC-12Bs are assigned to Stateside bases. The UC-12F is used at naval air facilities in Japan, while the UC-12M is used for base flights in Europe (and at NAS Norfolk, Virginia for type training). Two RC-12Fs (converted from UC-12Fs) support the Pacific Missile Range Facility in Hawaii and two new-build RC-12Ms assigned to NS Roosevelt Roads, Puerto Rico support the Atlantic Fleet Weapons Training Facility. Surplus UC-12Bs are being converted to TC-12Bs to augment the T-44A multi-engine training track with Training Air Wing 4.

In 1998, the Air National Guard transferred seven C-26Bs to the Navy at no cost to serve as on-call rapid-response modern air transport for high-priority resupply and the movement of key personnel to remote unserviced or feeder sites. The aircraft are replacing some UC-12Bs that are being converted to TC-12B trainers. The C-26Bs will be used to deliver repair parts, equipment, technical teams and mishap investigation teams and carry out such missions as range clearance, medical evacuation, administrative movement of personnel and courier services. Crew training commenced in January 1999, but at that time the bases destined to receive C-26Bs had not been finalised.

A few HH-1N helicopters remain in service in base flights as air station SAR aircraft. These aircraft, which may be required by the Marine Corps for conversion to the four-bladed rotor UH-1Y, may be candidates for replacement by the CH-60S; alternatively, replacement by contractor-operated helicopters is an option.

Adversaries

The once expansive adversary aircraft force is now concentrated in two reserve VFC squadrons flying F/A-18A/B Hornets (VFC-12) and F-5E/F Tiger IIs (VFC-13). The Navy's remaining F-5s are all based at NAS Fallon, Nevada.

Unmanned aerial vehicles (UAVs)

The Navy has used RQ-2A Pioneer unmanned aerial vehicles (UAVs) for reconnaissance since the late 1980s. The RQ-2A is a tactical system for near real-time reconnaissance, surveillance and target acquisition (RSTA) and battle damage assessment (BDA). The Pioneer is currently configured for operations from land-based sites and LPDs and will operate until the planned transition to the Tactical UAV (TUAV) system is completed.

The Pioneer is launched using rocket-assisted take-off or pneumatic rails and is recovered by net at sea, or by landing ashore in a 200 x 75-m (656 x 246-ft) unimproved field. The UAV can carry a payload of 65-100 lb (29-45 kg), including a day TV camera or IR camera and can patrol for periods of longer than five hours. Control of the RQ-2A can be handed from one control station to another, thereby increasing the vehicle's range and allowing launch from one site and recovery at another. The Pioneer system can control two air vehicles simultaneously (but the video downlink and positive control can be managed for only one air vehicle at a time).

The Pioneer fleet has flown over 17,000 hours during 11 years of operations by Army, Navy and Marine Corps tactical units. VC-6 deploys shipboard Pioneer detachments from NAS Patuxent River; the Marine Corps fields two Marine UAV squadrons, VMU-1 and VMU-2. Theatres of operation have included the Persian Gulf, Bosnia, Somalia and North Africa. A replacement has not been selected, but the Navy is considering procurement of a VTOL UAV to augment the Pioneer. Pioneer UAV, Inc. is developing an improved version, the RQ-2B.

Primary training aircraft

The Beech T-34C Turbo Mentor is operated in large numbers by the Naval Air Training Command for basic and intermediate training of naval aviators (including helicopter pilots) and flight officers. Six training squadrons are equipped with the Turbo Mentor. As of mid-1998, 318 T-34Cs remained in the Navy's inventory. A few T-34Cs serve as target-spotting aircraft for the Navy's F-14 and F/A-18 fleet-readiness squadrons. A single NT-34C serves as a development aircraft at the Naval Air Warfare Center, Aircraft Division and has been used to develop a collision-avoidance system.

The T-34C will be replaced by the Raytheon-built T-6A Texan II beginning in 2003. The T-6A, a variant of the Pilatus PC-9, was selected through the Joint Primary Aircraft Training System (JPATS) competition. The T-6A, equipped with a 'glass' cockpit, will be but one part of a comprehensive interactive training system. The T-6A will enter Air Force service in 2001 to replace the T-37 and will begin replacing Navy T-34Cs in 2003. Total Air Force and Navy procurement of 740 Texan IIs is planned, with the last scheduled for delivery in 2017.

Advanced training aircraft

The Beech T-44A Pegasus advanced maritime multi-engined training aircraft (a military version of the Beech King Air 90) has completed two decades of service and is busily engaged by one Navy training squadron (VT-31) in training Navy and Air Force pilots to fly multi-engined aircraft such as the P-3 and the C-130. Of 61 T-44As

built, 55 remained in service in mid-1998. A proposed T-44B follow-on version was cancelled before development. The shift of Air Force multi-engined turboprop pilot training to the Navy in 1997 increased the demand for training aircraft and some 20 Beech UC-12Bs are being converted to TC-12Bs.

Two training squadrons of North American T-2C Buckeyes take pilots and flight officers through basic and intermediate strike training. The 107 T-2Cs remaining in service experienced airframe problems and were grounded for a period in 1997. The T-2Cs still in the inventory are scheduled to be replaced by T-45Cs by 2010. Nine T-2Cs serve as chase aircraft and spin trainers at the US Naval Test Pilot School in Patuxent River, Maryland.

The TA-4J remains the only variant of the Skyhawk in US naval service. The TA-4J is used as an advanced strike trainer in one training squadron (VT-7) and serves as an adversary and target-tug in one composite squadron (VC-8). As of mid-1998, 49 TA-4Js remained in service. The T-45C is in production to replace the TA-4J in the strike training role. All TA-4Js were scheduled for phase-out by the end of 1999, but the phase-out may be adjusted because of delays in delivery of the T-45C.

The Boeing (formerly McDonnell Douglas) T-45 Goshawk is steadily replacing the T-2C and TA-4J in the strike-training role. A development of the British Aerospace Hawk with redesigned landing gear, a strengthened mid-section and a tailhook, the T-45 is one component of an entire interactive training system, the T45TS (T-45 Training System). The T-45A, which entered service during the mid-1990s, equips two training squadrons. Deliveries of the T-45A were completed in mid-1998. The proposed T-45B non-carrier-capable version was never developed. The Navy's total requirement for the T-45 is 187 aircraft. Through FY 1998, 123 aircraft had been funded; funding for another 15 was included in the FY 1999 budget. By mid-1998 78 T-45As (of 83 built) remained in service.

The T-45C, which first flew on 21 October 1997 and was first delivered in November 1997, features Cockpit-21, a 'glass' cockpit with an integral GPS/INS and a 1553 digital databus, compatible with modern military tactical aircraft. The first production T-45C was delivered in November 1997 to Training Air Wing One (TAW-1) as part of the stand-up of NAS Meridian, Mississippi as a T45TS training site. (The first six T-45Cs actually preceded the last T-45As off the production line.) TAW-1's VT-23 began training pilots in the T-45C, six of which were available for use by mid-1998. The T-45C will eventually replace the T-2C and TA-4J in VT-7 and VT-9. Conversion of the T-45As to the CP-21 configuration is expected to begin in 2001 and be fully completed by 2007.

The North American T-39N Sabreliner is used by one training squadron for advanced strike training for flight officers destined to crew the F-14, F/A-18D/F, S-3 and EA-6B. The 17 T-39Ns are modifications of a variety of earlier T-39 and CT-39 models with avionics suited for training in radar navigation and airborne radar intercepts. During the mid-1990s, the T-39Ns replaced the Cessna T-47A Citations, which earlier had replaced the T-39D. The T-39Ns were purchased by the Navy (and issued with new

VP-9 'Golden Eagles' (above) is one of the three Hawaii-based P-3C patrol units. VP-10 'Lancers' (above right) and VP-26 Tridents (left) are both based at NAS Brunswick, as part of Patrol Wing 5, Atlantic Fleet. VP-30 'Pro's Nest' (right) is the P-3 FRS. VP-40 (below) is one of the three NAS Whidbey Island-based Orion units.

Above: VP-47 'Golden Swordsmen' is one of the three Pacific Fleet P-3C units currently moving from NAS Barbers Point to MCAS Kaneohe Bay, in Hawaii.

In addition to their specialised EP-3Es, VQ-1 (above) and VQ-2 (below) – the Navy's dedicated Elint-gathering units – operate P-3 and UP-3 'bounce birds' for transport and training duties.

The US Navy has two shadowy special operations patrol units, VPU-1 'Old Buzzards' and VPU-2 'Wizards' (right). VPU-1 is the East Coast unit, based at NAS Brunswick, while VPU-2 is based in Hawaii. The two units operate a mix of largely unmarked, but modified, P-3s on classified tasks, believed to include reconnaissance.

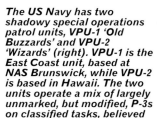

Based at Rota AB, in Spain, VQ-2 'Batmen' is one of the Navy's two EP-3E Aries units.

Above left: This VP-3A is the personal transport of the Commander in Chief, US Pacific Fleet (CINCPAC).

Left: Named Valkyria, this UP-3A is operated by the Keflavik base flight under the Commander, Fleet Air Keflavik, Iceland.

Above: The E-6Bs of VQ-3 and VQ-4 are now the USA's only strategic warfighting airborne command posts.

Bureau Numbers) having been owned and operated under contract by Boeing North American. Raytheon Systems Company won the contract to operate and maintain the Sabreliners beginning in 1998. One T-39D serves in test roles with the Naval Weapons Test Squadron in China Lake, California. (As of 1998, the CT-39G rapid-response airlift Sabreliners remained in service only with the Marine Corps.). Eleven Northrop T-38A Talons remain in service with the US Naval Test Pilot School.

Only one type of training helicopter, the Bell TH-57 Sea Ranger, is used to instruct the many helicopter pilots who serve with the Navy, Marine Corps and Coast Guard. The Navy trains several hundred student naval aviators with 47 TH-57Bs (for primary VFR training) and 77 TH-57Cs (for advanced IFR training) in two helicopter training squadrons at NAS Whiting Field, Milton, Florida. Two TH-57Cs configured for RDT&E are used for photo, chase and utility missions at the Naval Air Warfare Center, Aircraft Division at Patuxent River, Maryland.

Of note, with the advent of joint undergraduate pilot and navigator training during the mid-1990s, the following Air Force aircraft are used to train Navy, Marine Corps and Coast Guard pilots and flight officers: T-1A Jayhawk – large multi-engine jet pilot training and navigator training; T-37B – primary and intermediate pilot training; T-43A – navigator training.

Miscellaneous types

The Navy has long included in its inventory numerous aircraft in small quantities, many on loan from other services, for special purposes. Many continue to serve with the US Naval Test Pilot School in order to give students the opportunity to fly in a wide variety of flight conditions. Aircraft in service with the USN TPS include one de Havilland Canada NU-1B Otter, two DHC U-6A Beavers, four Beech U-21F Utes, two X-26A powered gliders, six Hughes TH-6B Cayuses and four Bell OH-58C Kiowas.

McDonnell Douglas QF-4N and QF-4S target drones are expended periodically in missile tests. They also serve (while manned) as chase planes for tests. A single YF-4J serves when needed as an ejection-seat test platform.

A single surviving X-31A high angle-of-attack research aircraft is owned by the Navy but is used by NASA on research activities.

A single Douglas EC-24A (a modified DC-8) is operated by Raytheon for the Navy as an electronic aggressor for fleet exercises. Two Boeing NKC-135A Stratotankers used for the same purpose were retired in the mid-1990s. Three DC-130A Hercules drone launcher aircraft are operated from NAWS Point Mugu under contract with Avtel.

Naval aircraft types or designations withdrawn from service 1990-1998

A-3B	A-4M	C-130F	HH-1K	RP-3A
EA-3B	NA-4M	LC-130F	TH-1L	EP-3B
EKA-3B	OA-4M	EC-130G	HH-2D	YP-3C
KA-3B	EA-6A	EC-130Q	SH-2F	RP-3D
NA-3B	NEA-6B	TC-130Q	HH-3A	S-3A
RA-3B	KA-6D	LC-130R	UH-3A	NS-3A
NRA-3B	A-6E	C-131H	SH-3D	US-3A
TA-3B	A-6F	NKC-135A	SH-3G	T-2B
NTA-3B	TA-7C	UC-880	OH-6A	T-34B
UA-3B	A-7E	RF-4B	NCH-53A	YT-34C
(NTRA-3B)	YA-7E	F-4S	CH-53A	CT-39E
A-4E	NA-7E	RF-8G	RH-53D	U-3A
A-4F	EA-7L	TH-57A	OH-58A	U-11A
NA-4F	TC-4C	TF-16N	U-21A	
TA-4F	UC-8A	QF-86F	YSH-60B	OV-10A
NTA-4F	DC-9-31	NUH-1E	O-2A	OV-10D
TA-4J	UC-27	AH-1J	EP-3A	V-22A
NTA-4J	C-28A	AH-1T	NP-3A	

US Navy organisation and operations

The Chief of Naval Operations (CNO) is the Department of the Navy's agent for training and equipping naval forces, including naval aviation and making them available for operational control by joint commanders to deploy in time of war or crisis or for routine peacetime operations. The CNO's staff (OPNAV), headquartered in the Pentagon in Arlington, Virginia, includes the Director, Air Warfare (N88), who co-ordinates air warfare and strike warfare policy and requirements. As a part of the move to reduce the power of the Navy's aviation, surface and submarine 'fiefdoms', the CNO in 1992 downgraded the Assistant Chief of Naval Operations (Air Warfare) position (a three-star admiral) to a two-star billet, the Director, Air Warfare.

Fleets

Most operational naval aviation forces are assigned to the US Atlantic Fleet or the US Pacific Fleet, which provide the forces used by joint commanders to execute US defence policy. An echelon below, five numbered fleets have both operational and administrative roles.

The Pacific Fleet includes the US Third, Fifth and Seventh Fleets. The Third Fleet conducts operations in the eastern Pacific and is available to serve as the naval component commander for a joint operation. The Fifth Fleet, created during the mid-1990s to command the forces that comprised the Middle East Force, operates in the Persian Gulf and northwest Indian Ocean. The Seventh Fleet operates in the Western Pacific and most of the Indian Ocean.

The US Second Fleet (Norfolk, Virginia) operates in the Atlantic, with a NATO role as Striking Force Atlantic. An adjunct to the Second Fleet, the Western Hemisphere Group (Mayport, Florida) is the naval component commander for the US Southern Command, which deploys ships to the Caribbean Sea, particularly in counter-drug operations. The Second Fleet trains forces for the US

Sixth Fleet (Gaeta, Italy), permanently deployed to the Mediterranean Sea, with a NATO role as Striking Force Southern Europe.

Type commanders

Virtually all naval aircraft and units are grouped administratively under a type commander, who is a flag officer with responsibility for administration, training and maintenance support. Operational aircraft, aircraft-carriers and units assigned to the Atlantic and Pacific Fleets are administered, respectively, by Commander Naval Air Force, US Atlantic Fleet (COMNAVAIRLANT, based at NAS Norfolk, Virginia) and Commander Naval Air Force, US Pacific Fleet (COMNAVAIRPAC, based at North Island, California). Training aircraft and units are the responsibility of the Chief of Naval Air Training (CNATRA). Commander Naval Air Reserve Force (CNARF) administers the Naval Air Reserve's aircraft and units (described separately). The Navy's test aircraft fleet falls under the Commander Naval Air Systems Command (NAVAIR, or NASC).

Additionally, there are overseas commands that act as agents for type commanders which provide similar support (under COMNAVAIRLANT or COMNAVAIRPAC) to aircraft stationed or deployed at forward bases. Commander Fleet Air, Western Pacific (NAF Atsugi, Japan), Commander Fleet Air, Mediterranean (NSA Naples, Italy) and Commander Fleet Air, Keflavik (NAS Keflavik, Iceland) provide such support and some have a few units directly assigned.

Naval air stations and facilities

The Navy's aviation infrastructure consists of naval air stations (NASs), naval air weapons stations (NAWSs) and naval air facilities (NAFs). Air stations host the wings and squadrons assigned to them and provide airfield services and personnel support, but do not exercise operational control over the tenant units. Most bases have UC-12

station liaison aircraft (a few have types such as UP-3, VP-3, C-26 or RC-12) and many have HH-1 or UH-3 SAR helicopters assigned. Some air stations operated by the Naval Air Reserve that host units of other services of the National Guard are designated NAS-JRBs (joint reserve base).

The airfields at Point Mugu and China Lake have been redesignated Naval Air Weapons Stations (NAWSs); they are under the command of their respective divisions of the Naval Air Warfare Center and host aircraft involved in weapons testing.

Some Navy airfields are operated by bases designated naval stations (NSs), such as Mayport, Florida, or Roosevelt Roads, Puerto Rico; or naval support activities (NSAs), such as Naples, Italy or Mid-South (Memphis, Tennessee). Some naval aviation units are hosted by Air Force bases or federal airfields.

Carrier air wings

The carrier air wing (CVW) projects the major conventional striking power of the Navy. Each wing includes a finely tuned balance of strike and support aircraft designed to maximise the operational effectiveness of the aircraft-carrier. The carrier air wing commander and his staff not only conduct the affairs of the wing, but advise the battle group commander in strike warfare doctrine and tactics.

Although the Navy operates 12 aircraft-carriers, the number of CVWs is set at 10, plus one reserve CVW (CVWR, described separately). With two carriers normally in long-term overhaul, the 10 wings are fully occupied with operational commitment, normally deploying for six months in each 18-month cycle. Over the last 10 years, the Navy has disbanded four CVWs (6, 10, 13 and 15) and most of their assigned squadrons.

CVWs are assigned five each to the Atlantic (1, 3, 7, 8, 17) and Pacific (2, 5, 9, 11, 14) Fleets. One Pacific Fleet air wing, CVW-5, is still permanently based at NAF Atsugi, Japan and deploys on USS *Kitty Hawk* (CV 63).

C-2A Greyhound COD aircraft are in service with VRC-40 'Rawhides' (above), VRC-30 'Providers' (right) and VAW-120, the E-2 FRS (below).

The Navy's two dedicated mine-countermeasures squadrons, equipped with the MH-53E Sea Dragon, are HM-14 'Sea Stallions' (above) and HM-15 'Blackhawks' (below).

Above: The LC-130Fs of VXE-6 'Ice Pirates' will soon be withdrawn as the Navy hands its Antarctic support role over to the US Air National Guard.

HC-3 'Packrats' (right) serves as the FRS for the Navy's CH/HH/UH-46D units. HC-8 'Dragon Whales' (below) is one of the four active H-46 squadrons (plus HC-3).

Above left: Based at NAS Sigonella, the MH-53Es of HC-4 provide heavylift support for Navy activities across Europe.

Left: HSL-47 'Sabrehawks' is one of the seven Pacific Fleet SH-60B squadrons, which are largely based at North Island.

Above: This HSL-43 'Battle Cats' SH-60B Sea Hawk is a Hellfire-capable aircraft with nose-mounted FLIR.

Squadron assignment to CVWs is more standardised now than at any time since before World War II, in terms of types of squadrons, detachments and assigned aircraft. During the early 1990s, the Navy's goal was to standardise its CVWs with the 'Roosevelt Air Wing', centred around a 60-aircraft strike force of two F-14, two F/A-18 and two A-6 squadrons. The cancellation of the proposed A-12 Avenger II and the accelerated retirement of the A-6E Intruder, along with the need to maximise the number of aircraft able to deliver air-to-ground ordnance, doomed the expensive 'Roosevelt Air Wing' in the early 1990s. The Navy switched to a 50-strike aircraft wing centred on one 14-aircraft F-14 squadron and three 12-aircraft F/A-18 squadrons.

The only significant anomaly is the assignment in two CVWs (7 and 8) of two F-14 fighter squadrons (versus one), with one of the VF units in each CVW displacing an F/A-18 squadron. As the F-14 squadrons transition to the F/A-18F, this anomaly is scheduled to disappear. Four CVWs each include one Marine Corps fighter-attack (VMFA) F/A-18 Hornet squadron in place of a Navy strike fighter (VFA) squadron. For several years during the mid-1990s, one Marine tactical electronic warfare (VMAQ) squadron deployed with one CVW in place of a Navy tactical electronic warfare (VAQ, now electronic attack) squadron.

Planners have earmarked aircraft replacements to 2015, but intend to retain the current structure of the air wing, barring significant future budget reductions. The Joint Strike Fighter (JSF) and the Common Support Aircraft (CSA) are still in the development or conceptual stage, respectively. Shown below is today's typical CVW composition and future replacement aircraft:

Squadron Type	Aircraft Type (current)	Type (future)	Quantity
VF (later VFA)	F-14A/B/D	F/A-18F	14
VFA or VMFA	F/A-18C	JSF	12
VFA	F/A-18C	JSF	12
VFA	F/A-18C	F/A-18E	12
VAQ	EA-6B	F/A-18G?	4
VAW	E-2C	E-2C or CSA	4
HS	SH-60F/HH-60H	SH-60R/CH-60S	6/2
VS	S-3B	CSA variant	8
VQ Detachment	ES-3A	(None)	2
VRC Detachment	C-2A	CSA variant	2

Type wings

For administrative convenience, squadrons flying the same type of aircraft in the same role are grouped into type wings and are usually assigned together at the same base. When deployed on aircraft-carriers or to overseas bases, they are assigned to an operational wing, such as a carrier wing.

The type wing commander provides administrative, training and maintenance support to the squadrons in the wing. The fleet readiness squadron (FRS) is normally assigned to the type wings (see below).

Generally, the Atlantic and Pacific Fleets each include one of each category of type wing. Many type wings were established during the 1990s as most larger functional wings were broken up. For some aircraft types, such as the EA-6B, E-6 and F-14, the fleets are both supported by only one type wing. In the case of patrol wings, each fleet is structured differently. The Atlantic Fleet has a functional-wing flag-level staff – Commander Patrol Wings, US Atlantic Fleet – who supervises the two type wings, Patrol Wings 5 and 11, as well as the P-3 FRS, VP-30. Commander Patrol

Wings, US Pacific Fleet, supervises Patrol Wing 10, but directly supervises the patrol squadrons based in Hawaii since Patrol Wing 2 was disbanded. Patrol Wing 1 in Japan supervises only squadrons and detachments deployed in its operational area.

Two naval air test wings were established in 1995 to perform the functions of type wings for the test aircraft fleet.

Fleet readiness squadrons

Often called fleet replacement squadrons, or by the obsolete term replacement air group (RAG), the fleet readiness squadrons (FRSs) provide type training for new aviation and maintenance personnel. The FRS assists operational squadrons with conducting tactical simulator training during work-up cycles. Many aircraft 'communities' have only one FRS that provides personnel to both fleets. In at least one case (HC-2), an FRS performs operational missions. Others have one FRS on each coast. In some cases, such as for MH-53E and HH-1Ns, Marine training squadrons train Navy personnel; in others, such as for EA-6Bs, Navy FRSs train Marines. In other cases, FRS training is conducted by an air station base fight (as NAS Norfolk does for C-12 crews), a training support unit (as for E-6 pilots) or the Air Force (such as for the C-130).

Fighter squadrons

The number of fighter (VF) squadrons per carrier air wing changed in most wings during the mid-1990s. Of the 10 CVWs, only two (CVW-7 and CVW-8) retain the traditional pair of F-14-equipped VF squadrons. The remaining eight wings deploy with a single larger, TARPS-capable, 14-aircraft VF squadron, the second squadron having been replaced by an F/A-18-equipped strike fighter squadron. This is the result of a restructuring that enshrines a 50-strike aircraft wing, ideally consisting of 36 Hornets and 14 Tomcats (eventually to be replaced by F/A-18Fs). Eleven active-duty F-14 squadrons (most non-TARPS-equipped) have been disestablished since the end of the Cold War.

The reduction in carrier-based VF squadrons has resulted in the consolidation of almost all of the Navy's VF squadrons at NAS Oceana, Virginia, with Fighter Wing, US Atlantic Fleet, commensurate with the transfer of NAS Miramar, California, to the Marine Corps. The 11 fleet VF squadrons at Oceana (three with F-14As, five with F-14Bs and three with F-14Ds) deploy onboard carriers from both coasts. VF-154 is permanently forward-deployed to NAF Atsugi, Japan, as the F-14A squadron assigned to CVW-5 onboard USS *Kitty Hawk* (CV 63). A 13th F-14 squadron, VF-101, is the FRS for the entire community. This unit operates F-14A/B/Ds and a few T-34C trainers for spotter missions.

Ten VF squadrons will transition to the F/A-18F, beginning in 1999, with the first two squadrons operational by 2001. The squadrons equipped with the F-14A, including VF-154 in Japan, will be the first to make the transition. Yet to be determined is whether any of the VF squadrons will move to the West Coast after they transition to the F/A-18F and whether the change to the two-seat Super Hornet will precipitate a redesignation to strike fighter (VFA) squadrons.

Several land-based fighter squadrons (VFs 43, 45 and 126) which performed the air combat manoeuvring adversary role were disbanded

during the mid-1990s when this mission was assumed completely by the Naval Air Reserve.

Strike fighter squadrons

The major striking power of carrier-based naval aviation resides in 24 strike fighter (VFA) squadrons, all of which operate the F/A-18C. The Hornet squadrons have both strike and air-superiority roles. The number of VFA squadrons is insufficient to provide three 12-aircraft squadrons in each of the 10 carrier air wings; the deficit is compensated for by two Tomcat-equipped VF squadrons (see above) and four Marine fighter-attack (VMFA) squadrons assigned to carrier duty. Most VFA squadrons are equipped with night-attack-capable F/A-18C(N) versions of the F/A-18C.

The F/A-18E Super Hornet and later the Joint Strike Fighter are scheduled to replace the F/A-18C. Each air wing is currently scheduled to operate one F/A-18E squadron.

The VFA squadrons are evenly divided between two strike-fighter wings, one each on the East and West Coasts. Three Pacific Fleet squadrons are stationed at NAF Atsugi, Japan, from where they deploy with CVW-5. The Atlantic Fleet VFA squadrons have begun moving to NAS Oceana, Virginia and MCAS Beaufort, North Carolina, as NAS Cecil Field is prepared for closure.

Each strike fighter wing includes an FRS. VFA-106 and VFA-125 conduct training for the East and West Coasts, respectively, using F/A-18A/B/C/Ds. These squadrons also train Marine Corps Hornet crews; in reciprocation, the Marine Corps Hornet FRS, VMFAT-101, trains Navy Hornet crews as well. This 'cross-pollination' promotes a high degree of standardisation in the large Hornet community.

The training of F/A-18E/F crews will begin in 1999 after the stand-up of the FRS, VFA-122, at NAS Lemoore, California in January 1999. An FRS is planned eventually for the East Coast at NAS Oceana.

Two VFA squadrons (132 and 161) – both equipped with F/A-18As – were disbanded during the last decade. One land-based VFA squadron, VFA-127, an air combat manoeuvring adversary squadron, was disbanded in 1996.

Electronic attack

The Navy operates 14 operational electronic attack (VAQ) squadrons (redesignated in March 1998 from 'tactical electronic warfare squadrons'). These units, all based with one electronic attack wing at NAS Whidbey Island, Washington, fly the EA-6B Prowler. Ten four-aircraft squadrons are assigned one each to the 10 carrier air wings. The remaining four squadrons (VAQs 128, 133, 134 and 142) were organised in the mid- to late 1990s as expeditionary squadrons to replace the EF-111A in USAF expeditionary wings. VAQ-134 was slated for disbanding, but survived in a cadre status until built up as an expeditionary squadron. VAQs 133 and 142 resumed the traditions of squadrons disestablished in the early 1990s. VAQ-128 honours the disbanded A-6 FRS, VA-128. (VAQ-137, carrying on the traditions of an earlier VAQ-137, originally was established as an expeditionary squadron but was soon reverted to carrier duty to replace a Marine Corps VMAQ squadron.) These expeditionary squadrons – which include some USAF flight crew – have

Above: This SH-60B
is operated by
HSL-49
'Scorpions'.

Top: This AGM-114-
armed SH-60B is
from HSL-41.

Right: This SH-60F
is an HS-10
'Warhawks'
aircraft.

The Navy's 10 front-line
helicopter anti-submarine
squadrons (plus the FRS)
operate a mix of SH-60Fs
(right) and HH-60Hs (above)
– the latter for planeguard
SAR and combat SAR duties.
HS-2 'Golden Falcons' (right)
and HS-4 'Black Knights'
(above) are based at North
Island. Both the SH-60F and
HH-60H will be replaced by
the SH-60R and the CH-60S.

Above: This SH-60F from HS-3 'Tridents' is one of the five
Atlantic Fleet HS squadrons, all based at NAS Jacksonville.

VC-8 'Red Tails' (above) operates UH-3Hs from NS Roosevelt
Roads, on range support duties. VC-8 is the last operator of
the Skyhawk, outside Training Command. UH-3Hs are on
strength with the NAS Key West base flight (below).

Above: Today, all
surviving Navy
H-3s are shore-
based, like this
SAR-tasked UH-3H
of the NAS
Patuxent River
base flight.

Left: HC-2 has
aircraft stationed
in the US, Italy and
Bahrain. This is
one of its VH-3As.

The C-12 serves widely in a number of essentially
similar variants, including this UC-12B of the
Lemoore base flight (above) and UC-12M from NAS
Norfolk (below).

The last HH-1Ns in Navy service survive as SAR
base flight aircraft. These examples are from NAS
Lemoore (left) and NAS Meridian (above).

deployed to the Middle East (replacing the EF-111A in April 1998) and to Japan to cover gaps (caused by commitments in Bosnia and the Middle East) in Marine Corps EA-6B deployments to MCAS Iwakuni, Japan.

FRS training of Navy and Marine Corps EA-6B crews and maintenance personnel is conducted by VAQ-129 at Whidbey Island.

The readiness of the EA-6B force has been severely stressed in the late 1990s by aircraft shortages aggravated by fatigued airframes and aircraft modification programmes. The demands of deployments to the Middle East (in support of 'No-Fly Zones' over Iraq) and to Italy (in support of operations over Bosnia) have exacerbated the stress on the EA-6B fleet.

Airborne early warning

Each carrier air wing includes one carrier airborne early warning (VAW) squadron equipped with four E-2C Hawkeye. Ten fleet VAW squadrons are evenly divided in two wings between the Atlantic and Pacific Fleets. All Pacific Fleet VAW squadrons operate the Group II version of the aircraft. One Pacific fleet unit, VAW-115, is stationed at NAF Atsugi, Japan and deploys onboard USS *Kitty Hawk* (CV 63) with CVW-5. The other four Pacific VAW squadrons moved in the second half of 1998 from MCAS Miramar, California to NAWS Point Mugu, California. The five Atlantic Fleet operational VAW squadrons operate either the Group 0 (VAWs 124, 125 and 126) or Group II version (VAWs 121 and 123) of the E-2C. The Group II is expected to equip the remaining Group 0 squadrons by 2001.

The E-2C FRS, VAW-120, conducts crew training at NAS Norfolk, Virginia, where the five Atlantic Fleet operational VAW units are based. VAW-120 operates E-2C and TE-2C aircraft, as well as C-2A Greyhound carrier onboard delivery (COD) aircraft to train C-2A crews. The West Coast FRS, VAW-110, was disbanded and its role was absorbed by VAW-120.

Sea control

Each carrier air wing includes one sea control (VS) squadron (formerly air anti-submarine squadron) equipped with eight S-3B Vikings. VS squadrons perform anti-submarine, anti-shipping, mine-laying and surveillance missions for the carrier battle group. An important secondary mission is aerial refuelling; with the 1997 retirement of the A-6 Intruder, the S-3B and ES-3A have been the only US carrier-based tankers available. For this reason, the number of S-3Bs per squadron, which had declined from 10 to six, has been increased to eight.

Fleet VS squadrons are evenly divided in two wings between the Atlantic and Pacific Fleets. The Atlantic fleet squadrons moved from NAS Cecil Field, Florida to nearby NAS Jacksonville during late 1997. One Pacific Fleet unit, VS-21, is based at NAF Atsugi, Japan, for duty with CVW-5 onboard USS *Kitty Hawk* (CV 63). S-3 FRS training is handled by an additional unit, VS-41 at North Island, California. (The Atlantic Fleet FRS, VS-27, was disbanded in 1994.) All S-3A versions have been withdrawn from service.

In a surprise move in late 1998, the Navy decided to delete ASW as a role of the S-3B, choosing to rely on P-3 and SH-60 aircraft for aerial ASW protection for carrier battle groups.

ASW training at VS-41 has ended and S-3B ASW systems have been rendered inoperative. Four aircraft in each squadron are maintained as surface surveillance and strike aircraft with a secondary tanker role; four others are assigned permanent tanker duty, retaining limited surveillance capability.

Maritime patrol

The Navy maintains a force of 12 active-duty operational patrol (VP) squadrons, a force half the size of that maintained at the height of the Cold War; 12 squadrons have been disestablished since 1990. The squadrons are evenly divided between East and West Coasts. Six squadrons under Commander Patrol wings, US Atlantic Fleet (Norfolk, Virginia) are based, three each, at NAS Brunswick, Maine (Patrol Wing 5) and NAS Jacksonville, Florida (Patrol Wing 11). The six West Coast squadrons, under Commander Patrol Wings, US Pacific Fleet are based, three each, at NAS Whidbey Island, Washington (Patrol Wing 10) and NAS Barbers Point, Hawaii (directly under Patrol Wings, US Pacific Fleet, to move to MCAF Kaneohe Bay, Hawaii by 2 July 1999). Patrol Wing 10 maintains a detachment at NAS North Island, California to support fleet training and exercise requirements. VP squadrons from Washington and Hawaii alternate in providing aircraft to support this detachment.

Commander Patrol Wing Two at NAS Barbers Point was disestablished when Commander Patrol Wings Pacific moved from NAS Moffett Field to Barbers Point. The Navy is considering establishing a new Commander Patrol Wing Two to command the P-3 squadrons moving to Kaneohe Bay.

All VP squadrons operate P-3C Orion patrol aircraft. Since the late 1980s, the Navy has been upgrading older P-3Cs to the Update III configuration. As this process is not yet complete, many squadrons operate a mixture of Update II, II.5 and III versions, but shuffle aircraft to be equipped with nine Update III aircraft (10, in the case of Hawaii-based squadrons) when deployed.

All MPA crew and maintenance training is conducted by the FRS, VP-30, at Jacksonville. VP-30, which reports directly to Commander Patrol Wings Atlantic, operates P-3Cs and two remaining TP-3A versions. The squadron maintains a VIP transport detachment comprised of three VP-3A aircraft, assigned to support the Chief of Naval Operations and the Commander in Chief, US Atlantic Fleet.

Four VP squadrons are deployed at any given time, two from each fleet. The Pacific squadrons deploy for six months to Misawa AB, Japan, or to Diego Garcia, BIOT. These squadrons both maintain detachments in Kadena AB, Okinawa, Japan and the Diego Garcia squadron keeps a detachment in the Middle East, normally at Al Masirah, Oman, in support of Fifth Fleet operations in the Persian Gulf. One Atlantic Fleet squadron is deployed to NAS Sigonella, Sicily and recently was engaged in operations in the Adriatic and over Bosnia and Kosovo. A second Atlantic Fleet squadron is split between NAS Keflavik, Iceland and NS Roosevelt Roads, Puerto Rico, from where it supports drug-interdiction operations in the Caribbean. Routine MPA operations are no longer conducted from Bermuda; Lajes, Azores; Rota, Spain; Cubi Point, Republic of the Philippines; Agana, Guam; Midway Island; and Adak, Alaska.

Patrol squadrons primarily engage in anti-submarine and anti-shipping missions, as well as reconnaissance, shipping surveillance, rescue, logistics, range support, threat simulation and communications relay. Improved optical sensors have made the P-3C useful in overland surveillance in Bosnia and central Africa. Advancements, embodied in the Anti-surface Improvement Programme (AIP) in the form of long-range optics, improved command and control and weaponry (such as the SLAM-ER missile), will make the MPA force potent in a stand-off land-attack role.

VP special projects units

For three decades the Navy has fielded a small number of specialised reconnaissance versions of the P-3. Initially, these aircraft were operated by special projects departments of selected VP squadrons. In 1982, however, the departments became separate units, designated Patrol Squadron Special Projects Units (VPUs), VPU-1 at NAS Brunswick, Maine and VPU-2 at NAS Barbers Point, Hawaii (to move to MCAF Kaneohe Bay, Hawaii by July 1999). In 1996, these units became full commands, although they remain designated as units instead of squadrons. The VPUs fly modified P-3B and P-3C aircraft for tactical and strategic intelligence collection and maintain a P-3C or UP-3A for logistic support and crew training. VPU detachments typically deploy on short notice, frequently for short periods.

Fleet air reconnaissance

The Navy operates six active-duty fleet air reconnaissance (VQ) squadrons, two each of three types, one of each assigned to each coast. Two of the squadrons have a strategic communications role and are described separately.

Two VQ squadrons, VQ-1 and VQ-2, collect signals intelligence with EP-3E Orions fitted with the Aries II collection suite. These 12 aircraft are P-3Cs modified in the early 1990s under a conversion-in-lieu-of-procurement (CILOP) programme and replaced 10 earlier EP-3E Aries I and two EP-3B 'Batrack' versions. Flying reconnaissance missions, typically along the periphery of foreign nations, these aircraft collect Elint and Comint for further analysis. They also operate UP-3A, UP-3B and P-3C aircraft for crew training and logistics. VQ-1 moved from NAS Agana, Guam and is now based at NAS Whidbey Island, Washington with Patrol Wing 10. VQ-1 keeps a permanent detachment at NAF Misawa, Japan and routinely deploys aircraft to sites in the Pacific and Indian Oceans and the Persian Gulf. VQ-2, based at NS Rota, Spain under Commander, Fleet Air Mediterranean, typically deploys aircraft in the Mediterranean, Europe and the Middle East and frequently maintains a detachment at Souda Bay, Crete. Consideration has been given by Navy planners to relocating VQ-2 to either NAS Brunswick, Maine, or NAS Jacksonville, Florida, but no decision has been announced.

For carrier-based intelligence collection, the Navy has maintained one VQ squadron on each coast. These VQ squadrons were formed in the early 1990s during the gap in carrier-based VQ presence precipitated by the retirement of the EA-3B Skywarrior aircraft flown by VQs 1 and 2. VQ-5, which moved from NAS Agana, Guam to NAS North Island, California, has deployed two ES-3A Shadow aircraft with each carrier in the

Formally established at NAS Fallon on 12 July 1996, the Naval Strike and Air Warfare Center (NSAWC) centralised the training tasks of the Naval Fighter Weapons School ('Topgun'), the Strike Warfare Center ('Strike U') and the Carrier AEW School ('Top Dome'). 'Topgun' remains as a distinct entity within the organisation of NSAWC and its badge appears on every aircraft – as part of a combined logo. NSAWC operates its own Hornets (above, left), Tomcats (below left and right) and SH-60Fs (top left), the latter for C-SAR training. E-2s are deployed from fleet units, as required. Apart from the SH-60s, most NSAWC aircraft wear standard Navy TPS grey.

Above and below: **The Naval Air Warfare Center, Aircraft Division (NAWC-AD) at NAS Patuxent River is the Navy's principal RDT&E organisation. Its Strike Aircraft Test Squadron handles all F-14, F/A-18 and EA-6B flight testing.**

Above and right: **VX-1 'Pioneers' is the Navy's ASW operational test unit and flies a mix of P-3Cs, S-3Bs and SH-60B/Fs from its base at NAS Patuxent River.**

Left: **This F/A-18 is one of those attached to the NAWC-AD's Naval Strike Aircraft Test Squadron.**

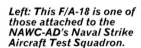

VX-9 'Vampires' was formed through the merger of VX-4 and VX-5 in April 1994. It handles strike fighter, ECM aircraft and combat helicopter operational testing. F-18 (above left) and EA-6B (left) operations are conducted at NAWS China Lake – as are AV-8B and AH-1W flying for the Marines. A detachment of F-14s is maintained at NAS Point Mugu (above).

Pacific Fleet. A permanent VQ-5 detachment at Misawa, Japan has deployed with the USS *Kitty Hawk*, which is based in Japan. VQ-6, which moved in January 1998 from NAS Cecil Field, Florida to nearby NAS Jacksonville, has deployed two ES-3As with each Atlantic Fleet carrier. Only 16 ES-3As were modified from S-3As. VQ-5 has operated two S-3Bs for crew training. The ES-3As have performed a secondary mission – aerial refuelling – which has become all the more important since the retirement of the A-6/KA-6.

During mid-1998, the Navy decided to phase out the ES-3A because of the expense of upgrading the aircraft's mission suite to be interoperable with the Joint Sigint Avionics Family of the future. VQ-5's last detachment deployed in November onboard USS *Carl Vinson*. Retirement of the ES-3A began in January 1999. VQ-5 and VQ-6 will be disestablished in July and September 1999, respectively.

Strategic communications

Two VQ squadrons are not reconnaissance squadrons at all, but strategic communications units, with the mission of maintaining links between the National Command Authority and the strategic nuclear deterrent forces. VQ-3 and VQ-4, both based with Strategic Communications Wing One at Tinker AFB, Oklahoma, operate the Boeing E-6 Mercury. The 16 E-6As are being upgraded to E-6Bs, with the last scheduled for completion in 2001. The E-6B not only supports the ballistic missile submarine fleet, but by October 1998 had assumed the Looking Glass command post role from USAF EC-135Cs in support of the Minuteman ICBM force. E-6s operate from permanent detachments at Travis AFB, California, NAS Patuxent River, Maryland and, since 1998, Offutt AFB, Nebraska. Flight crew training for the E-6 fleet is conducted at the USAF's Tinker AFB by the Naval Training Support Unit, which operates two modified Boeing 707s, designated TC-18F.

Carrier onboard delivery

Although its requirements have not lessened even with the post-Cold War drawdown, the Navy has consolidated its COD operations from four squadrons to two and changed its mode of operations from forward-deployed squadrons servicing deployed carriers to that of assigning COD detachments to each deploying carrier air wing.

Each carrier now deploys with a detachment of two C-2A aircraft. When operating on station in areas such as the Mediterranean, Persian Gulf or Western Pacific, the C-2As normally are staged at shore bases, each flying one to three sorties per day to the carrier and back. Atlantic Fleet carriers draw C-2As from Fleet Logistics Support (VRC) Squadron 40. West Coast carriers deploy with C-2As from VRC-30, which maintains a permanent detachment in Atsugi, Japan to support the USS *Kitty Hawk*'s CVW-5. FRS training for the C-2A is conducted by the E-2 FRS, VAW-120, at NAS Norfolk, Virginia (VAW-110 also conducted C-2A training at NAS Miramar, California before it was disbanded). The C-2As normally wear the tailcode of the CVW to which they are assigned.

VR-24 and VRC-50, the COD squadrons in the Mediterranean and Western Pacific, respectively, were disbanded in the early 1990s. The long-range US-3A COD aircraft, which proved so useful in supporting carriers in the North Arabian Sea from Diego Garcia, were withdrawn from service shortly before VRC-50 was disbanded and have been placed in storage.

CompRons and contractors

The number of Navy composite (VC) squadrons has steadily dwindled as budget cutbacks reduced squadrons and economies were achieved with a shift to the use of contractors to provide aircraft services for fleet training. Only two VC squadrons, distinctly different in composition, remain in service.

VC-8, based at NS Roosevelt Roads, Puerto Rico, provides UH-3H helicopters for rescue, torpedo recovery and logistics for ships exercising in the Puerto Rican Op Area (PROA), including the torpedo range at St Croix. VC-8 is the only operational squadron in the Navy still flying the Skyhawk; its TA-4Js are used to tow targets and to simulate enemy aircraft and cruise missiles. The TA-4Js are due to be retired in 1999 or later; a replacement has not been identified, but turnover of their duties to a contractor has been considered.

VC-6, based at NAS Norfolk, Virginia, has long been an operator of drones for target services. The squadron also operates a number of fast boats to simulate fast patrol craft. VC-6 led the way for the introduction of the RQ-2A Pioneer UAV during the 1980s. The squadron sent two detachments to the Persian Gulf during Operation Desert Storm, one each deployed onboard the battleships USS *Missouri* and USS *Wisconsin*. VC-6's UAV detachments are based at NAS Patuxent River, Maryland and are available for deployment onboard amphibious warfare ships.

A number of aircraft bearing Navy markings are operated by companies providing services under contract to the Navy. DC-130A Hercules aircraft, operated by AVTEL Services, a contractor based at NAWS Point Mugu, California, perform drone launch services for missile shots. A single EC-24A (modified DC-8) operated by Raytheon Systems Company for the Fleet Information Warfare Center (FIWC, formerly Fleet Tactical Readiness Group (FTRG), formerly Fleet Electronic Warfare Support Group (FEWSG)) provides electronic threat simulation to Navy ships during exercises. Raytheon (formerly Hughes) also operates EA-3B, ERA-3B, NRA-3B, TA-3B and NTA-3B Skywarriors for a variety of test services from Van Nuys, California.

Carrier-based ASW helicopters

Since the early 1970s, each carrier air wing has included one helicopter anti-submarine (HS) squadron for ASW, rescue, plane guard, logistics, radar calibration and other duties. The SH-3H was phased out in 1995 and all fleet HS squadrons operate a mixture of eight SH-60F and HH-60H helicopters. The HH-60Hs were added to give the carrier a more survivable combat SAR capability. The originally intended normal mix for deployment is six SH-60Fs and two HH-60Hs, but this mix has frequently been modified in favour of the HH-60H in such areas as the Adriatic Sea and the Persian Gulf. Future plans call for the SH-60Fs and HH-60Hs to be remanufactured into an SH-60R configuration and replacement of the HH-60H with the CH-60S Knighthawk.

The 10 active-duty HS squadrons are divided evenly between the Atlantic and Pacific Fleets, with one Pacific Fleet squadron (HS-14) forward-deployed at Atsugi, Japan for duty with CVW-5 onboard USS *Kitty Hawk*. The HS FRS, HS-10, trains pilots and crews for the SH-60F and HH-60H at North Island, California.

LAMPS HSL squadrons

Ten helicopter anti-submarine squadrons light (HSL) operate the SH-60B Seahawk Light Airborne Multi-Purpose System (LAMPS) Mk III helicopter, which is deployed in detachments of one or two aircraft (depending on ship capacity) onboard cruisers, destroyers and frigates. These detachments provide ASW, anti-shipping, rescue, logistics and utility services for surface warships.

The 10 fleet squadrons are divided evenly between the Atlantic and Pacific Fleets. One Pacific squadron, HSL-37, is based permanently in Hawaii (at NAS Barbers Point, to move to MCAF Kaneohe Bay by 1999) to deploy with ships based at Pearl Harbor. A second Pacific squadron, HSL-51, is based at NAF Atsugi, Japan to operate from destroyers based in Yokosuka, Japan. HSL-51 operates a VIP detachment (Detachment 11) that flies two UH-3Hs in support of the Commander, US Seventh Fleet from his flagship, USS *Blue Ridge* (LCC 19).

The LAMPS community employs two FRSs. The West Coast FRS, HSL-41, is based at NAS North Island, California and the East Coast FRS, HSL-40, is based at NS Mayport, Florida.

Helicopter combat support

Seven helicopter combat support (HC) squadrons provide the Navy with the vertical lift capability necessary to keep its ships at sea properly provisioned. HC squadrons also undertake rescue detachments and a variety of utility missions.

Four HC squadrons, two each with the Atlantic and Pacific Fleets, provide H-46 Sea Knight vertical replenishment (VertRep) detachments to ships of the Combat Logistics Force and the Military Sealift Command that replenish Navy ships at sea. These helicopters shuttle supplies, spare parts, ordnance and personnel to other ships in a battle group. During the early 1990s, these HC squadrons assigned detachments to assume the rescue and utility role formerly performed by UH-1N and later HH-1Ns onboard amphibious assault ships. An H-46 detachment deploys onboard the MCM command ship USS *Inchon* (MCS 12). These HC squadrons operate a mixture of essentially similar CH-46D, HH-46D and UH-46Ds. HC-11, based at North Island, California, operates a single UH-3H from the command ship USS *Coronado* (AGF 11) to support the commander of the Third Fleet. The Navy has experimented with civil contractor helicopters, such as the Kaman K-Max and Bell 214, but is considering the CH-60 as well to replace the H-46. FRS training for the Navy's H-46 fleet is performed by a fifth H-46 squadron, HC-3 at NAS North Island, California.

Vertical onboard delivery missions in the Mediterranean, Europe, Africa and the Middle East are handled by HC-4, based at NAS Sigonella, Sicily. HC-4 operates MH-53E Sea Dragons, having acquired them during the mid-1990s when the Navy turned over all of its CH-53E Sea Stallions to the Marine Corps. FRS training for HC-4 personnel is accomplished by the Marine Corps CH-53E training squadron, HMT-302 at MCAS New River, North Carolina, which has MH-53Es on strength.

This NVH-3A (left) is operated by NAWC-AD's Rotary-Wing Test Squadron. The NAWC-AD is charged with testing USMC aircraft, such as this AV-8B (below).

The Rotary-Wing Test Squadron operates this SH-60F (above) and SH-60B (below) as part of its ongoing SH-60R test effort.

Left: Most types attached to the Naval Force Warfare Aircraft Test Squadron now wear a distinctive fin-flash.

Above: This TH-57C Sea Ranger is another type on strength with the RWTS at Patuxent River.

Above and below: The Navy's distinctive NP-3Ds (each fitted with the large EATS antenna) are assigned to the Naval Weapons Test Squadron, at Point Mugu. Originally designated EP-3As, they were redesignated as RP-3As in the early 1990s and later became RP-3Ds then NP-3Ds.

The Naval Force Warfare Aircraft Test Squadron handles all P-3C (above), S-3B, E-3C and other multi-engined aircraft testing – including the C-2A (above left) – for the NAWC-AD. NFWATS operates a small number of T-34C Turbo Mentors.

Left and below: Aircraft attached to the NAWC-AD's Strike Aircraft Test Squadron now wear revised markings highlighting their strike role. The 'SD' tailcode stands for 'Strike Directorate'.

Above: The Naval Research Laboratory's Flight Support Detachment operates NP-3Ds from NAS Patuxent River on a range of military and civil test and survey duties.

HC-2, based at NAS Norfolk, Virginia, has three assigned roles. The squadron's VH-3As (former presidential support helicopters) provide VIP transportation to flag officers assigned to the Norfolk area, including the Commander in Chief, US Atlantic Command and to the Commander in Chief, US Atlantic Fleet. The unit's UH-3Hs operate in several detachments. One, formed as needed, transports the commander of the Second Fleet, operating from the command ship USS *Mt Whitney* (LCC 20). Detachment 1, based at NSA Naples, Italy, supports the Sixth Fleet commander onboard his flagship, USS *LaSalle* (AGF 3). Detachment 2, the 'Desert Ducks', is based in Bahrain and supports the Fifth Fleet in the Persian Gulf. HC-2 serves as the FRS (succeeding HS-1 in this role in 1996) for the Navy's H-3 helicopter fleet, training pilots and crews for HC-2 detachments, several air station rescue units and the Pacific Missile Range Facility in Barking Sands, Hawaii. HC-2's H-3s are planned for replacement by the CH-60S.

Mine countermeasures

Only two airborne mine countermeasures (AMCM) squadrons remain on strength, HMs 12 and 16 having been disestablished. Both operate the MH-53E Sea Dragon and perform vertical onboard delivery duties as well. These squadrons deploy detachments overseas for exercises and deploy onboard the mine countermeasures command ship USS *Inchon* (MCS 12). During the early 1990s, HM-14 and HM-15 absorbed their reserve counterpart squadrons, HM-18 and HM-19, respectively, becoming joint active-duty/reserve squadrons. With the closure of NAS Alameda, California, HM-15 moved to NAS Corpus Christi, Texas, near the mine warfare forces based at Ingleside. Plans to move HM-14 from Norfolk, Virginia to Corpus Christi have been delayed indefinitely by funding constraints.

FRS training for the HM squadrons, conducted until 1994 by now-disbanded HM-12, is handled by Marine Corps H-53E training squadron HMT-302, which operates several MH-53Es at MCAS New River, North Carolina. Tactical training takes place at the AMCM School at Norfolk.

In order to reduce the variety of helicopters in service, the Navy is considering replacing the MH-53E with the CH-60S. The probability of such a step would depend upon the success of matching AMCM technology with the H-60 airframe. Navy planners are considering assigning three CH-60Ss to amphibious assault ships (LHAs and LHDs), replacing the two HH-46D SAR helicopters and assuming a minesweeping role for amphibious ready groups (ARGs).

Naval Air Systems Command

Beginning in 1992, the Navy's research, development, test and evaluation community underwent a complete reorganisation. Gone are such familiar organisations as the Naval Air Test Center and its directorates, the Pacific Missile Test Center, the Naval Weapons Center, the Naval Weapons Evaluation Facility, VX-4, VX-5 and VXN-8. In their place is a streamlined establishment under the supervision of the Naval Air Systems Command (NAVAIR, or NACS), which moved in 1996 from Arlington, Virginia to NAS Patuxent River, Maryland. Development, procurement and depot-level maintenance of

Navy and Marine Corps aircraft and aviation weapons and systems remain the responsibility of the NAVAIR.

Naval Air Warfare Center

Much of NAVAIR's structure was subordinated into a new command, the Naval Air Warfare Center (NAWC), also headquartered at Patuxent River. Most of its work is performed by the Center's three main divisions – the NAWC, Aircraft Division (NAWC-AD) at Patuxent River, Maryland, Trenton, New Jersey and Lakehurst, New Jersey; the NAWC, Weapons Division (NAWC-WD) at China Lake and Point Mugu, California; and the Training Systems Division in Orlando, Florida.

The NAWC-AD's aircraft fleet is assigned to Commander Naval Air Test Wing Atlantic. The four squadrons assigned to the wing were organised in 1995 from the directorates of the former Naval Air Test Center at Patuxent River. The Naval Strike Aircraft Test Squadron performs RDT&E for fighter, attack and electronic attack aircraft. The Naval Rotary-Wing Test Squadron does the same for Navy and Marine Corps helicopters. The Naval Force Warfare Test Squadron has test responsibilities for anti-submarine, electronic reconnaissance, early warning, communications, aerial refuelling and transport aircraft. The US Naval Test Pilot School (USNTPS), now considered a squadron, trains test pilots and flight officers on a variety of aircraft.

When new aircraft are being evaluated at NAWC-AD, integrated test teams (ITTs), comprising naval and industry pilots, engineers and support personnel, are formed to shepherd new aircraft through development. Current ITTs are evaluating the F/A-18E/F and the MV-22B.

The NAWC-AD facilities at Lakehurst, New Jersey are still used for aircraft-carrier catapult and arresting gear trials. The activities formerly conducted at Naval Air Development Center at Warminster, Pennsylvania have been consolidated at Patuxent River. The Trenton, New Jersey facility used for aircraft engine test and development closed in 1998; its functions were transferred to NADEP North Island, California.

The NAWC-WD was formed largely from the facilities of the Pacific Missile Test Center at Point Mugu, California and the Naval Weapons Center in China Lake, California. NAWC-WD is responsible for development and testing of air-launched weapons and (along with NAWC-AD) integrating them with aircraft weapons systems. NAWC-WD operates two major sites, at China Lake and Point Mugu, with two naval weapons test squadrons (NWTS) under Commander Naval Air Test Wing Pacific. NAWS (Naval Air Weapons Station) China Lake, with purview of testing air-to-ground weapons, is the home of NWTS China Lake. NAS Point Mugu (NAWS Pt Mugu until October 1998) operates the Pacific Missile Range and hosts the NWTS Point Mugu air-to-air weapons test unit. NWTS Point Mugu operates QF-4 drones as targets for missile test shots. NWTS China Lake operates the station's HH-1N rescue helicopters.

NWEF Albuquerque, New Mexico was disestablished as part of the reorganisation.

The Navy's test ranges remain an important element in the development of the Navy's weapons and tactics. The Navy maintains an extensive test range off the island of Kauai in the Hawaiian Islands, used for missile shots and exercise

torpedo firings. The Pacific Missile Range Facility operates UH-3Hs for torpedo recovery and RC-12Fs for range clearance. The Atlantic Fleet Weapons Test Facility, with ranges in Puerto Rico and at St Croix in the Virgin Islands, is supported by UH-3Hs from VC-8 and RC-12Ms from NS Roosevelt Roads, Puerto Rico. The Advanced Underwater Test and Evaluation Center (AUTEC) at Andros Island in the Bahamas is now supported by contractor helicopters and UH-3Hs from reserve squadron HS-75.

Naval aviation depots

NASC operates three major industrial facilities, called Naval Aviation Depots (NADEPs), which overhaul and modify Navy and Marine Corps aircraft. Formerly called Naval Air Rework Facilities (NARFs), these depots now compete with commercial companies for some contracts. The number of depots has been halved since the end of the Cold War; the depots at NAS Alameda, California, Pensacola, Florida and Norfolk, Virginia were closed and their work moved to the other depots, to similar facilities of the other services, or to commercial contractors. NADEP North Island, California handles work for F/A-18, S-3, E-2 and C-2 aircraft; NADEP Jacksonville, Florida overhauls F-14, EA-6B and P-3 aircraft; and NADEP Cherry Point, North Carolina conducts work on AV-8, H-46 and H-53 aircraft. Many aircraft are overhauled by commercial contractors, some affiliated with aircraft manufacturers, such as Northrop Grumman.

Air test and evaluation squadrons

The Navy maintains two air test and evaluation (VX) squadrons operationally assigned to the Commander, Operational Test and Evaluation Force (COMOPTEVFOR), headquartered in Norfolk, Virginia. These squadrons, co-located but separate from the NASC organisation, put new aircraft and systems through operational testing after they have gone through developmental testing with the Naval Air Warfare Centers' squadrons and ITTs. The VX squadrons test the new systems under 'real world' conditions and make recommendations to COMOPTEVFOR regarding the suitability of the system for fleet introduction. VX-1 at Patuxent River is responsible for operational testing of anti-submarine, electronic reconnaissance and strategic communications aircraft, and associated weapons and systems. VX-9, based at China Lake with a detachment at Point Mugu, conducts operational tests of strike fighter and ECM aircraft, helicopter gunships and associated weapons. (VX-9 was formed in 1994 from elements of VX-4 and VX-5 and assumed their roles. VX-9 retained the nickname 'Vampires' and code ('XE') from VX-5, but its F-14 detachment in Point Mugu continues to use the 'XF' code formerly assigned to VX-4.)

Strike warfare development

The Naval Strike and Air Warfare Center (NSAWC), established in 1995 at NAS Fallon, Nevada, is an expansion of the Naval Strike Warfare Center ('Strike University') that was set up in the mid-1980s to improve strike warfare doctrine and tactics following the flawed December 1983 strike on anti-aircraft sites in Lebanon. The increasing use of cruise missiles in war at sea and in strikes against land targets led to an expanded syllabus for students (aviators, surface warriors and

These Naval Weapons Test Squadron F-14s – an F-14D (above right) and NF-14A (left) – wear differing NWTS markings.

Below: The NWTS operates this unique YF-4J Phantom as an ejection-seat testbed, from NAS Point Mugu.

Above and below: The Naval Weapons Test Wing, which is an element of the Naval Air Warfare Center, Weapons Division, maintains two Test Squadrons at NAS Pt Mugu and NAWS China Lake. All F/A-18s are based at China Lake.

Jet types flown by the NAS Patuxent River-based Naval Test Pilots School include the T-2C Buckeye (above) and several F/A-18A Hornets (above right).

Above: The TPS still has a number of U-6As (de Havilland Canada DHC-2 Beaver) on strength.

Below: Alongside a naval NSH-60B Seahawk the TPS operates this UH-60A bailed from the US Army.

Above, clockwise from top left: The TPS operates T-38s on loan from the USAF, a TH-6B and OH-58C on loan from the Army and Schweizer X-26A gliders – the only gliders in the entire Navy.

Right: Another of the unusual types in service with the Naval Test Pilots School is this NU-1B, better known as a de Havilland Canada DHC-3 Otter.

147

submariners) attending the NSWC. The Navy decided to consolidate the Navy Fighter Weapons School ('Topgun') and the Carrier Airborne Early Warning School ('Topdome') into the Fallon facility, accompanying its all-encompassing mission expansion.

The NSAWC operates a small inventory of fleet aircraft – as of early 1999 this comprised eight F-14As, 25 F/A-18As, four F/A-18Bs and four SH-60Fs – for tactical development. Fleet E-2C aircraft are assigned on a temporary basis as needed. The famous 'Topgun' school offers a syllabus in air combat manoeuvring for fleet aviators and flight officers in fighter and strike fighter squadrons.

The Navy's long association with aerial support of Antarctic scientific research operations –

performed by the ski-equipped LC-130 Hercules aircraft owned by the National Science Foundation and assigned to Antarctic Development Squadron Six (VXE-6), home-based at NAS Point Mugu – has come to an end. VXE-6 will be disestablished on 31 March 1999, but has already turned over its role to the New York Air National Guard's 109th Mobility Air Wing. VXE-6's last Operation Deep Freeze deployment ended in March 1998. Since then, the squadron has been operating with the 109th MAW to complete the transition. VXE-6's LC-130Fs (and TC-130Q trainer) have been retired and three LC-130Rs are programmed for modification to LC-130H standard. (VXE-6's HH-1N helicopters were withdrawn from service in 1996, replaced by a private contractor's helicopters.)

The Naval Research Laboratory (NRL) in Washington, DC maintains a Flight Support Detachment (FSD) at Patuxent River, Maryland which operates several NP-3D Orion aircraft in support of a variety of scientific and military research projects. NRL-FSD assumed some of the aircraft and oceanographic survey missions formerly assigned to Oceanographic Development Squadron 8 (VXN-8) when that squadron was disbanded in 1993.

The Naval Surface Warfare Center operates a small facility, Coastal Systems Station Panama City, Florida, for the development of undersea warfare systems, particularly mine countermeasures systems. For these purposes, two MH-53E and one NMH-53E Sea Dragons are assigned, as is an HH-1N for utility support.

Naval Air Training Command

The Naval Air Training Command, headed by the Chief of Naval Air Training (CNATRA) and headquartered at NAS Corpus Christi, Texas, trains aviators and navigators for the Navy, Marine Corps, Coast Guard and, increasingly, for the Air Force. In turn, the Air Force now conducts some phases of pilot and navigator training for the Navy, Marine Corps and Coast Guard. CNATRA trains a number of pilots and navigators for foreign navies and air forces. In addition to training functions, CNATRA operates Naval Aviation Schools Command and the Naval Flight Demonstration Squadron (the 'Blue Angels') and maintains the National Museum of Naval Aviation.

Training air wings

CNATRA supervises five training air wings (TAWs), each based at a separate airfield in Florida, Mississippi or Texas. Two wings, TAW-1 at NAS Meridian, Mississippi and TAW-2 at NAS Kingsville, Texas, conduct strike syllabus training. TAW-4 conducts primary training and multi-engined turboprop training at NAS Corpus Christi, Texas. TAW-5 trains primary students and conducts all basic and advanced helicopter training at NAS Whiting Field, Florida. All basic and some advanced navigator training is conducted by TAW-6 at NAS Pensacola, Florida. TAW-6 includes the German Luftwaffe's 2nd Training Squadron. Upon completion of primary training, student naval aviators proceed through one of six different training tracks. Navigators (naval flight officers) and Air Force navigators have five training tracks after primary training.

Primary training

After aviation pre-flight indoctrination (API), student aviators undergo 23 weeks of primary flight training at TAW-4 (with VTs 27 or 28, flying the T-34C), TAW-5 (with VTs 2, 3 or 6, flying the T-34C), or with the USAF at Vance AFB, Oklahoma, flying the T-37B. After primary training, students proceed on one of the six pilot training tracks.

Strike training

After primary training, student aviators beginning the strike aviator syllabus are channelled into one of two tracks, determined by the type of training aircraft available. Students assigned to TAW-2

will complete their advanced strike training flying the T-45A with VTs 21 or 22 in a 39-week syllabus. Students assigned to TAW-1 will undergo a 23-week intermediate phase with VT-9 (redesignated from VT-19 on 1 October 1998) in the T-2C Buckeye, followed by a 25-week advanced phase with VT-7 in the TA-4J Skyhawk, or a 29-week advanced phase with VT-23 in the T-45C. The T-45C, introduced in early 1998 with VT-23 (which moved from TAW-2 to TAW-1), will eventually replace the TA-4J in 1999 and the T-2C by 2010. At that point, the TAW-1 and TAW-2 syllabi will be identical. TAW-2 T-45As are programmed to be modified as T-45Cs. Strike training includes carrier qualification and weapons employment. Graduates proceed to FRS training in the F/A-18, F-14, EA-6B and S-3.

E-2/C-2 track

These students complete a 15-week intermediate phase in the T-44A and TC-12B with TAW-4's VT-31, followed by a 22-week carrier qualification phase flying the T-2C with TAW-1's VT-9. Upon graduation, aviators undergo FRS training at VAW-120 at NAS Norfolk, Virginia.

Maritime training

Students destined to fly large multi-engined turboprop aircraft undergo a six-week intermediate syllabus flying the T-34C with TAW-4's VT-27 or -28 or with TAW-5's VTs 2, 3 or 6. Upon completion, students train in a 20-week syllabus (25 for Air Force students) flying the T-44A and TC-12B with TAW-4's VT-31. TAW-4 has assumed all training for future Air Force C-130 pilots. Graduates of the maritime syllabus proceed to FRS training in the P-3, EP-3, HU-25 or C-130.

TACAMO training

These students complete the 26-week intermediate phase with TAW-4's VT-27 or VT-28 or TAW-5's VTs 2, 3 or 6 in the T-34C, or with the Air Force in the T-37B. A 26-week advanced phase follows, conducted by the Air Force in the T-1A. Graduates report to the Navy Training Support Unit at Tinker AFB, Oklahoma for transition into the E-6 using the TC-18F.

Helicopter training

Helicopter pilot trainees complete a 26-week T-34C syllabus with TAW-4's VT-27 or VT-28,

or TAW-5's VTs 2, 3, or 6. The students are introduced to helicopters with a 21-week syllabus flying the TH-57B and TH-57C Sea Ranger with TAW-5's helicopter training (HT) squadrons HT-8 or HT-18. Graduates proceed to FRS training in the H-1, H-3, H-46, H-53, H-60 or H-65 helicopters.

Naval flight officer training

Student naval flight officers (NFOs) and Air Force navigators undergo 14 weeks of primary training after completion of API. Students fly the T-34C at TAW-6 (with VTs 4 or 10). Upon completion, students are funnelled into one of five training tracks.

Maritime navigation training

Upon completion of primary training, NFO students selected for long-range maritime navigator training are sent to Randolph AFB, Texas for 26 weeks of advanced navigation training in the T-43A aircraft operated by the Air Force's 562nd FTS. Navy graduates proceed to FRS training in the P-3, EP-3 and E-6 aircraft. EP-3 NFOs will complete electronic warfare officer school at Corry Field, Pensacola, Florida. Air Force graduates will fly the E-3, E-8, C-5, C-130, C-135 and C-141 aircraft.

Strike syllabus

NFOs and navigators destined to fly non-fighter tactical jets or Air Force bombers will remain with TAW-6 and undergo a 14-week intermediate syllabus flying the T-34C and T-1A with VTs 4 or 10. Strike training consists of 19 weeks flying the T-2C and T-39N. Navy graduates proceed to FRS training in the S-3 or EA-6B; NFOs destined for the latter two types will complete electronic warfare officer school at Corry Field. USAF graduates will fly the B-1 or B-52.

Strike fighter syllabus

Students bound for fighter aircraft as radar intercept officers (RIOs) or weapon system operators (WSOs) receive 14 weeks of intermediate training with TAW-6 in the T-34C and T-1A operated by VTs 4 and 10. VT-86 conducts 26 weeks of training (including air combat manoeuvring) in the T-2C and T-39N. Navy graduates undergo FRS training to become F-14 RIOs. Marine Corps graduates (and eventually Navy

The **QF-4** drones of Point Mugu's Naval Weapons Test Squadron (part of the Naval Air Warfare Center, Weapons Division) serve as targets for missile trials. Both **QF-4N** (above) and **QF-4S** (right) drones are in use.

Specialist contractor-operated aircraft include the **DC-130A** drone directors (above) flown by **AVTEL** from **NAS Pt Mugu**, and Raytheon's **EC-24A** (below) that acts as an electronic aggressor for the Fleet Information Warfare Center.

TW-1, based at NAS Meridian, currently operates a mix of **TA-4Js** (VT-7), **T-2Cs** (VT-9) and **T-45Cs** (VT-23, as seen below). TW-2 has two T-45C squadrons, including **VT-21 'Fighting Red Hawks'** (right).

Above: **VT-22 'Golden Eagles'** is one of the two T-45C units that make up **TW-2**, at NAS Kingsville.

Above right: **VT-86 'Sabre Hawks'** flies T-2Cs as part of TW-6, along with VT-4 and VT-10, which fly T-34Cs.

Above: **VT-9 'Tigers'**, part of TW-1 at NAS Meridian, is the second of two remaining T-2C Buckeye squadrons.

Right: One squadron of TA-4Js, **VT-7 'Strike Eagles'**, remains in Training Command service, as part of TW-1.

graduates) will become F/A-18 WSOs. Air Force graduates will become F-15E WSOs.

ATDS syllabus

Students destined to become airborne intercept controllers onboard E-2C aircraft undergo 14 weeks of intermediate training with TAW-6 in the T-34C and T-1A. Advanced training in the

air tactical data system (ATDS) is provided in 32 weeks of training at VAW-120, the E-2 FRS at NAS Norfolk, Virginia. During the FRS ATDS training, the students are designated NFOs.

The Naval Flight Demonstration Squadron, known as the 'Blue Angels', is based at NAS Pensacola and conducts its winter training at NAF El Centro, California. The aerobatic team

keeps an intensive air show schedule, performing throughout the United States and occasionally in other nations. The squadron's Navy and Marine Corps pilots fly F/A-18A Hornets (one two-seat F/A-18B also is assigned). A Marine Corps TC-130G Hercules ('Fat Albert'), painted in the full team colours, provides logistic support for the team – and participates in the display.

US Naval Air Reserve

United States naval aviation is augmented by a powerful reserve force that provides reinforcement in time of national emergency and in some cases provides capabilities not found in the active-duty forces. The Naval Air Reserve today reflects the reserve force squadron structure created in 1970 in wake of the lack of readiness displayed with the failed reserve call-up during the 1968 *Pueblo* Crisis off North Korea. Today, the Naval Air Reserve, headquartered in New Orleans, Louisiana under the command of Commander, Naval Air Reserve Force, consists of five wings (soon to be four) and 37 squadrons. Since the end of the Cold War, 21 reserve force squadrons (as well as two patrol squadron master augmentation units and most squadron augmentation units) have been disbanded and only two squadrons have been formed (VAW-77 and VQ-11).

In certain mission areas, the Naval Air Reserve operates all of the Navy's aircraft assigned those missions. Today, all non-carrier-capable airlift squadrons, combat SAR helicopter squadrons and air combat manoeuvring adversary squadrons are part of the reserve force structure.

The Naval Air Reserve is manned largely by experienced officers and sailors who have been released from active duty following their initial service. A core of reservists on active duty, designated TARs (Training and Administration of Reserves), ensure day-to-day operation of the reserve force squadrons and wings.

Reserve carrier aviation

The Navy's determined effort to maintain two reserve carrier air wings (CVWRs) on strength since 1970 – and to continuously upgrade their aircraft common to fleet standard – was dashed with the end of the Cold War. Budget reductions forced the disestablishment of the West Coast's CVWR-30 and most of its squadrons (VF-301, VF-302, VFA-303, VA-304, VFA-305, VAQ-309 and VAW-88), leaving only East Coast-based CVWR-20, minus VF-202 and VA-205. The Navy's effort to modernise the CVWRs was largely successful, with their aircraft and squadron composition mirroring those of the active-duty CVWs for the most part. Their aircraft were usually earlier models of the fleet-standard aircraft. Unlike active-duty CVWs, CVWRs were never equipped with VS squadrons, relying instead on squadron augmentation units that would draw aircraft from the S-3 FRSs. The CVWRs have to rely on active-duty squadrons, whose aircraft are in short supply, for fleet air reconnaissance and COD detachments. With the dissolution of the fleet's three electronic adversary squadrons (VAQs 33, 34 and 35), the CVWR's VA, VAQ and VFA assumed the role of providing electronic adversary services to Navy ships (using special pods mounted on F/A-18As, A-6Es and EA-6Bs).

In recent years, for convenience, the CVWRs assumed administrative command of land-based VFC and VAW units that had no carrier mission. Despite their level of training and readiness, the Navy's CVWRs have never made a combat deployment – even during Operation Desert Storm, when Navy resources were stretched to the limit. Many within the organisation feel there is a lack of faith in the Reserve from higher-up and that its long-term future may yet be called into question.

CVWR-20, which moved its headquarters from NAS Cecil Field, Florida to NAS Atlanta, Georgia, is nominally assigned to USS *John F. Kennedy* (CV 67), which is part of the Naval Reserve Force. This carrier, however, is still integrated in the overseas deployment cycle with active-duty CVWs.

Fighter squadrons

The retirement of CVWR-30 and the consolidation in most active-duty carrier air wings of the two F-14A fighter squadrons resulted in the disestablishment of VFs 202, 301 and 302 and the retention of only one reserve fighter squadron, VF-201. The Navy's initiative to accelerate retirement of the F-14A led to the decision to transition VF-201 to F/A-18A Hornet strike fighters in 1999, which left CVWR-20 with four Hornet squadrons and no Tomcat fighters. VF-201 was redesignated VFA-201 on 1 January 1999.

Strike fighter squadrons

Most of CVWR-20's combat capability resides in four F/A-18A Hornet strike fighter squadrons. One of the assigned squadrons is Marine Fighter-Attack Squadron (VMFA) 142, which replaced VA-205 in the wing's structure when the A-6 Intruder was retired. The three VFA squadrons have a secondary mission of electronic adversary training support.

Electronic attack squadrons

CVWR-20 is assigned one electronic attack (formerly tactical electronic warfare) squadron, VAQ-209, which performs suppression of enemy air defences with electronic countermeasures and missile strikes. VAQ-209 crews and EA-6B Prowler aircraft have augmented active-duty VAQ units operating from carriers off Bosnia and have served in rotation in support of Air Force expeditionary deployments to Turkey in support of Operations Northern Watch over Iraq. A shortage of EA-6Bs in the fleet has produced mounting pressure to relocate VAQ-209 from NAF Washington to the fleet's main EA-6B base, NAS Whidbey Island, Washington, to allow the squadron's aircraft to be used to support fleet deployments. In the meantime, the squadron has had some of its aircraft siphoned off to support

active fleet squadrons and therefore would have difficulty mustering a full complement in the event of mobilisation.

Airborne early warning squadrons

CVWR-20 has two E-2C Hawkeye squadrons assigned, but only one, Carrier Airborne Early Warning (VAW) Squadron 78, is intended to operate onboard aircraft-carriers. Airborne Early Warning Squadron (also designated VAW) 77 was formed in 1995 to replace active-duty squadron VAW-122 as a specialist dedicated drug-interdiction and fleet exercise support squadron. VAW-77, assigned to CVWR-20 as a matter of administrative convenience, has greatly relieved the operational tempo required of active-duty VAW squadrons.

Adversary services

The Navy's once expansive active-duty air combat adversary force (VF-43, VF-45, VF-126, VFA-127) has been disbanded and adversary services are provided by only two squadrons, both units of the Naval Air Reserve. Fighter Composite Squadron (VFC) 12 flies F/A-18A/B Hornets on the East Coast. VFC-13, which moved in 1996 to NAS Fallon, Nevada from NAS Miramar, Calif., retired its A-4Fs, A-4Ms and TA-4Js, transferred its F/A-18As and F/A-18Bs and now flies the F-5E/F Tiger II in support of carrier air wing work-ups at Fallon. Both VFC units are administratively assigned to CVWR-20, having been transferred from CFLSW. The A-4M adversary detachment maintained by NAS Dallas has long since been disbanded.

Patrol squadrons

For nearly three decades, one third of the Navy's patrol (VP) squadrons have been operated by the Naval Air Reserve. Reserve VP units routinely augment active-duty VP squadrons at overseas deployment sites and in fleet exercises in what has long been a remarkably successful active-reserve operational integration. Since the end of the Cold War, the number of reserve VP squadrons, however, has declined at a pace commensurate with that of the active-duty patrol force, from 13 squadrons in 1990 to seven by the first quarter of 1999 (with the 1 April 1999 scheduled disestablishment of VP-91). The units disbanded included VPs 60, 67, 68, 90 and 93, as well as the two VP-Master Augmentation Units (VP-MAUs) at Brunswick and Moffett Field, which were equipped with a small number of Orions. The drawdown will further result in the April 1999 consolidation of Commander Reserve Patrol Wing, US Pacific Fleet (also designated Commander Patrol Wing 4), based at Moffett Federal Air Field, with Commander Reserve Patrol Wing, US Atlantic Fleet, at NAS Norfolk,

T-34C operations are concentrated at TW-4 (above) and TW-5 (left). TW-4 has two Turbo Mentor squadrons, VT-27 and VT-28, while TW-5 has three, VT-2, VT-3 and VT-6.

Right: Some Training Command T-34Cs, such as this VT-27 aircraft, have adopted a more tactical colour scheme.

Below: The Navy's last T-39s are the T-39Ns operated by VT-86 at NAS Pensacola, for NFO training.

Above: VT-31 'Wise Owls', the third squadron at TW-4, flies the T-44A Pegasus from NAS Corpus Christi.

Below: TH-57 flying is split between HT-8 and HT-18. Both squadrons are attached to TW-5, at NAS Whiting Field.

Like the other F/A-18 units of Reserve Carrier Air Wing 20 (CVWR-20), VFA-203 'Blue Dolphins' has a 'part-time' Adversary training role and maintains some of its Hornets in a typical dissimilar Adversary scheme (below).

Left: VFA-204 'River Rattlers', the third regular Reserve Hornet squadron, flies from NAS New Orleans JRB.

Above: VFC-12 'Fighting Omars' is one of just two surviving Adversary units in the entire Navy. It flies only F/A-18As.

Top: VFA-201 'Hunters' was the last Reserve F-14 unit and began its transition to the F/A-18A in early 1999.

151

into one organisation, Reserve Patrol Wing, at NAS Norfolk.

During the mid-1990s, the reserve VP squadrons retired their last P-3Bs, helping the Navy to finally reach its goal of an all P-3C patrol force. The reserve VP squadrons operate a mixture of Update I, II, II.5 and III variants of the P-3C Orion; eventually, all units will operate a common Update III version.

Fleet air reconnaissance squadron

In 1997, the Naval Air Reserve formed its first fleet air reconnaissance (VQ) squadron, VQ-11, to operate two EP-3J Orion electronic adversary aircraft formerly operated by VAQ-33 and later VP-66, plus one P-3C for training and support. The squadron's name does not reflect its true mission; its aircraft do not perform reconnaissance, but simulate enemy electronic threats during work-up training of Navy ships. One of the EP-3Js was damaged beyond economic repair in a ground mishap in April 1998. In late 1998, the Navy was considering disbanding VQ-11 in 1999 and transferring the remaining EP-3J to another unit.

Airlift

The Navy's entire organic airlift force continues to reside in the Naval Air Reserve. Drawing on former active-duty aviators, many of whom are airline pilots, Commander Fleet Logistic Support Wing's (CLSW's) 14 fleet logistic support (VR) squadrons transport high-priority cargo and passengers throughout the United States and overseas. A major responsibility of the VR units is to transport carrier air wing personnel and cargo from their bases to ports to meet deploying aircraft-carriers. The logistic support wing's squadrons fly a mixture of C-9B, DC-9, C-130T, C-20D and C-20G aircraft. Normally, one C-130T and one C-9B or DC-9 each are deployed to the Mediterranean and Western Pacific to support airlift requirements in the Sixth and Seventh Fleets, respectively, partially filling the gap caused by the disestablishment in the early 1990s of active-duty squadrons VR-22 and VRC-50. Two DC-9 squadrons (VR-51 and VR-60) were disbanded in the early 1990s and two other C-9 squadrons (VR-55 and VR-62) transitioned to the C-130T during the mid-1990s, but the redistribution of their aircraft to other VR units resulted in no reduction in C-9B/DC-9 aircraft inventory. When NAF Detroit closed, VR-62 moved to NAS South Weymouth and transitioned to the C-130T; when NAS South Weymouth closed, VR-62 moved to NAS Brunswick. Another C-130T unit, VR-55, is slated to move from Moffett Federal Airfield, California to NAS Point Mugu, California in 1999.

The replacement for the ageing C-9Bs and DC-9s has been selected: three Boeing C-40As, versions of the Boeing 737-700 IGW (increased gross weight) airliner, are on order for initial delivery in 2001.

The six C-20 aircraft, based in Maryland and Hawaii, are used for rapid-response airlift and for transport of senior Navy Department officials and flag officers. The two C-20Ds, formerly flown by Commander Fleet Logistics Support Wing Detachment Washington, are now flown by a squadron formed in 1997 at NAF Washington: VR-1. VR-51 was formed the same year from a CFLSW detachment to operate two C-20Gs based at MCAF Kaneohe Bay, Hawaii. VR-48 operates two C-20Gs from NAF Washington. VR-48 briefly operated the C-130Ts that eventually equipped VR-53 while the basing decision for the future VR-53 was being made. Plans to base VR-53 in Martinsburg, West Virginia were cancelled and the unit remained at NAF Washington.

Helicopter wing reserve

All of the Navy's reserve helicopter squadrons are administratively assigned to Helicopter Wing Reserve, headquartered at NAS North Island, California.

Helicopter anti-submarine squadrons

One carrier-based helicopter anti-submarine (HS) squadron, administratively assigned to Helicopter Wing Reserve, operates as the helicopter component for CVWR-20 in performing anti-submarine, rescue and utility missions. HS-75 is the only Navy squadron still operating the SH-3H Sea King and flies the UH-3H version in the rescue and torpedo recovery role.

Light Airborne Multi-Purpose System (LAMPS) units

Since the mid-1990s, the Navy's remaining SH-2G Super Seasprite LAMPS helicopters have been operated by the Naval Air Reserve's helicopter anti-submarine squadron light (HSL) units, two of three such units (HSL-84 and HSL-94) still being in operation. In recent years, detachments of these squadrons have deployed in support of drug-interdiction operations. Their SH-2Gs are the only aircraft currently configured to operate the Magic Lantern laser mine detection system. These HSL squadrons have been kept in operation to provide LAMPS helicopters to the Naval Reserve's early 'Oliver Hazard Perry'-class guided-missile frigates, which were incapable of operating the SH-60B LAMPS Mk III helicopter flown by active-duty squadrons. The imminent retirement of these ships has resulted in the planned disestablishment of the two reserve HSL units by 2000.

Combat search and rescue and Special Operations

The Naval Air Reserve operates the Navy's only two helicopter combat support squadron special (HCS) squadrons, HCS-4 and HCS-5, which operate the HH-60H Seahawk for combat SAR missions and support of special warfare forces, such as the Navy's Sea-Air-Land (SEAL) commandos. In recent years, HCS personnel and helicopters have augmented active-duty HS squadrons onboard carriers operating off Bosnia. The HH-60Hs are scheduled to be withdrawn over the next decade for conversion to SH-60Rs and to be replaced by new CH-60S variants.

Mine countermeasures

Helicopter Wing Reserve once operated two helicopter mine countermeasures (HM) squadrons (HM-18 at NAS Norfolk and HM-19 at NAS Alameda), initially equipped with RH-53D Sea Stallions. Both squadrons transitioned to the MH-53E Sea Dragon but were disbanded during the mid-1990s, when their aircraft and many of their personnel were absorbed by their active-duty counterpart squadrons, HM-14 and HM-15, respectively, which became the Navy's first joint active-reserve squadrons. (See mine countermeasures in the Navy section above.)

Utility helicopter operations

Helicopter Wing Reserve operates one helicopter combat support (HC) squadron, HC-85, which provides rescue, utility and torpedo recovery services in the southern California area. HC-85, which replaced its SH-3Hs with UH-3H utility versions, was redesignated from HS-85 when CVWR-30 was disbanded. HC-85 assumed the duties of the now-disbanded active-duty HC-1.

Air stations

Four naval air stations and one naval air facility (Washington, D.C.) operate under management of the Naval Air Reserve. Most have been redesignated Naval Air Station-Joint Reserve Bases (Atlanta, Fort Worth, New Orleans, Willow Grove). NAS Fort Worth-JRB, established on the site of the former Carswell AFB, Texas, is now the home of units formerly based at NAS Dallas (disestablished on 30 September 1998) and some units relocated from NAS Glenview and NAS Memphis. Since the early 1990s, the naval air stations at Glenview, Memphis and South Weymouth, as well as NAF Detroit, have been closed. NAS Memphis became Naval Support Activity Memphis and finally, in October 1998, became NSA Mid-South, home of the Navy Personnel Command, retaining an active airfield. VR-62 moved to NAS South Weymouth when NAF Detroit closed and then to NAS Brunswick when South Weymouth closed.

Many reserve squadrons are based at air stations and facilities operated by the active-duty Navy and some are based at other federal facilities. VP-91 (soon to be disbanded) and VR-55 are based at Moffett Federal Airfield (formerly Naval Air Station Moffett Field) in Mountainview, California and supported by Naval Air Reserve Center Santa Clara. VR-55, soon to move to NAS Point Mugu, will be last the Navy aviation unit based in the San Francisco Bay area.

Like many air stations managed by active-duty type commanders, the Naval Air Reserve operates several UC-12B aircraft in base flights for air station liaison support. **Richard R. Burgess**

US Navy Aviation

Chief of Naval Operations, Arlington, Va.

Commander in Chief, US Atlantic Fleet, Norfolk, Va.
Commander, Naval Air Force, US Atlantic Fleet, NAS Norfolk

Commander, Carrier Group 2	NAS Norfolk, Va.
Commander, Carrier Group 4	NAS Norfolk, Va.
Commander, Carrier Group 6	NS Mayport, Fla.
Commander, Carrier Group 8	NAS Norfolk, Va.
USS *Enterprise* (CVN 65)	NS Norfolk, Va.
USS *Nimitz* (CVN 68)	Newport News, Va.
	(3-year refuelling and overhaul)
USS *Dwight D. Eisenhower* (CVN 69)	NS Norfolk, Va.
USS *Theodore Roosevelt* (CVN 71)	NS Norfolk, Va.
USS *George Washington* (CVN 73)	NS Norfolk, Va.
USS *Harry S. Truman* (CVN 75)	NS Norfolk, Va.
Commander, Carrier Air Wing 1	AB	NAS Oceana, Va.
Commander, Carrier Air Wing 3	AC	NAS Oceana, Va.
Commander, Carrier Air Wing 7	AG	NAS Oceana, Va.
Commander, Carrier Air Wing 8	AJ	NAS Oceana, Va.
Commander, Carrier Air Wing 17	AA	NAS Oceana, Va.

Commander, Patrol Wings, US Atlantic Fleet   NAS Norfolk
VP-30 (FRS)   Pro's Nest   P-3C, TP-3A, VP-3A   LL

NAS Jacksonville, Fla.

Above: Proudly wearing its Darth Vader badge, this EA-6B is from the Reserve's single Prowler squadron, VAQ-209.

Below: VFC-13 shares its Nevada base with NSAWC, working closely with that unit and 'Topgun' in particular.

Right: NAS Fallon-based VFC-13 'Saints' is the last Navy F-5 unit and is the only provider of dissimilar Adversary training to US Navy units.

Below: VP-62 'Broadarrows' flies its P-3Cs from NAS Jacksonville.

Two E-2C Hawkeye squadrons are attached to Reserve Carrier Air Wing 20. They are VAW-77 'Night Wolf' and VAW-78 'Fighting Escargots' (above).

Reserve Patrol Wing has eight P-3C patrol squadrons, including VP-65 'Tridents' (above left), VP-69 'Totems' (above), VP-91 'Black Cats' (above right) and VP-94 'Crawfish' (left). However, one Reserve Orion squadron, VP-91, will disappear in 1999. The Reserve's only special duties P-3 squadron, the short-lived VQ-11 (right), is scheduled to be disestablished during 1999.

The last SH-2G Seasprites in US service are flown by HSL-84 'Thunderbolts' (above left) and HSL-94 'Titans' (left). The Reserve has two HH-60H squadrons, HCS-4 'Red Wolves' (above) and HCS-5 'Firehawks' (above right). Two H-3 units round out the assets of Helicopter Wing Reserve. The first of these is HS-75 'Emerald Knights' (right).

Air Power Analysis

Commander, Patrol Wing 5, NAS Brunswick, Maine
VP-8 Tigers P-3C LC NAS Brunswick, Maine
VP-10 Lancers P-3C LD NAS Brunswick, Maine
VP-26 Tridents P-3C LK NAS Brunswick, Maine
VPU-1 Old Buzzards P-3B, P-3C OB NAS Brunswick, Maine
Note: OB code for VPU-1 is unofficial.

Commander, Patrol Wing 11, NAS Jacksonville, Fla.
VP-5 Mad Foxes P-3C LA NAS Jacksonville, Fla.
VP-16 Eagles P-3C LF NAS Jacksonville, Fla.
VP-45 Pelicans P-3C LN NAS Jacksonville, Fla.

Commander, Fighter Wing, US Atlantic Fleet, NAS Oceana, Va.
VF-2 Bounty Hunters F-14D NAS Oceana, Va.
VF-11 Red Rippers F-14B NAS Oceana, Va.
VF-14 Tophatters F-14A NAS Oceana, Va.
VF-31 Tomcatters F-14D NAS Oceana, Va.
VF-32 Swordsmen F-14B NAS Oceana, Va.
VF-41 Black Aces F-14A NAS Oceana, Va.
VF-101 (FRS) Grim Reapers F-14A/B/D, T-34C NAS Oceana
VF-102 Diamondbacks F-14B NAS Oceana, Va.
VF-103 Jolly Rogers F-14B NAS Oceana, Va.
VF-143 Pukin Dogs F-14B NAS Oceana, Va.
VF-154 Black Knights F-14A NAS Atsugi, Japan
VF-211 Flying Checkmates F-14A NAS Oceana, Va.
VF-213 Black Lions F-14D NAS Oceana, Va.
VC-8 Red Tails (GF) TA-4J, UH-3H NS Roosevelt Roads, Puerto Rico

Commander, Strike Fighter Wing, US Atlantic Fleet, NAS Oceana, Va.
VFA-15 Valions F/A-18C NAS Oceana, Va.
VFA-34 Blue Blasters F/A-18C NAS Oceana, Va.
VFA-37 Bulls F/A-18C NAS Oceana, Va.
VFA-81 Sunliners F/A-18C NAS Oceana, Va.
VFA-82 Marauders F/A-18C MCAS Beaufort, S.C.
VFA-83 Rampagers F/A-18C NAS Oceana, Va.
VFA-86 Sidewinders F/A-18C MCAS Beaufort, S.C.
VFA-87 Golden Warriors F/A-18C NAS Oceana, Va.
VFA-105 Gunslingers F/A-18C NAS Oceana, Va.
VFA-106 (FRS) Gladiators (AD) F/A-18A/B/C/D NAS Oceana, Va.
VFA-131 Wildcats F/A-18C NAS Oceana, Va.
VFA-136 Knighthawks F/A-18C NAS Oceana, Va.
Strike Fighter Weapons School T-34C NAS Oceana, Va.
***Note:** VFA-131 and VFA-136 moved from NAS Cecil Field, Fla., to NAS Oceana in December 1998; VFA-34 in March 1999; VFA-81 and VFA-83 in April 1999; VFA-37 and VFA-105 in July 1999 and VFA-15 and VFA-87 in October 1999. VFA-82 and VFA-86 depart Cecil Field in September 1999 for deployment and move to MCAS Beaufort, S.C., in March 2000. Bases listed above reflect eventual destinations.*

Commander, Airborne Early Warning Wing, US Atlantic Fleet, GE, NAS Norfolk,Va.
VAW-120 (FRS) Greyhawks (AD) E-2C, TE-2C, C-2A NAS Norfolk, Va.
VAW-121 Bluetails E-2C NAS Norfolk, Va.
VAW-123 Screwtops E-2C NAS Norfolk, Va.
VAW-124 Bear Aces E-2C NAS Norfolk, Va.
VAW-125 Tigertails E-2C NAS Norfolk, Va.
VAW-126 Seahawks E-2C NAS Norfolk, Va.
VRC-40 Rawhides C-2A NAS Norfolk, Va.
***Note:** CAEWW-12 is assigned the code GE, which has been used in the past by VAW squadrons not assigned to a CVW. VAW-122, now disestablished, used this code during its long assignment as a counter-drug squadron. VRC-40 aircraft normally wear the code of the CVW to which they are assigned. The JK code formerly assigned is now assigned to VR-1.*

Commander, Sea Control Wing, US Atlantic Fleet, NAS Jacksonvile, Fla.
VS-22 Checkmates S-3B NAS Jacksonville, Fla.
VS-24 Scouts S-3B NAS Jacksonville, Fla.
VS-30 Diamondcutters S-3B NAS Jacksonville, Fla.
VS-31 Topcats S-3B NAS Jacksonville, Fla.
VS-32 Maulers S-3B NAS Jacksonville, Fla.
VQ-6 (ET) Black Ravens ES-3A NAS Jacksonville, Fla.
***Note:** VQ-6 is scheduled to be disestablished in September 1999. Its ET code, due to an administrative oversight, was assigned despite the fact that the code has been assigned to HMM-262 for decades. VQ-6 aircraft normally wear the codes of the CVW to which they are assigned.*

Commander, Helicopter Antisubmarine Wing, US Atlantic Fleet, NAS Jacksonville, Fla.
HS-3 Tridents SH-60F, HH-60H NAS Jacksonville, Fla.
HS-5 Night Dippers SH-60F, HH-60H NAS Jacksonville, Fla.
HS-7 Dusty Dogs SH-60F, HH-60H NAS Jacksonville, Fla.
HS-11 Dragonslayers SH-60F, HH-60H NAS Jacksonville, Fla.
HS-15 Red Lions SH-60F, HH-60H NAS Jacksonville, Fla.
***Note:** HS-7 is also known as the Shamrocks.*

Commander, Helicopter Antisubmarine Wing Light, US Atlantic Fleet, NS Mayport, Fla.
HSL-40 (FRS) Air Wolves SH-60B HK NS Mayport, Fla.
HSL-42 Proud Warriors SH-60B HH NS Mayport, Fla.
HSL-44 Swamp Foxes SH-60B HP NS Mayport, Fla.
HSL-46 Grandmasters SH-60B HQ NS Mayport, Fla.
HSL-48 Vipers SH-60B HR NS Mayport, Fla.

Commander, Helicopter Tactical Wing, US Atlantic Fleet, NAS Norfolk, Va.
HC-2 (FRS) Circuit Riders UH-3H, VH-3A HU NAS Norfolk, Va.
Det 1 UH-3H NSA Naples, Italy
Det 2 UH-3H ASU Bahrain
HC-4 Black Stallions MH-53E HC NAS Sigonella, Sicily
HC-6 Chargers CH/HH/UH-46D HW NAS Norfolk, Va.
HC-8 Dragon Whales CH/HH/UH-46D BR NAS Norfolk, Va.
HM-14 Sea Stallions MH-53E BJ NAS Norfolk, Va.
HM-15 Blackhawks MH-53E TB NAS Corpus Christi, Tx.
VC-6 Skeet of the Fleet RQ-2A NAS Norfolk, Va.
***Note:** HM squadrons are joint active/reserve squadrons. HC-2 serves as both an FRS and an operational squadron.*

VX-1 Pioneers P-3C, S-3B, SH-60B/F JA NAS Patuxent River, Md.

NAS Brunswick HH-1N 7F
NAS Oceana UH-3H 7R
NAS Norfolk UC-12B/M 7M
NAS Jacksonville UC-12B 7E
NAS Cecil Field None 7U
NAS Key West UC-12B, UH-3H 7Q
NS Mayport None 8U
NS Roosevelt Roads RC-12M 8E
NS Guantanamo Bay UC-12B, HH-1N 8F

Commander, Fleet Air Keflavik, NAS Keflavik, Iceland
VP-xx (Rotation) P-3C
NAS Keflavik UP-3A

Commander, US Naval Forces Europe, London, UK
NAF Mildenhall, UK UC-12M 8G

Commander, Fleet Air Mediterranean, NSA Naples, Italy
VQ-2 Batmen EP-3E, P-3C JQ NS Rota, Spain
VP-xx (Rotation) P-3C NAS Sigonella, Sicily
***Note:** HC-4, based at NAS Sigonella, is part of Helicopter Tactical Wing, US Atlantic Fleet, but operates under control of Commander, Fleet Air Mediterranean.*

NAS Sigonella, Sicily UC-12M, VP-3A 8C
NS Rota, Spain UC-12M 8D
NSA Naples, Italy UC-12M
NSA Souda Bay, Crete None
Admin Support Unit Bahrain UC-12B

Commander in Chief, US Pacific Fleet, NB Pearl Harbor, Hawaii
Commander, Naval Air Force, US Pacific Fleet NAS North Island, Hawaii
Commander, Carrier Group 1 NAS North Island, Calif.
Commander, Carrier Group 3 NS Bremerton, Wash.
Commander, Carrier Group 5 NS Yokosuka, Japan
Commander, Carrier Group 7 NAS North Island, Calif.
USS *Kitty Hawk* (CV 63) NS Yokosuka, Japan
USS *Constellation* (CV 64) NAS North Island, Calif.
USS *Carl Vinson* (CVN 70) NS Bremerton, Wash.
USS *Abraham Lincoln* (CVN 72) NS Everett, Wash.
USS *John C. Stennis* (CVN 74) NAS North Island, Calif.
Commander, Carrier Air Wing 2 NE NAS Lemoore, Calif.
Commander, Carrier Air Wing 5 NF NAF Atsugi, Japan
Commander, Carrier Air Wing 9 NG NAS Lemoore, Calif.
Commander, Carrier Air Wing 11 NH NAS Lemoore, Calif.
Commander, Carrier Air Wing 14 NK NAS Lemoore, Calif.

Commander, Patrol Wings (to become Patrol Wing 2), US Pacific Fleet, MCAF Kaneohe Bay, Hawaii
VP-4 Skinny Dragons P-3C YD MCAF Kaneohe Bay, Hawaii
VP-9 Golden Eagles P-3C PD MCAF Kaneohe Bay, Hawaii
VP-47 Golden Swordsmen P-3C RD MCAF Kaneohe Bay, Hawaii
VPU-2 Wizards P-3C, UP-3A SP MCAF Kaneohe Bay, Hawaii
***Note:** Move of these units from NAS Barbers Point, Hawaii, to MCAF Kaneohe Bay by July 1999 is reflected here.*

Commander, Patrol and Reconnaissance Wing 10, NAS Whidbey Island, Wash.
VP-1 Screaming Eagles P-3C YB NAS Whidbey Island, Wash.
VP-40 Fighting Marlins P-3C QE NAS Whidbey Island, Wash.
VP-46 Grey Knights P-3C RC NAS Whidbey Island, Wash.
VQ-1 World Watchers EP-3E, P-3C, UP-3A/B PR NAS Whidbey Island, Wash.

Commander, Electronic Attack Wing, US Pacific Fleet, NAS Whidbey Island, Wash.
VAQ-128 Fighting Phoenix EA-6B NL NAS Whidbey Island, Wash.
VAQ-129 Vikings (FRS) EA-6B NJ NAS Whidbey Island, Wash.
VAQ-130 Zappers EA-6B NAS Whidbey Island, Wash.
VAQ-131 Lancers EA-6B NAS Whidbey Island, Wash.
VAQ-132 Scorpions EA-6B NAS Whidbey Island, Wash.
VAQ-133 Wizards EA-6B NL NAS Whidbey Island, Wash.
VAQ-134 Garudas EA-6B NL NAS Whidbey Island, Wash.
VAQ-135 Black Ravens EA-6B NAS Whidbey Island, Wash.
VAQ-136 Gauntlets EA-6B NAF Atsugi, Japan
VAQ-137 Rooks EA-6B NAS Whidbey Island, Wash.
VAQ-138 Yellowjackets EA-6B NAS Whidbey Island, Wash.
VAQ-139 Cougars EA-6B NAS Whidbey Island, Wash.
VAQ-140 Patriots EA-6B NAS Whidbey Island, Wash.
VAQ-141 Shadowhawks EA-6B NAS Whidbey Island, Wash.
VAQ-142 Gray Wolves EA-6B NL NAS Whidbey Island, Wash.
***Note:** VAQs 128, 133, 134 and 142, all coded NL, provide electronic warfare support to Air Force expeditionary wings. Modexes as follows: VAQ-128: NL570; VAQ-133: NL530; VAQ-134: NL540; VAQ-142: NL520.*

Commander, Strike Fighter Wing, US Pacific Fleet, NAS Lemoore, Calif.
VFA-22 Fighting Redcocks F/A-18C NAS Lemoore, Calif.
VFA-25 Fist of the Fleet F/A-18C NAS Lemoore, Calif.
VFA-27 Chargers F/A-18C NAF Atsugi, Japan
VFA-94 Mighty Shrikes F/A-18C NAS Lemoore, Calif.
VFA-97 Warhawks F/A-18A NAS Lemoore, Calif.
VFA-113 Stingers F/A-18C NAS Lemoore, Calif.
VFA-115 Eagles F/A-18C NAS Lemoore, Calif.
VFA-122 (NJ) F/A-18E/F NAS Lemoore, Calif.
VFA-125 Rough Raiders (FRS) F/A-18A/B/C/D, T-34C NJ NAS Lemoore, Calif.
VFA-137 Kestrels F/A-18C NAS Lemoore, Calif.
VFA-146 Blue Diamonds F/A-18C NAS Lemoore, Calif.
VFA-147 Argonauts F/A-18C NAS Lemoore, Calif.
VFA-151 Vigilantes F/A-18C NAS Lemoore, Calif.
VFA-192 World Famous Golden Dragons F/A-18C NAF Atsugi
VFA-195 Dambusters F/A-18C NAF Atsugi, Japan
***Note:** VFA-97's transition to the F/A-18C was stalled; the unit is the last carrier-assigned active-duty unit to fly the F/A-18A.*

Commander, Airborne Early Warning Wing, US Pacific Fleet, NAS Point Mugu, Calif.
VAW-112 Golden Hawks E-2C NAS Point Mugu, Calif.
VAW-113 Black Hawks E-2C NAS Point Mugu, Calif.
VAW-115 Sentinels E-2C NAF Atsugi, Japan
VAW-116 Sun Kings E-2C NAS Point Mugu, Calif.
VAW-117 Wallbangers E-2C NAS Point Mugu, Calif.
VRC-30 (RW) Providers C-2A, UC-12B NAS North Island, Calif.
***Note:** VRC-30 aircraft normally wear codes of the CVWs to which their detachments are assigned.*

Commander, Sea Control Wing, US Pacific Fleet, NAS North Island, Calif.
VS-21 Fighting Redtails S-3B NAF Atsugi, Japan
VS-29 Screaming Dragonfires S-3B NAS North Island, Calif.
VS-33 Screwbirds S-3B NAS North Island, Calif.
VS-35 Blue Wolves S-3B NAS North Island, Calif.
VS-38 Red Griffins S-3B NAS North Island, Calif.
VS-41 (FRS) Shamrocks S-3B NAS North Island, Calif.
VQ-5 (SS) Sea Shadows ES-3A, S-3B NAS North Island, Calif.
***Note:** VQ-5 is scheduled for disestablishment in July 1999. Its aircraft usually wear the codes of the CVWs to which its detachments are assigned.*

Commander, Strategic Communications Wing 1, Tinker AFB, Okla.
VQ-3 Ironmen E-6A/B TZ Tinker AFB, Okla.
Det Travis Travis AFB, Okla.
VQ-4 Shadows E-6A/B HL Tinker AFB, Okla.
Det Patuxent River NAS Patuxent River, Md.
NTSU (FRS) TC-18F Tinker AFB, Okla.
***Note:** In 1998, CSCW-1 stood up a detachment at Offutt AFB, Neb., for Looking Glass ABNCP operations. Both VQ-3 and VQ-4 provide aircraft to this detachment.*

Commander, Helicopter Antisubmarine Wing, US Pacific Fleet, NAS North Island, Calif.
HS-2 Golden Falcons SH-60F, HH-60H NAS North Island, Calif.
HS-4 Black Knights SH-60F, HH-60H NAS North Island, Calif.
HS-6 Indians SH-60F, HH-60H NAS North Island, Calif.
HS-8 Eightballers SH-60F, HH-60H NAS North Island, Calif.
HS-10 (FRS) Warhawks SH-60F, HH-60H (RA) NAS North Island, Calif.
HS-14 Chargers SH-60F, HH-60H NAF Atsugi, Japan

Commander, Helicopter Antisubmarine Wing Light, US Pacific Fleet, NAS North Island, Calif.
HSL-37 Easy Riders SH-60B TH MCAF Kaneohe Bay, Hawaii

Left: HC-85 'Golden Gaters' flies its UH-3Hs from NAS North Island.

Below: VR-48 'Capital Skyliners', based at NAF Washington, is one of the Reserve's two C-20G squadrons.

The Navy's C-20s are split between three squadrons. The C-20Ds (above) are all flown by VR-1 'Starlifters'. VR-51 'Windjammers' flies C-20Gs from MCAF Kaneohe Bay (below).

Above: VR-53, the aptly named 'Capital Express', is based at NAF Washington DC, with C-130Ts.

Below: VR-55 'Minutemen' fly C-130Ts from Moffett Field (now Moffett Federal Airfield).

Above: The Reserve has four C-130 squadrons which, with the disestablishment of VXE-6, will become the only Navy Hercules. This C-130T is a VR-54 'Revelers' aircraft.

All of the Navy's seven C-9 transport squadrons come under Reserve control. These aircraft are from VR-46 'Peach Airlines' (right) and VR-52 'Taskmasters' (above left).

The Navy's extensive C-9 fleet includes VR-56 'Globemasters' (above), VR-57 'Conquistadors' (right), VR-58 'Sun Seekers' (below), VR-59 'Lone Star Express' (below right) and VR-61 'Islanders' (below far right).

155

HSL-41 (FRS) Sea Hawks   SH-60B   TS   NAS North Island, Calif.
HSL-43   Battle Cats   SH-60B   TT   NAS North Island, Calif.
HSL-45   Wolfpack   SH-60B   TZ   NAS North Island, Calif.
HSL-47   Sabrehawks   SH-60B   TY   NAS North Island, Calif.
HSL-49   Scorpions   SH-60B   TX   NAS North Island, Calif.
HSL-51   Warlords   SH-60B, UH-3H   TA   NAF Atsugi, Japan

Note: *HSL-51 Det 11 operates maintains the UH-3H helicopters that transport Commander Seventh Fleet. List reflects move of HSL-37 from NAS Barbers Point by July 1999.*

Commander, Helicopter Tactical Wing,
US Pacific Fleet, NAS North Island, Calif.
HC-3 (FRS)   Packrats   CH/HH-46D   SA   NAS North Island, Calif.
HC-5   Providers   CH/HH/UH-46D   RB   Andersen AFB, Guam
HC-11   Gunbearers CH/HH/UH-46D, UH-3H   VR   NAS North Island, Calif.
VXE-6   Ice Pirates   LC-130F/R   XD   NAS Point Mugu, Calif.

Note: *VXE-6 is scheduled for disestablishment in March 1999. HC-11 operates the UH-3H assigned to transport Commander Third Fleet.*

VX-9   Vampires   XE   F/A-18A/B/C/D, EA-6B, AV-8B, AH-1W   NAS China Lake, Calif.
Detachment Point Mugu   F-14A/B/D   XF

Naval Strike and Air Warfare Center, Naval Fighter Weapons School
F/A-18A/B, F-14A, SH-60F   NAS Fallon, Nev.

Pacific Missile Range Facility   RC-12F, UH-3H   Barking Sands, Hawaii

NAS Barbers Point, Hawaii   UP-3A, UP-3A
NAS North Island, Calif.   UC-12B   7M
NAS Lemoore, Calif.   UC-12B, HH-1N   7S
NAS Fallon, Nev.   UC-12B, HH-1N   7H
NAS Whidbey Island, Wash.   UC-12B, UH-3H   7G
NAF El Centro, Calif.   UC-12B   8N

Commander, Fleet Air Western Pacific
NAF Atsugi, Japan
Note: *HC-5, part of Helicopter Tactical Wing, US Pacific Fleet, operates under control of Commander Fleet Air, Western Pacific.*
Commander, Patrol Wing One   **Kamiseya, Japan**
VP-xx (Rotation)   P-3C   NAF Misawa, Japan
VP-xx (Rotation)   P-3C   NSA Diego Garcia, BIOT
VP-xx Det (Rotation)   P-3C   NAF Kadena, Okinawa
VQ-1 Det   EP-3E   NAF Misawa, Japan

NAF Atsugi, Japan   UC-12F
NAF Misawa, Japan   UC-12F   8M
NAF Kadena, Okinawa, Japan   UC-12F   8H
NSA Diego Garcia, BIOT   None

Chief of Naval Education and Training
NAS Pensacola, Fla.
Commander, Naval Air Training Command,
NAS Corpus Christi, Texas

Commander, Training Air Wing 1   A   NAS Meridian, Miss.
VT-7   Strike Eagles   TA-4J   A   NAS Meridian, Miss.
VT-9   Tigers   T-2C   A   NAS Meridian, Miss.
VT-23   Professionals   T-45C   A   NAS Meridian, Miss.
Note: *VT-19 was redesignated VT-9 on 1 October 1998.*

Commander, Training Air Wing 2   B   NAS Kingsville, Texas
VT-21   Fighting Red Hawks   T-45A   B   NAS Kingsville, Texas
VT-22   Golden Eagles   T-45A   B   NAS Kingsville, Texas

Commander, Training Air Wing 4   G   NAS Corpus Christi
VT-27   Boomers   T-34C   G   NAS Corpus Christi, Texas

VT-28   Rangers   T-34C   G   NAS Corpus Christi, Texas
VT-31   Wise Owls   T-44A, TC-12B   G   NAS Corpus Christi, Texas

Commander, Training Air Wing 5   E   NAS Whiting Field
HT-8   Eightballers   TH-57B/C   E   NAS Whiting Field, Milton, Fla.
HT-18   Vigilant Eagles   TH-57B/C   E   NAS Whiting Field, Milton, Fla.
VT-2   Doer Birds   T-34C   E   NAS Whiting Field, Milton, Fla.
VT-3   Red Knights   T-34C   E   NAS Whiting Field, Milton, Fla.
VT-6   Shooters   T-34C   E   NAS Whiting Field, Milton, Fla.

Commander, Training Air Wing 6   F   NAS Pensacola, Fla.
VT-4   Mighty Warbucks   T-34C, T-1A   F   NAS Pensacola, Fla.
VT-10   Wildcats   T-34C, T-1A   F   NAS Pensacola, Fla.
VT-86   Sabre Hawks   T-2C, T-39N   F   NAS Pensacola, Fla.

NFDS ('Blue Angels')   F/A-18A/B, TC-130G (BA)   NAS Pensacola, Fla.

NAS Meridian, Miss.   HH-1N   A
NAS Corpus Christi, Texas   UC-12B, HH-1N   G
NAS Kingsville, Texas   None   B
NAS Pensacola, Fla.   UC-12B, UH-3H   F
NAS Whiting Field, Fla.   None   E
NSA Mid-South (Memphis, Tenn.)   UC-12B   6M

Commander, Naval Air Systems Command
NAS Patuxent River, Md.
Commander, Naval Air Warfare Center
NAS Patuxent River, Md.
Commander, Naval Air Warfare Center, Aircraft Division
NAS Patuxent River, Md.
Commander, Naval Test Wing Atlantic   NAS Patuxent River, Md.
Naval Force Warfare Aircraft Test Squadron
P-3C, UP-3A, NP-3C/D, S-3B, E-2C, C-2A, KC-130F, T-34C, NT-34C, NC-130H   NAS Patuxent River, Md.

Naval Rotary-Wing Aircraft Test Squadron
UH-1N, AH-1W, NVH-3A, CH-46E, CH-53E, NSH-60B, SH-60B/F, YSH-60F, HH-60H, TH-57C   NAS Patuxent River, Md.

Naval Strike Aircraft Test Squadron   SD   NAS Patuxent River, Md.
F/A-18A/B/C, NF/A-18A/C/D, F-14A, NF-14A/D, EA-6B

US Naval Test Pilot School
F/A-18B, T-2C, T-38A, NP-3D, NU-1B, U-6A, U-21F, TH-6B, OH-58C, UH-60A, NSH-60B, X-26A

NAS Patuxent River, Md.   UC-12B, UH-3H   7A

Commander, Naval Air Warfare Center, Weapons Division
NAWS China Lake, Calif.
Commander, Naval Test Wing Pacific   NAS Point Mugu, Calif.
Naval Weapons Test Squadron China Lake
F/A-18A/C/D, F-14A, NF/A-18D, AV-8B, NAV-8B, TAV-8B, T-39D, AH-1W, HH-1N   NAWS China Lake, Calif.

Naval Weapons Test Squadron Point Mugu
NF-14A/B/D, NP-3D, QF-4N, QF-4S, YF-4J   NAS Point Mugu, Calif.

NAS Point Mugu, Calif.   None   7L
NAWS China Lake, Calif.   None   7P

Naval Research Laboratory   NS Washington, D.C.
Flight Support Detachment   NP-3D   NRL   NAS Patuxent River, Md.

Naval Surface Warfare Center   Arlington, Va.
Naval Coastal Systems Station   MH-53E, NMH-53E, HH-1N   Panama City, Fla.

Chief of Naval Reserve   NAS New Orleans, La.
USS *John F. Kennedy* (CV 67)   NS Mayport, Fla.

Commander, Naval Air Reserve Force, NAS New Orleans, La.
Commander, Reserve Patrol Wing, NAS Norfolk, Va.
VP-62   Broadarrows   P-3C   LT   NAS Jacksonville, Fla.
VP-64   Condors   P-3C   LU   NAS Willow Grove JRB, Pa.
VP-65   Tridents   P-3C   PG   NAS Point Mugu, Calif.
VP-66   Liberty Bells   P-3C   LV   NAS Willow Grove JRB, Pa.
VP-69   Totems   P-3C   PJ   NAS Whidbey Island, Wash.
VP-91   Black Cats   P-3C   PM   Moffett Federal Airfield, Calif.
VP-92   Minutemen   P-3C   LY   NAS Brunswick, Maine
VP-94   Crawfish   P-3C   PZ   NAS New Orleans JRB, La.
VQ-11   Bandits   EP-3J, P-3C   LP   NAS Brunswick, Maine

Note: *VP-91 was deactivated on 1 April 1999. On the same date, Commander Reserve Patrol Wing Pacific/Commander Patrol Wing Four merged with Commander Patrol Wing Atlantic to form Reserve Patrol Wing, headquartered at NAS Norfolk, Va. VQ-11 is scheduled for deactivation in 1999.*

Commander, Reserve Carrier Air Wing 20, AF
NAS Atlanta, Ga.
VFA-201   Hunters   F/A-18A   NAS Fort Worth JRB, Texas
VFA-203   Blue Dolphins   F/A-18A   NAS Atlanta JRB, Ga.
VFA-204   River Rattlers   F/A-18A   NAS New Orleans JRB, La.
VAQ-209   Star Warriors   EA-6B   NAF Washington, D.C.
VAW-77   Night Wolf   E-2C   NAS Atlanta JRB, Ga.
VAW-78   Fighting Escargots   E-2C   NAS Norfolk, Va.
VFC-12   Fighting Omars   F/A-18A/B   NAS Oceana, Va.
VFC-13   Saints   F-5E/F   NAS Fallon, Nev.

Note: *VF-201 was redesignated VFA-201 on 1 January 1999 upon transition to the F/A-18A. A Marine Corps Reserve F/A-18A squadron, VMFA-142, is assigned to CVWR-20.*

Commander, Helicopter Wing Reserve, NW
NAS North Island, Calif.
HC-85   Golden Gaters   UH-3H   NAS North Island, Calif.
HCS-4   Red Wolves   HH-60H   NAS Norfolk, Va.
HCS-5   Firehawks   HH-60H   NAS Point Mugu, Calif.
HS-75   Emerald Knights   SH-3H, UH-3H   NAS Jacksonville, Fla.
HSL-84   Thunderbolts   SH-2G   NAS North Island, Calif.
HSL-94   Titans   SH-2G   NAS Willow Grove JRB, Pa.

Commander, Fleet Logistics Support Wing   NAS Fort Worth
VR-1   Starlifters   C-20D   JK   NAF Washington, D.C.
VR-46   Peach Airliners   C-9B, DC-9   JS   NAS Atlanta JRB, Ga.
VR-48   Capital Skyliners   C-20G   JR   NAF Washington, D.C.
VR-51   Windjammers   C-20G   RG   MCAF Kaneohe Bay, Hawaii
VR-52   Taskmasters   DC-9   JT   NAS Willow Grove JRB, Pa.
VR-53   Capital Express   C-130T   WV   NAF Washington, D.C.
VR-54   Revelers   C-130T   CW   NAS New Orleans JRB, La.
VR-55   Bicentennial Minutemen   C-130T   RU   Moffett Federal Airfield, Calif.
VR-56   Globemasters   C-9B   JU   NAS Norfolk, Va.
VR-57   Conquistadors   C-9B, DC-9   RX   NAS North Island, Calif.
VR-58   Sun Seekers   C-9B   JV   NAS Jacksonville, Fla.
VR-59   Lone Star Express   C-9B, DC-9   RY   NAS Ft Worth JRB, Texas
VR-61   Islanders   DC-9   RS   NAS Whidbey Island, Wash.
VR-62   Downeasters   C-130T   JW   NAS Brunswick, Maine

Note: *VR-55 moving to NAS Point Mugu in 1999. VR-62 was nicknamed the 'Motowners' while based at NAF Detroit and 'Mass Transit' during its subsequent sojourn at NAS South Weymouth.*

NAS New Orleans JRB, La.   UC-12B   7X
NAS Fort Worth JRB, Texas   UC-12B   7D
NAS Atlanta JRB, Ga.   UC-12B   7B
NAS Willow Grove JRB, Pa.   UC-12B   7W
NAF Washington, D.C.   UC-12B   7N
NARC Santa Clara, Calif.   UC-12B   7Y

US Navy Fleet Readiness Squadrons (FRSs)

Fleet Readiness Squadrons
Type conversion training is conducted by fleet readiness squadrons (FRSs) or other units assigned similar additional duties.

Unit Type	Aircraft	FRS	Site
HC	H-3	HC-2	NAS Norfolk, Va.
	H-46	HC-3	NAS North Island, Calif.
HC, HM	MH-53	HMT-302	MCAS New River, N.C.
HS	SH-60F/HH-60H	HS-10	NAS North Island, Calif.
HSL	SH-60B	HSL-40	NS Mayport, Fla.
		HSL-41	NAS North Island, Calif.
VAQ	EA-6B	VAQ-129	NAS Whidbey Island, Wash.
VAW	E-2C	VAW-120	NAS Norfolk, Va.
VF	F-14	VF-101	NAS Oceana, Va.

Unit Type	Aircraft	FRS	Site
VFA	F/A-18A/C	VFA-106	NAS Oceana, Va.
		VFA-125	NAS Lemoore, Calif.
		VMFAT-101	MCAS Miramar, Calif.
	F/A-18E/F	VFA-122	NAS Lemoore, Calif.
VP, VPU	P-3	VP-30	NAS Jacksonville, Fla.
VQ	EP-3E	VP-30	NAS Jacksonville, Fla.
	E-6	NTSU	Tinker AFB, Okla.
VR	C-12	NAS Operations	NAS Norfolk
		VRC-30	NAS North Island, Calif.
	C-130	USAF	Little Rock AFB, Ark.
VRC	C-2A	VAW-120	NAS Norfolk, Va.
VS	S-3B	VS-41	NAS North Island, Calif.
NAS	H-1	HMT-303	MCAF Camp Pendleton, Calif.

Note: *The FRSs listed below have been disestablished since 1987:*

Type	Squadron
A-3	VAQ-33
A-6	VA-42, VA-128
A-7	VA-122, VA-125, VA-174
E-2/C-2	VAW-110
F-14	VF-124
H-1	HC-16
H-2	HSL-30, HSL-31
H-3	HC-1
H-60	HS-1
P-3	VP-31
S-3	VS-27

US Navy disestablished units 1988-1999

Carrier Air Wings Disestablished 1988-1998

Wing	Code	Official Date	Ceremonial date
CVW-6	AE	1 Apr 92	1 Apr 92
CVW-10	NM	1 Jun 88	
CVW-13	AK	1 Jan 91	16 Jan 91
CVW-15	NL	31 Mar 95	16 Feb 95
CVWR-30	ND	31 Dec 94	11 Sep 94

Navy Squadrons Disestablished 1988-1999

Unit	Nickname	Code	Official date	Ceremonial Date
HC-1	Fleet Angels	UP	29 Apr 94	29 Apr 94
HC-9	Protectors	NW	31 Jul 90	9 Jun 90
HC-16	Bullfrogs	BF	1 Apr 94	18 Feb 94
HM-12	Sea Dragons	DH	30 Sep 94	30 Sep 94
HM-18	Norsemen	NW	4 Mar 95	4 Mar 95
HM-19	Golden Bears	NW	5 Nov 94	5 Nov 94
HS-1	Sea Horses		30 Jun 97	19 Jun 97
HS-9	Sea Griffins		30 Apr 93	23 Apr 93
HS-12	Wyverns		30 Nov 94	23 Sep 94
HS-16	Night Hawks		1 Jun 88	
HS-17	Valkyries		30 Jun 91	2 Jul 91
HSL-30	Scooters	HT	30 Sep 93	28 Jul 93
HSL-31	Archangels	TD	31 Jul 92	9 Jul 92
HSL-32	Tridents	HV	31 Jan 94	21 Jan 94
HSL-33	Sea Snakes	TF	29 Apr 94	23 Mar 94
HSL-34	Gray Checkers	HX	30 Nov 93	19 Nov 93
HSL-35	Magicians	TG	4 Dec 92	19 Nov 92
HSL-36	Lamplighters	HY	30 Sep 92	30 Sep 92
HSL-74	Demon Elves	NW	1 Apr 94	19 Mar 94
VA-35	Panthers		31 Jan 95	24 Jan 95
VA-36	Roadrunners		31 Mar 94	11 Mar 94
VA-42	Thunderbolts*	AD	30 Sep 94	23 Sep 94
VA-46	Clansmen		30 Jun 91	23 May 91
VA-52	Knight Riders		31 Mar 95	17 Mar 95
VA-55	War Horses		1 Jan 91	22 Feb 91
VA-65	Fighting Tigers		31 Mar 93	26 Mar 93
VA-72	Blue Hawks		30 Jun 91	23 May 91
VA-75	Sunday Punchers		31 Mar 97	28 Feb 97
VA-85	Black Falcons		30 Sep 94	22 Sep 94
VA-95	Green Lizards		31 Oct 95	18 Nov 95
VA-122	Flying Eagles	NJ	31 May 91	5 Apr 91
VA-128	Golden Intruders	NJ	30 Sep 95	29 Sep 95
VA-145	Swordsmen		1 Oct 93	13 Oct 93
VA-155	Silver Foxes		30 Apr 93	27 Apr 93
VA-165	Boomers		30 Sep 96	26 Jul 96
VA-174	Hell Razors	AD	30 Jun 88	30 Jun 88
VA-176	Thunderbolts		30 Sep 92	18 Sep 92
VA-185	Knighthawks		30 Aug 91	6 Aug 91

Unit	Nickname	Code	Official date	Ceremonial Date
VA-196	Main Battery		28 Feb 97	28 Feb 97
VA-205	Green Falcons		31 Dec 94	25 Sep 94
VA-304	Firebirds		31 Dec 94	17 Sep 94

Note: *VA-42 was nicknamed Green Pawns until the demise of the VA-176 Thunderbolts.*

Unit	Nickname	Code	Official date	Ceremonial Date
VAK-208	Jockeys		30 Sep 89	30 Sep 89
VAK-308	Griffins		30 Sep 88	30 Sep 88
VAQ-33	Firebirds	GD	1 Oct 93	1 Oct 93
VAQ-34	Electric Horsemen	GD	1 Oct 93	5 Oct 93
VAQ-35	Grey Wolves	GD	1 Oct 93	7 Oct 93
VAQ-133	Wizards		1 Jun 92	24 Apr 92
VAQ-137	Rooks		30 Sep 94	26 May 94
VAQ-142	Grim Watchdogs		1 Jul 91	30 Apr 91
VAQ-309	Axemen		31 Dec 94	10 Sep 94
VAW-88	Cottonpickers		31 Dec 94	27 Aug 94
VAW-110	Firebirds	NJ	30 Sep 94	28 Sep 94
VAW-111	Seabats		30 Apr 88	
VAW-114	Hormel Hawgs		31 Mar 95	16 Feb 95
VAW-122	Steeljaws		31 Mar 96	14 Mar 96
VAW-127	Seabats		30 Sep 91	30 Sep 91
VC-1	Blue Aliis	UA	30 Sep 92	30 Sep 92
VC-5	Checkertails	UE	31 Aug 92	1 May 92
VC-10	Challengers	JH	15 Aug 93	6 Aug 93
VF-1	Wolfpack		30 Sep 93	1 Jul 93
VF-21	Freelancers		31 Jan 96	12 Jan 96
VF-24	Fighting Renegades		31 Aug 96	27 Jun 96
VF-33	Starfighters		1 Oct 93	24 Sep 93
VF-43	Challengers		1 Jul 94	24 Jun 94
VF-45	Blackbirds	AD	31 Mar 96	8 Mar 96
VF-51	Screaming Eagles		31 Mar 95	16 Feb 95
VF-74	Bedevilers		30 Apr 94	28 Apr 94
VF-84	Jolly Rogers		1 Oct 95	29 Sep 95
VF-111	Sundowners		31 Mar 95	16 Feb 95
VF-114	Aardvarks		30 Apr 93	28 Jan 93
VF-124	Gunfighters	NJ	30 Sep 94	30 Sep 94
VF-126	Bandits	NJ	1 Apr 94	1 Apr 94
VF-142	Ghostriders		30 Apr 95	7 Apr 95
VF-191	Satan's Kittens		30 Apr 88	
VF-194	Red Lightnings		30 Apr 88	
VF-202	Superheats		31 Dec 94	9 Jul 94
VF-301	Devil's Disciples		31 Dec 94	11 Sep 94
VF-302	Stallions		31 Dec 94	11 Sep 94
VFA-127	Desert Bogeys	NJ	31 Mar 96	23 Mar 96
VFA-132	Privateers		1 Jun 92	15 May 92
VFA-161	Chargers		1 Apr 88	

Unit	Nickname	Code	Official date	Ceremonial Date
VFA-303	Goldenhawks		31 Dec 94	11 Sep 94?
VFA-305	Lobos		31 Dec 94	20 Aug 94
VP-6	Blue Sharks	PC	31 May 93	19 Mar 93
VP-11	Proud Pegasus	LE	15 Jan 97	02 Aug 97
VP-17	White Lightnings	ZE	31 Mar 95	17 Dec 94
VP-19	Big Red	PE	31 Aug 91	17 May 91
VP-22	Blue Geese	QA	31 Mar 94	22 Jan 94
VP-23	Sea Hawks	LJ	28 Feb 95	7 Dec 94
VP-24	Batmen	LR	30 Apr 95	13 Apr 95
VP-31	Black Lightnings	RP	1 Nov 93	26 Aug 93
VP-44	Golden Pelicans	LM	28 Jun 91	31 May 91
VP-48	Boomerangs	SF	26 Jun 91	23 May 91
VP-49	Woodpeckers	LP	1 Mar 94	14 Jan 94
VP-50	Blue Dragons	SG	30 Jun 92	21 May 92
VP-56	Dragons	LQ	28 Jun 91	28 Jun 91
VP-60	Cobras	LS	1 Sep 94	20 Mar 94
VP-67	Golden Hawks	PL	30 Sep 94	5 Mar 94
VP-68	Blackhawks	LW	31 Dec 96	2 Nov 96
VP-90	Lions	LX	30 Sep 94	19 Mar 94
VP-91	Black Cats	PM	1 Apr 99	
VP-93	Executioners	LH	30 Sep 94	17 Sep 94
VP-MAU Brunswick	Northern Sabres	LB	30 Jun 91	2 Jun 91
VP-MAU Moffett	Rolling Thunder	PS	30 Sep 91	17 Aug 91
VQ-5	Sea Shadows	SS	Jul 99	
VQ-6	Black Ravens	ET	Sep 99	
VQ-11	Bandits	LP	1999?	
VR-22	Med Riders	JL	31 Mar 93	2 Apr 93
VR-24	Lifting Eagles	JM	31 Jan 93	29 Jan 93
VR-51	Flamin' Hookers	RV	30 Sep 94	
VR-60	Volunteer Express	RT	1 Apr 95	Mar 95
VRC-50	Foo Dogs	RG	7 Oct 94	29 Sep 94
VS-27	Seawolves	AD	30 Sep 94	29 Sep 94
VS-28	Gamblers		1 Oct 92	28 Jul 92
VS-35	Boomerangs		1 Jun 88	25 May 88
VS-37	Sawbucks		31 Mar 95	17 Feb 95
VT-24	Bobcats	C	30 Oct 92	18 Sep 92
VT-25	Cougars	C	30 Oct 92	18 Sep 92
VT-26	Tigers	C	29 May 92	22 May 92
VX-4	Evaluators	XF	30 Sep 94	30 Sep 94
VX-5	Vampires	XE	29 Apr 94	29 Apr 94
VXE-6	Ice Pirates	XD	31 Mar 99	27 Mar 99
VXN-8	World Travellers	JB	1 Oct 93	21 Sep 93

Lists compiled by Michael Weeks and Rick Burgess

US Navy unit and vessel changes 1988-1999

Squadrons Established 1988-1999

HCS-5	Firehawks	NW	01 Oct 1988
HM-19	Golden Bears	NW	09 Jan 1989
HSL-46	Grandmasters	HQ	07 Apr 1988
HSL-48	Vipers	HR	07 Sep 1989
HSL-49	Scorpions	TX	23 Mar 1990
HSL-51	Warlords	TA	01 Oct 1991
Naval Force Aircraft Test Squadron			21 Jul 1995
Naval Rotary-Wing Aircraft Test Sqn			21 Jul 1995
Naval Strike Aircraft Test Sqn		SD	21 Jul 1995
Naval Weapons Test Squadron China Lake, Calif.			08 May 1995
Naval Weapons Test Squadron Point Mugu, Calif			08 May 1995
VAQ-35	Grey Wolves	GD	14 Aug 1991
VAQ-128	Fighting Phoenix	NL	01 Oct 1997
VAQ-133	Wizards	NL	01 Apr 1996
VAQ-137	Rooks	NL	01 Oct 1996
VAQ-142	Grim Watchdogs		01 Jun 1988
VAQ-142	Gray Wolves	NL	01 Apr 1997
VAW-77	Night Wolf	AF	01 Oct 1995
VFA-122	Flying Eagles	NJ	01 Oct 1998
VQ-5	Sea Shadows	SS	15 Apr 1991
VQ-6	Black Ravens	ET	05 Aug 1991
VQ-11	Bandits	LP	01 Jul 1997

VR-1	Starlifters	JK	01 May 1997
VR-51	Windjammers	RG	01 Jun 1997
VR-53	Capital Express	WV	01 Oct 1993
VR-54	Revelers	CW	01 Jun 1991
VS-35	Blue Wolves	VS	04 Apr 1991
VX-9	Vampires	XE/XF	30 Apr 1994

Note: *VS-35 was temporarily assigned the tailcode VS until assigned to a CVW.*

Squadrons Redesignated 1988-1999

HAL-4 to HCS-4	Red Wolves		1 Oct 1989
HS-85 to HC-85	Golden Gaters		1 Oct 1994
VA-22 to VFA-22	Fighting Redcocks		4 May 1990
VA-27 to VFA-27	Chargers		24 Jan 1991
VA-34 to VFA-34	Blue Blasters		30 Sep 1996
VA-37 to VFA-37	Bulls		28 Nov 1990
VA-81 to VFA-81	Sunliners		04 Feb 1988
VA-83 to VFA-83	Rampagers		01 Mar 1988
VA-94 to VFA-94	Mighty Shrikes		28 Jun 1990
VA-105 to VFA-105	Gunslingers		17 Dec 1990
VA-97 to VFA-97	Warhawks		24 Jan 1991
VA-115 to VFA-115	Eagles		30 Sep 1996
VA-146 to VFA-146	Blue Diamonds		21 Jul 1989
VA-147 to VFA-147	Argonauts		20 Jul 1989

VA-203 to VFA-203	Blue Dolphins		01 Oct 1989
VA-204 to VFA-204	River Rattlers		01 May 1991
VF-201 to VFA-201	Hunters		01 Jan 1999
VC-12 to VFC-12	Fighting Omars		22 Apr 1988
VC-13 to VFC-13	Saints		22 Apr 1988
VT-19 to VT-9	Tigers		01 Oct 1998

Note: *The following Air Antisubmarine Squadrons (VS) were redesignated Sea Control Squadrons (VS) on 16 Sep 1993: VS-21, -22,-24, -27, -28, -29, -30, -31,-32, -33, -35, -37, -38, -41*
The following Tactical Electronic Warfare Squadrons (VAQ) were redesignated Electronic Attack Squadrons (VAQ) on 31 Mar 1998: VAQ-128, -129, -130, -131, -132, -133, -134,-135, -136, -137, -138, -139, -140, -141, -142

Aviation Ship Changes 1988-1999

Commissioned
USS *Bataan* (LHD 5)		20 Sep 1997
USS *Bonhomme Richard* (LHD 6)		15 Aug 1998
USS *Boxer* (LHD 4)		11 Feb 1995
USS *Essex* (LHD 2)		17 Oct 1992
USS *Kearsarge* (LHD 3)		16 Oct 1993
USS *Abraham Lincoln* (CVN 72)		11 Nov 1989
USS *John C. Stennis* (CVN 74)		09 Dec 1995

USS *Harry Truman* (CVN 75)		25 Jul 1998
USS *George Washington* (CVN 73)		04 Jul 1992
USS *Wasp* (LHD 1)		29 Jul 1989

Decommissioned
USS *America* (CV 66)		30 Sep 1996
USS *Coral Sea* (CV 43)		30 Apr 1990
USS *Forrestal* (AVT 59)		11 Sep 1993
USS *Independence* (CV 62)		30 Sep 1998
USS *Iwo Jima* (LPH 2)		14 Jul 1993
USS *Guadalcanal* (LPH 7)		31 Aug 1994
USS *Guam* (LPH 9)		25 Aug 1998
USS *Lexington* (AVT 16)		08 Nov 1991
USS *Midway* (CV 41)		11 Apr 1992
USS *New Orleans* (LPH 11)		31 Oct 1997
USS *Okinawa* (LPH 3)		17 Dec 1992
USS *Ranger* (CV 61)		10 Jul 1993
USS *Saratoga* (CV 60)		30 Sep 1994
USS *Tripoli* (LPH 10)		08 Sep 1995

Redesignated
USS *Forrestal* (CV 59) to (AVT 59)		04 Feb 1992
USS *Inchon* (LPH 12) to (MCS 12)		01 Mar 1995

Note: *Some official dates differ from those on which ceremonies were actually held.*

INDEX

INDEX

Picture acknowledgments

Front cover: Zoltan Buza. **4:** David Donald (two), Alexander Mladenov. **5:** Robin Polderman, René J. Uijthoven, Roberto Yañez. **6:** Robin Polderman, Yefim Gordon. **7:** Westland (two), Yefim Gordon. **8:** Dylan Eklund, John Winchester. **9:** Peter Steinemann/Skyline APA (two), Richard Marchant, Simon Watson (four). **10:** Nikola Dimitrijevic (two), Yoshitomo Aoki. **11:** Craig P. Justo, Iván Siminic. **12:** Mario Roberto V. Carneiro (two), Iván Siminic. **13:** Boeing (two), Stephen J. Brennan/Eagle Aviation Photos. **14:** Jonathan Chuck, Carl L. Richards (two). **15:** Craig Kaston (two), Boeing. **16:** Kaman, David Donald. **17:** Nigel Pittaway, David Donald, Nate Leong. **18-21:** Yefim Gordon (10). **22:** Yefim Gordon, via Richard Fisher. **23:** via Richard Fisher (two). Mike Vines/Photolink (two) **24:** via Richard Fisher (10). **25:** via Richard Fisher (three), Mike Vines/Photolink. **26-29:** Cees-Jan Van der Ende and Roland van Maarseveen (25). **30-33:** Captain John Rahe/USMC (17). **34-41:** Dick Lohuis (42). **42-43:** Eddie De Kruyff (main), Robert Hewson (inset). **44:** Yefim Gordon Archive (two), David F. Brown. **45:** US DoD (inset). **46:** Yefim Gordon Archive (five). **47:** Yefim Gordon Archive (two). **48:** Yefim Gordon, Frank Rozendaal (two), Hugo Mambour, Paul Jackson, Chris Ryan. **49:** US DoD, Yefim Gordon Archive. **50:** Yefim Gordon Archive (three), Robert Hewson. **51:** Gabor Szekeres, Yefim Gordon Archive. **52:** Alexander Mladenov, Aerospace. **53:** Peter R. March, Jozef Gal (inset), Alexander Mladenov. **54:** Yefim Gordon Archive, Tieme Festner, Keith Wilson/SFB Photographic. **55:** Yefim Gordon Archive (three). **57:** Hugo Mambour, Frank Rozendaal. **58:** Stefan Petersen, Yefim Gordon Archive (two), Frank Rozendaal. **59:** Frank Spooner, GAMA/Frank Spooner. **60:** Yefim Gordon Archive (three), Peter Steinemann/Skyline APA. **61:** GAMMA/Frank Spooner (two). **62:** GAMMA/Frank Spooner, SIPA-Press/Rex Features. **63:** SIPA-Press/Rex Features (three). **64:** SIPA-Press/Rex Features, Yefim Gordon Archive (three), GAMA/Frank Spooner, Yefim Gordon Archive. **65:** SIPA-Press/Rex Features (two). **66:** Zoltan Buza (two). **67:** Peter Steinemann/Skyline APA, Eddie De Kruyff. **68:** GAMMA/Frank Spooner, Aerospace (two). **69:** Peter Steinemann/Skyline APA, Pushpindar Singh. **70:** Frank Rozendaal, Marcus Fülber, Jens Schymura. **71:** Yefim Gordon Archive (five), Paul Jackson (two). **72:** Sergey Sergeyev (two), Keith Wilson/SFB Photographic, Tieme Festner, David R. Hames, Georg Mader, Paul Jackson, Gabor Szekeres, Robert Hewson, Paul Jackson, Gabor Szekeres (two). **77:** F. Robineau/Dassault, SIPA-Press/Rex Features, SIPA-Press/Rex Features. **77:** FANA/FAPLA via Vasco Henrique. **78:** ITAR-TASS va Dimitri Komissarov, GAMMA/Frank Spooner (two). **79:** Press Association, via Yefim Gordon. **80:** Chris Ryan, Tim Senior, Sergey Sergeyev. **81:** Press Association, Tim 'no, it's my secret clubhouse' Ripley. **82:** Marcus Fülber. **83:** Yefim Gordon, Paul Jackson, Frank Rozendaal. **84:** GAMMA/Frank Spooner, FANA/FAPLA via Vasco Henrique, Alexander Mladenov. **85:** Dragisa Brasnovic, Hugo Mambour, Timm Ziegenthaler. **86:** Jens Schymura, Hugo Mambour, Timm Ziegenthaler. **87:** Gabor Szekeres, Peter Steinemann/Skyline APA, via Simon Watson, Paul O'Driscoll/REX Features, Patrick Lareau. **88:** Jens Schymura, Hugo Mambour, Robin Polderman, Peter R. March, Jens Schymura. **89:** Eddie De Kruyff, David F. Brown, Frank Rozendaal, David F. Brown. **90-95:** SrA Greg 'Cactus' Davis/1st CTCS, USAF. **96:** Dassault via Paul Jackson. **97:** F. Robineau/Dassault. **100:** Ian Black (two). **99:** Stefan Petersen, Aerospotiale. **100:** Luigino Caliaro, Claude Haller/SIRPA AIR via Frédéric Lert. **102:** F. Robineau/Dassault, J.P. Gauthier/SIRPA AIR via Frédéric Lert, Ian Black. **103:** F. Robineau/Dassault (two), Armée de l'Air. **104:** Patrick Laureau, Aerospace, Armée de l'Air. **105:** MATRA/BAe Dynamics, Dassault (two), Paul Jackson. **106:** F. Robineau/
Dassault (two). **107:** Ian Black, Frédéric Lert, Ian Black, Hugo Mambour (two), MATRA/CEV. **108:** Gilles Rolle/SIRPA AIR, Dassault (three). **109:** Dassault, MATRA/CEV, Dassault (two). **110:** MATRA/BAe Dynamics, SIRPA AIR via Frédéric Lert, Ian Black,F. Robineau/Dassault. **111:** Yves Debay, Ian Black. **112:** Thomson-TRT,Peter R. Foster, GIFAS, Chris Schmidt. **113:** Armée de l'Air, US DoD, Ian Black, Aérospatiale. **114:** Paul Jackson, Aérospatiale, MATRA/CEV, Dassault (two), Stefan Petersen. **115:** Claude Haller/SIRPA AIR, Paul Jackson, GIFAS. **116:** Dassault, Jelle Sjoerdsma, Peter R. Foster, Dassault, Paul Jackson, Dassault. **117:** Dassault, Aérospatiale, J. P. Gauthier/SIRPA AIR, Yves Debay. **118:** F. Robineau/Dassault, Derek Bower, Dassault. **119:** F. Robineau/Dassault, J. P. Gauthier/SIRPA AIR via Frédéric Lert, F. Robineau/Dassault. **120:** Dassault, MATRA/Dassault, F. Robineau/ Dassault via Paul Jackson. **121:** F. Robineau/ Dassault, Claude Haller/SIRPA AIR, F. Robineau/ Dassault. **122:** François Brévot, F. Robineau/ Dassault, David Donald, François Brévot. **123:** F. Robineau/ Dassault, Peter Steinemann, Dassault (two). **125:** Jamie Hunter, Werner Münzenmaier, Ted Carlson/Photodynamics, Jose Ramos/Ramos Aviation Photography, Ted Carlson/Photodynamics, Frédéric Lert, Peter J. Cooper. **127:** Jamie Hunter, Alan Key, Mark Munzel, Ted Carlson/Photodynamics, L/Cdr David Baranek, Ted Carlson/Photodynamics, Airshots, Ted Carlson/Photodynamics, Alan Key, Werrner Münzenmaier (two), Robert Hewson. **129:** Dylan Eklund, Peter J. Cooper, Marcus Fülber, Werner Münzenmaier, Airshots, Werner Münzenmaier, Marcus Fülber, Ted Carlson/Photodynamics, Geoff Stockle, Jim Kippen, Robert Hewson (two), Robert Hewson. **131:** Ted Carlson/Photodynamics, McDonnell Douglas, Cees-Jan Van der Ende and Roland van Maarseveen, Mark Munzel, Ted Carlson (four), Godfrey Mangion, Airshots, Ted Carlson/Photodynamics, Geoff Stockle, Tieme Festner, Jose Ramos/Ramos Aviation Photography. **133:** Alan Key, Frédéric Lert, Geoff Stockle, Lockheed, Geoff Stockle (two), Alan Key, Mark Munzel, Werner Münzenmaier. **135:** Robert Hewson, Airshots (three), Ted Carlson/Photodynamics, Airshots, Henry B. Ham, Geoff Stockle, Keith Wilson/SFB Photography, Ted Carlson/Photodynamics, Marcus Fülber (three), Ted Carlson/Photodynamics. **137:** Ted Carlson/Photodynamics, Godfrey Mangion (two), Dylan Eklund, Ted Carlson/Photodynamics (three), Mark Munzel, Roberto Yañez, Robert Hewson, Ted Carlson/Photodynamics, Bob Archer, Rene J. Uijthoven. **139:** Keith Wilson/SFB Photographic, Airshots, Tieme Festner, Airshots, Geoff Stockle (three), Airshots (four), Ted Carlson/Photodynamics (four). **141:** Ted Carlson/Photodynamics, Airshots (three), Airshots, Alan Key, Frédéric Lert, US Navy, Jamie Hunter, Paul van den Elsaker, Geoff Stockle, Airshots, Geoff Stockle, Rene J. Uijthoven (three). **143:** Airshots, Antoine Roels, Robert Hewson, Mark Munzel (two), Werner Münzenmaier (three), Jamie Hunter, Richard Cooper, Jim Winchester, Ted Carlson/Photodynamics, Airshots. **145:** Werner Münzenmaier (two), Jamie Hunter (three), Richard Cooper (two), Robert Hewson, Ted Carlson/Photodynamics, Richard Cooper (three), Ted Carlson/Photodynamics. **147:** Robin Polderman, Airshots, Ted Carlson/Photodynamics, Airshots, Geoff Stockle, Airshots, Werrner Münzenmaier, jamie Hunter, Fred van Horrik (six). **149:** Airshots (three), Robin Polderman, Ted Carlson/Photodynamics (two), Mark Munzel (three), Henry B. Ham, Mark Munzel. **151:** Tieme Festner, Geoff Stockle, Airshots (two), Ted Carlson/Photodynamics, Tieme Festner, Peter J. Cooper (two), Carl L. Richards, Airshots, Jamie Hunter. **153:** Carl L. Richards, Robert Hewson (two), Airshots, Chris Ryan, Robin Polderman, Ted Carlson/Photodynamics, Geoff Stockle, Tieme Festner, John W. Binford, Robert Hewson, Dylan Eklund, Ted Carlson/Photodynamics, Robert F. Dorr, Carl L. Richards. **155:** Werner Münzenmaier, Geoff Stockle, Gulfstream, Jonathan Chuck, Alan Key (two), Airshots, Marcus Fülber, Ted Carlson/Photodynamics, Peter J., Cooper, Airshots, Ted Carlson/Photodynamics (two).